UNDERSTANDING
ROBOTICS

Understanding Robotics

V. Daniel Hunt

Technology Research Corporation

ACADEMIC PRESS, INC.

Harcourt Brace Jovanovich, Publishers

San Diego   New York   Boston

London   Sydney   Tokyo   Toronto

21041370

Cover photo: Courtesy of ASEA Brown Boveri (ABB)

This book is printed on acid-free paper. ∞

Academic Press, Inc.
San Diego, California 92101

United Kingdom Edition published by
Academic Press Limited
24–28 Oval Road, London NW1 7DX

Library of Congress Cataloging-in-Publication Data

Hunt, V. Daniel.
    Understanding robotics / V. Daniel Hunt.
        p.   cm.
    data
    Includes bibliographical references.
    ISBN   0-12-361775-8   (alk. paper)
    1. Robotics.   I. Title.
    TJ211.H863   1990
    629.8'92--dc20   90-30649
                                                                      CIP

Printed in the United States of America
90   91   92   93   9   8   7   6   5   4   3   2   1

Dedicated to a Gentleman
Samuel S. Scherr

CONTENTS

3. SENSORS FOR ROBOTIC SYSTEMS   64

4. APPLICATION OF ROBOTICS   93

5. JUSTIFICATION OF ROBOTICS   144

6. ROBOTS—A MANUFACTURING TOOL   173

7. ROBOTS AND PEOPLE   194

8. A GLIMPSE OF THE FUTURE   209

PREFACE

Robotics technology made its debut in the 1960s. However, in the early 1980s, the automobile industry actually created the market for robotics. At present, the automobile industry's share of robotics orders booked annually runs above 50 percent, down substantially from the beginning of the decade. As a result of the decline in automotive-related capital expenditures between 1985 and 1989, the robotics industry has increased research and development in vertical applications which will allow other industries to apply robotics technology to their manufacturing processes.

The developing U.S. robotics industry currently consists of approximately 56 robot producers and a number of robot accessories and component manufacturers. Accessories include, but are not limited to, machine vision recognition systems, sensing and proximity devices, end-of-arm tooling devices for robots, interface modules, compliance devices, joint locating and guidance systems for welding, and guard/safety devices.

Manufacturing application technology advancements, such as those made during 1989 in surface mount and thru-hole technologies, will reduce the robotic industry's dependence on orders from the automotive industry. These types of applications particularly suit the revitalized U.S. electronics and appliance industries. Also, the flexibility, quality control, productivity, and automation requirements of today's manufacturing manager ensure expanding use of the robot in the factory. The robotic industry's recent profitability will enable U.S. producers to devote more time, attention, and funding to application research, a priority of offshore producers such as Japan.

In the automotive industry, robot applications have become saturated, resulting in flat or declining revenues. The fastest growing markets for robotics are in light manufacturing assembly operations. The spread to light manufacturing industries is influenced by developments in robot sensors, artificial intelligence, network communications, enhanced accuracy, and system integration.

Between 1987 and 1994, U.S. robot revenues could have a compound annual growth rate of 9.7 percent and may reach $879 million by 1994. The light industry use of robots has been increasing despite the overall situation in the robot market. In 1987 the U.S. light industrial revenues were $183.6 million, up from $161 million in 1986. Revenues for light industrial robots are expected to exceed 50 percent of the total U.S. robot market by 1994. The compound annual growth rate of the U.S. light industrial robot market may be 16.3 percent from 1987 to 1994. The light industrial market may reach $462 million in 1994.

Internationally, the world market for robots was $2.83 billion in 1987 and may reach $5.93 billion by 1994. Imports of robots are estimated to be at least 30 percent of domestic consumption. Japan is the source of more than 80 percent of these imports. Japan is the dominant force in the world in the manufacture of robots, producing more than half the total. The United States and Europe each produce about 20 percent of the world total. There are about 300 firms producing robots in Japan, one-third of which are for in-house use only.

One of the reasons that the Japanese control the world robot market is due to support by the Japanese government. Government incentives include funded research and development programs, low interest loans, tax incentives, and a government-funded robot leasing company. European governments have also encouraged robot manufacturers but have not been nearly as successful as the Japanese in promoting industry growth.

In general, the U.S. government has not been very supportive in promoting the increased use of robots in the industrial base. Most funding has been directed at space and military applications. Recent efforts by the National Institute of Standards and Technology to assist in the area of factory automation have just begun in their "Shop of the 90's" program for small and mid-size manufacturing companies.

Moreover, U.S. robot suppliers depend on foreign sources for components used to create robots and robotic systems. Growth in robotics in the next 10 years will be affected by software developments, diversification of vertical application areas, systems integration including CIM, developments of robot intelligence, and sensor systems.

V. Daniel Hunt

ACKNOWLEDGMENTS

Understanding Robotics has been developed based on information from a wide variety of authorities who are specialists in their respective fields.

We especially appreciate John Wiley & Sons' permission to reprint material from articles by Jerry W. Saveriano (Pioneers of Robotics), Paul Chapman (Sensor Evolution), and Azriel Rosenfeld, Nello Zuech, and Jim Dunseth (Vision Systems) from the *International Encyclopedia of Robotics,* 1988, edited by Richard C. Dorf and Shimon Y. Nof.

The following publications were used as the basic technical resources for this book. Portions of these publications have been used in the book. The definitions or artwork used have been reproduced with the permission of the respective publisher.

A Competitive Assessment of the U.S. Robotics Industry, U.S. Department of Commerce, International Trade Administration, March 1987.

An Overview of Robotics Technology, V. Daniel Hunt, Technology Research Corporation, Report Number TRC-85-111, Revision A, March 1987.

Computerized Manufacturing Automation: Employment, Education, and the Workplace U.S. Congress, Office of Technology Assessment, OTA-CIT-235, April 1984.

Industrial Robots—A Summary and Forecast, Tech Tran Corporation, Naperville, Illinois, 1986.

Robotics and Automated Manufacturing, Richard C. Dorf, Reston Publishing Company, 1983, Reston, Virginia.

Robotics in Practice, Joseph F. Engelberger, American Management Association, 1980.

A Glossary of Terms for Robotics, National Bureau of Standards, U.S. Department of Commerce, NBS Report PB82-251216.

Robotics Technology: An Assessment and Forecast, Aerospace Industrial Modernization Office of the Air Force Systems Command, July 1984.

ICAM Robotics Application Guide, Air Force Report, Report No. AFWAL-TR-8042.

Robot Motion, M. Brady, MIT Press, 1982.

The preparation of a book is dependent on an excellent staff, and I have been fortunate in this regard. Special thanks to Janet C. Hunt for research assistance. Special thanks to Margaret W. Alexander for the word processing of the manuscript.

ACRONYMS AND ABBREVIATIONS

AC Alternating Current
A/D Analog-to-Digital
AI Artificial Intelligence
ALU Arithmetic/Logic Unit
AM Amplitude Modulation
AML Advanced Manipulator Language
AMT Advanced Manufacturing Technology
ANSI American National Standards Institute
API All-Purpose Interface
APT Automatically Programmed Tools
APU Auxiliary Power Unit
AROM Alterable Random-Access Memory
ART Average Response Time
ASA American Standards Association
ASCII American Standard Code for Information Interchange
ASY Assembly
BCD Binary Coded Decimal
BIU Bus Interface Unit
BNA Boeing Network Architecture
BOM Bill of Materials
BPI Bits per Inch
BPS Bits per Second

BRA British Robot Association
BREP Boundary Representation
BSC Binary Synchronous Communications
CAD Computer-Aided Design
CAD/CAM Computer-Aided Design/Computer-Aided Manufacturing
CADD Computer-Aided Design and Drafting
CAM Computer-Aided Manufacturing
CASE Common Application Service Elements
CCD Charge-Coupled Device
CID Charge Injection Device
CIM Computer-Integrated Manufacturing
CL Cutter Location
CLF Cutter Location File
CLI Cutter Location Information
CLS Clear Screen
CNR Carrier-to-Noise Ratio
COPICS Communications-Oriented Production Information and Control System
CP Continuous Path
CPC Continuous Path with Controlled Path Motion

CPM   Critical Path Method
CPS   Characters per Second
CPS   Controlled Path System
CPU   Central Processing Unit
CRT   Cathode Ray Tube
CYL   Cylindrical
DA   Design Automation or Destination Address
DAA   Data Access Arrangement
DAS   Data Acquisition System
DASD   Direct Access Storage Device
DAT   Dynamic Address Translation
DBMS   Data Base Management System
DDAS   Digital Data Acquisition System
DDC   Direct Digital Control
DF   Degree of Freedom
DIP   Dual-In-Line Package
DIS   Draft International Standard
DLC   Data Link Control
DMA   Direct Memory Access
DML   Data Manipulation Language
DOS   Disk Operating System
DT   Developed Template
EPROM   Erasable Programmable Read-Only Memory
ES   Expert System or Electrical Schematic
ESC   Escape Character
FBL   Form Block Lines
FEA   Finite Element Analysis
FEM   Finite Element Modeling
FMC   Flexible Manufacturing Cell or Flexible Manufacturing Center
GKS   Graphics Kernal System
GMAW   Gas Metal Arc Welding
GMF   General Motors Fanuc
GTAW   Gas Tungsten Arc Welding
HDLC   High-Level Data Link Control
HZ   Hertz
IC   Integrated Circuit
ICAM   Integrated Computer-Aided Manufacturing (USAF)
IDEF$_0$ ICAM Definition Method, Version Zero
IDSS   ICAM Decision Support System

IDU   Interface Data Unit
IEEE   Institute of Electrical and Electronic Engineers
IFR   International Federation of Robotics
IGES   Initial Graphics Exchange Specification
IGS   Interactive Graphics Systems
IMS   Information Management System
I/O   Input/Output
IPDU   Internet Protocol Data Unit
IPL   Initial Program Load
IPS   Inches per Second
IS   International Standard
ISO   International Standards Organization
JCL   Job Control Language
JCS   Job Control Statement
JIRA   Japanese Industrial Robot Association
JNT   Jointed
JTM   Job Transfer and Manipulation
JUPITER   Juvanescent Pioneering Technology for Robots (Japan)
KBS   Knowledge-Based System
KE   Knowledge Engineer
KIPS   Knowledge Information Processing System
KR   Knowledge Representation
KWIC   Keyword-in-Context
LAN   Logical Area Network/Local Area Network
LCD   Liquid Crystal Display
LED   Light-Emitting Diode
LISP   List Processing Language
LPM   Lines per Minute
LSB   Least Significant Bit
LSI   Large-Scale Integration
LUT   Look-Up Table
MAP   Manufacturing Automation Protocol
MCC   Microelectronics and Computer Technology Corporation
MIG   Metal Inert Gas welding
MIS   Management Information System
MITI   Ministry of International Trade and Industry (Japan)

MMFS Manufacturing Message Format Standard
MOS Metal Oxide Semiconductor
MPS Master Production Schedule or Multi-Processing System
MRP Material Requirements Planning
MRPS Manufacturing Resource Planning System
MSB Most Significant Bit
MSI Medium-Scale Integration
MTBF Mean-Time-Between-Failures
MTP Machine Tool Program
MTTR Mean-Time-to-Repair
MUF Machine Utilization Factor
MUM Methodology for Unmanned Manufacturing
NAPLPS North American Presentation-Level Protocol Syntax
NC Numerical Control
NEC National Electrical Code
NGS Numerical Geometry System
NIST National Institute of Standards and Technology
NL Natural Language
NLI Natural Language Interface
NLP Natural Language Processing
NLU Natural Language Understanding
OEM Original Equipment Manufacturer
OMR Optical Mark Recognition
OS Operating System
OSHA Occupational Safety and Health Act
OSI Open System Interconnection
PC Personal Computer, Program Counter, Programmable Controller, or Printed Circuit
PCM Pulse Code Modulation
PD Programmable Device/Phase Modulation

P&ID Piping and Instrumentation Diagram
PID Proportional, Integral, Derivative Control
PIP Peripheral Interchange Program
PLA Programmed Logic Arrays
PLC Programmable Logic Controller
PM Phase Modulation
PTC Point-to-Point with Controlled Path Motion
PTP Point-to-Point Control System
RAM Random-Access Memory
RCC Remote Center Compliance
RGB Red, Green, Blue
RJE Remote Job Entry
ROM Read-Only Memory
ROS Read-Only Storage
RPG Report Program Generator
SA Source Address
SAP Service Access Point
SASE Specific Application Service Element
SCARA Selective Compliance Assembly Robot Arm
SDU System Data Unit
SPH Spherical
SSI Small-Scale Integration
SYSGEN System Generation
SYSLOG System Log
TCP Tool Center Point
TIG Tungsten Inert Gas Welding
TOP Technical and Office Protocols
TPDU Transport Protocol Data Unit
TPOP Time-Phased Order Point
VLSI Very-Large-Scale Integration
VMM Virtual Device Coordinates
VSAM Virtual Storage Access Method
WD Working Draft
XID Exchange Identification

ROBOTICS COMES
OF AGE

INTRODUCTION TO ROBOTICS

The primary thrust of domestic U.S. interest in robotics is the belief that robots, along with other automation technology, will be an important tool for improving the competitiveness of U.S. manufacturing. The use of robots can lower production costs, improve the quality of manufactured goods, and reduce workplace hazards. A clear theme has been the concern that foreign competitors, such as the Pacific Rim Countries (Japan) and Europe (Sweden and Germany), have gained a significant edge over the United States both in using this new production technology and in establishing a competitive position in the major export market for robots.

United States manufacturers are investing increasing amounts in new forms of automation to increase productivity, reduce product cost, and improve product quality and reliability in order to regain some of the domestic and world market share lost to foreign competitors. Robotics is one technology that is being applied successfully to accomplish these objectives. Firms that have incorporated robots into their manufacturing processes have demonstrated increases in productivity and reductions in manufacturing costs. The technology is flexible. Robots can perform as stand-alone machines or as components of an advanced computer-integrated manufacturing system, along with computer-aided design/computer-aided manufacturing (CAD/CAM) systems, automated materials-handling equipment, and computer numerically controlled (CNC) machine tools.

For a robot to function in the manufacturing environment it must perform successfully with respect to repeatability, accuracy, intelligence, and communication. The first two work hand in hand, since accuracy is the quality that makes repeatability usable. Accuracy is how close the robot can come to a commanded position. Repeatability is how close the robot can return to the previously ''touched'' position. Intelligence operates through the various sensory capabilities and through high-level language programming. Finally, the robot must have the ability to accept and feed back information and—in a growing number of cases—interact with other equipment in a manufacturing systems setting.

Robots have always excelled in applications where freeing humans from repetitious tasks or dangerous operating environments was a goal. Advances in visual, tactile, acoustic, and magnetic sensing capabilities have provided robots with the ability to perform many of the basic manufacturing functions, including visual inspection and intricate welding operations. New generations of robots are being applied in areas such as finishing, laser and water-jet cutting, assembly, and inspection. Clearly this technology is important now and in the future as one of the tools U.S. manufacturers can use to regain competitiveness, both in the domestic market and overseas. These same perceived advantages are spurring many other industrial nations to devote substantial resources to further development of robotics technology, thereby guaranteeing an intensely competitive global robot market into the foreseeable future. Figure 1-1 shows the growth in annual sales of robots in the United States.

Robots have become one of the more visible indicators of the trend toward factory automation. Robots are replacing human workers in the factories and on the production lines. Where there were once machinists, welders, and painters, there are now robots and their support systems, many of which are maintained and controlled by the workers that were initially displaced by the robots.

At first, robots competed on an economic basis with the workers they replaced. The early robots were extremely expensive and, with a life span of approximately 8 years, could hardly compete with human workers. But as worker benefits and wages began to increase, the fixed costs associated with robots became a reasonable cost alternative.

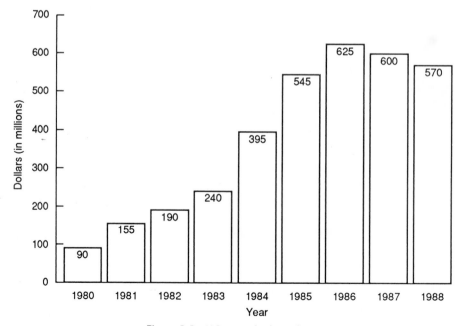

Figure 1-1 U.S. annual robot sales.

In the 1970s a few hundred robots were in use. They performed jobs that were too hazardous for human workers, or were too physically difficult or boring. The job required of the robot what it required of the worker: limited skill and the ability to cope with the specific working conditions.

Automobile manufacturers began emphasizing the use of robots in the middle and late 1970s. As the wages of workers spiraled even higher, management sought to replace manual labor with robots. The result was factories with lines of robots that had replaced human welders. The robots performed more consistently, which resulted in increased quality. Painting robots were developed next because humans could also not paint as consistently as the robots.

Today, robots are working in a wide variety of manufacturing operations across the entire spectrum of the economy. The trend is for robots to continue to become cost-effective in more and more fields as the wages of human workers continue to increase relative to robot operating costs. Table 1-1 shows the major robotic application areas by their percentage of current application. These trends show areas of primary interest in robot usage.

Although one faction of futurists believes that humans are in danger of being replaced tomorrow by the robot, don't plan on seeing this happen. Like humans, who have taken several millenia to evolve, in much the same fashion the robot will develop into a more complete entity over time. Presently the robot, even in its current state of evolution, is capable of performing many of the menial, tedious, repetitive, dangerous, and otherwise unpleasant chores that occur in the production world.

To perform tasks usually performed by a human, the robot will require some human capacities, namely, adaptable hands or grippers, wrist and arms with sufficient joints to allow range of motion, strength to meet the task at hand, memory to learn and repeat tasks once learned, vision to locate itself and parts in production, and the ability to permit control or supervision of the work performed. Finally, the robot must be as reliable and operate at a speed no less than the human it is to replace.

Several attributes are missing from the qualifications of our current robot, as shown in Table 1-2. A robot cannot react to unforeseen circumstances or changing environments and it lacks the ability to improve performance based on prior experience.

Table 1-1
Estimate of U.S. Robot Population by Application

Task	Percentage of total
Welding	26
Materials handling	22
Machine loading/unloading	17
Assembly	15
Casting	11
Painting and finishing	8
Other applications	1

Table 1-2
Comparison of Robot versus Human Skills and Characteristics[a]

Robot	Human
Action and Manipulation	
• One or more arms; automatic hand change is possible.	• Two arms and two legs; multipurpose hands.
• Incremental usefulness per each additional arm can be relatively higher than in humans.	• Two hands cannot operate independently.
• Movement time related to distance moved by speed acceleration, and deceleration, and will increase with higher accuracy requirements.	• Movement time and accuracy governed by Fitt's law. High-precision movements may interfere with calculation processes.
Brain and Control	
• Fast, e.g., up to 10,000 bits/sec for a small minicomputer control.	• Slow—5 bits/sec.
• Not affected by meaning and connotation of signals.	• Affected by meaning and connotation of signals.
• No valuation of quality of information unless provided by program.	
• Error detection depends on program.	• Good error detection/correction at cost of redundancy.
• Very good computational and algorithmic capability by computer.	
• Negligible time lag.	• Time lags increased, 1 to 3 sec.
• Ability to accept information is very high, limited only by the channel rate.	• Limited ability to accept information (10 to 20 bits/sec).
• Good ability to select and execute responses.	• Very limited response selection; execution (1 sec) responses may be "grouped" with practice.
Memory	
• Memory capacity from 20 commands to 2,000 commands and can be extended by secondary memory such as cassettes.	• No indication of capacity limitation.
• Can forget completely but only on command.	
• "Skills" must be specified in programs.	• Memory contains basic skills accumulated by experience.
	• Slow storage access/retrieval.
	• Very limited working register (5 times).
Training	
• Requires training by an experienced human or machine.	• Requires human teacher.
• Training does not have to be individualized.	• Usually individualized is best.
• No need to retrain once the program taught is correct.	• Retraining often needed due to forgetting.
Social	
• No social and psychological needs.	• Needs considerable support.

[a] From G. Nof, A. Knight, and D. Salvendy, "Effective Utilization of Industrial Robots—A Job and Skills Analysis Approach," *AIIE Transactions*, Vol. 12, No. 3, September 1980.

WHY USE ROBOTS?

Over the past several years, robots have become common in manufacturing facilities around the world. If advanced manufacturing technology is to become a viable reality, robots will need to become much more capable in every aspect: from precision to weight capacity to multipurpose programming and applications. Automation will be a hallmark of the future factory, a world of computer-integrated (Fig. 1-2) and computer-directed work cells each performing a specific part of the overall process of manufacture, from crude metal cutting to precision assembly and subsequent packaging.

The application of a robot will be based on considerable analysis of the entire system implications and how this new equipment will affect the overall operation. Robots can clearly be identified in terms of the functions they perform.

- Pick-and-place robots move objects from one place to another and position materials for the manufacturing process. They can perform material handling, grasping, transporting, and heavy-duty handling.
- Machine-loading robots can, in support of another machine such as a numerically controlled machine, accomplish the task of material loading and tool changing.

Figure 1-2 General Electric's computer-integrated manufacturing diesel engine plant. (Courtesy of General Electric.)

- Continuous path applications such as welding, spray painting, and heat treating, in which precise rates of motion are required, are within the robot's capability.
- Assembly robots can perform many operations in the production process. The design of such robots will be a challenge to the ingenuity of the designer, who must grapple with the problems of the sophisticated sensing of the parts and their orientation in the workstation. Central to this effort will be the advances required in the development of software algorithms to recognize and identify parts in a random orientation and a variety of lighting conditions. Tooling and parts feeders will also be required to support this new capability as it comes on line.
- Inspection robots will depend on the knowledge derived in the world of assembly robots and will perform sophisticated measurements. The robots will position parts, use some measuring devices, determine suitable production definition, and check for rejection criteria.

What additional new jobs will be created in the factory of the future is still to be determined. There will certainly be new challenges as we proceed into the next century, as well as new dangers to cope with and new requirements for our robotized work force. Table 1-3 lists the prime reasons for using robots.

The laws governing safety in the workplace and the threat of potential injuries are excellent reasons to consider robots. Many dangerous tasks are performed in factories, and some of these tasks are not appropriate for human workers. A good example of such a task is loading and unloading a die cast machine, a job performed at high temperature in an environment polluted with fumes and vapors. Many other hazardous situations are currently handled by robots. These robots include:

- welding robots, which are subjected to sparks, oil leaks, and water spray;
- machining robots, which are subjected to flying chips;
- painting robots, which operate in hazardous paint fume environments.

Today's robots can be usefully employed to accomplish highly structured industrial tasks for which variability can be controlled or engineered out. These are generally repetitive and programmable tasks, such as assembly, spot welding, spray painting, palletizing and unloading metal forming, and metal cutting.

Many hands-on tasks that are currently performed by workers will soon be done by robots. Expected uses for robots include heat treating, grinding and buffing, and inspection and assembly. The next generation of robots, which will

Table 1-3
Reasons for Using Robots (in Rank Order)

1. Increased profit
2. Reduced labor costs
3. Elimination of dangerous jobs
4. Increased output rate
5. Improved product quality
6. Increased product flexibility
7. Reduced materials waste
8. Reduced labor turnover

have integral machine vision, tactile sensors, or audio sensors, will be able to perform a much broader range of tasks in less structured environments.

The robot generally will outperform the human in extended, repetitive, well-defined tasks. Significant productivity increases can be expected because of the robot's constant pace and ability to operate in a multishift environment. A robot is impervious to fatigue and can repeatedly perform complex tasks, resulting in increased production over extended periods. Its ability to perform repetitive tasks guarantees that after learning a task, the robot will create less waste in production and less rework, both of which mean less material input to the process.

While outperforming human labor, the robot suffers few of the weaknesses inherent in humans. The robot does not get sick, take leave or breaks, or go on strike, and is not susceptible to injury. Its costs are mostly up front and, unlike human workers, it does not get annual raises, health benefits, and retirement pay.

ROBOTS DEFINED

Although everyone uses the word "robot," the mental images conjured up vary from person to person. In the wake of the movie *Star Wars*, many people visualize R2D2 and C3PO (Fig. 1-3) or androids shuttling around the landscape and carrying on intellectual discussions with each other. However, by human standards, robots are still in the embryonic stages of development.

Robots come in all sizes and shapes; from a Lincoln Electric Company Laser Vision MIG Trak Welding Robot (Fig. 1-4) to the robot arm on the space shuttle lifting over 500 kilograms in a zero-gravity environment. More typical robots are seen in some of the latest automobile commercials in which Lee Iacocca takes you for a tour of an auto plant, where you see a row of industrial robots all taking their turn on a chassis passing before them. This industrial robot is not nearly as flashy as the *Star Wars* duo previously mentioned. It doesn't walk, talk, or see; however, it does perform work. It is usually bolted to the floor, but eventually they will become part of a fully mobile system on the factory floor in which they move from one task to another.

It has been difficult to establish a usable, generally agreed upon international definition of a robot. Experts use different approaches in defining the term. It is important to have some common understanding to help define the state of the art, to project future capabilities, and to compare efforts between countries. Depending on the definition used, for example, estimates of the number of robots installed in Japan vary from 20,000 to over 100,000. This variation stems in part from the difficulty of distinguishing simple robots from very flexible robot systems.

A textbook definition of an industrial robot is "a programmable multifunctional device designed to both manipulate and transport parts, tools, or specialized implements through variable programmed paths for the performance of specific manufacturing tasks." Taking this definition apart:

- Programmable—capable of executing stored program or routines resident in its memory. The memory may be on magnetic tape, on computer floppy disk, or in a random-access microprocessor.

- Multifunctional—capable of being applied to a variety of operations. By inserting other learned operations stored in one of the memory media, the robot becomes capable of performing other tasks.
- Manipulate—to handle or use with skill. This will include gripping, holding, and rotating objects.
- Transport—carry or convey from one place to another. The work space for any robot will depend on its design, but once determined the robot must be capable of effective operation in that space.
- Tools or specialized manufacturing implements—unique tools like spray guns for painting or welding guns for welding, and more common tools like drills, grinders, routers, etc.
- Variable programmed paths—predetermined and stored directions or maps on the correct and sequential moves necessary to perform a task. The path may be defined only by its end points, by many points along its path, or continuously from end to end.
- Specific manufacturing tasks—those work elements defined or definable, with certain repeatability, that is, not requiring any additional human intervention once learned. The tasks will be limited by our ability to define the step-by-step processes involved in completing the task.

Figure 1-3 Science fiction robots. (Courtesy of *Star Wars,* Lucas Films, Inc.)

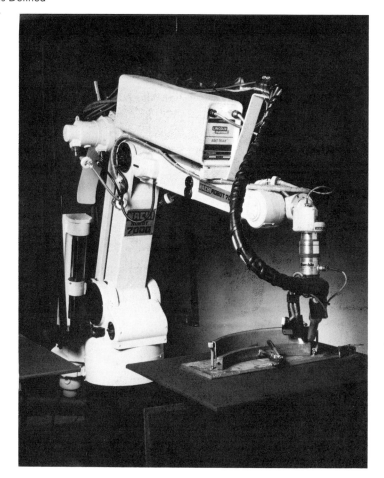

Figure 1-4   Lincoln's "Laser Vision MIG Trak" welding robot. (Courtesy of Lincoln Electric Company.)

Robots meeting the definition elements are evolving from less complex to more complex machines as follows:

1. Manual manipulators operated by humans. A common example of a manual manipulator is a backhoe, which is an arm guided by an operator.
2. Fixed-sequence pick-and-place robots—manipulators performing a series of steps specified by mechanical cams, switches, or valves.
3. Variable-sequence robots—instructions are specified by resetting electrical connections.
4. Playback robots—can remember and repeat any operation after being trained by an operator.
5. Numerically controlled robots—can receive instructions via magnetic tape or directly from a computer.
6. Smart or intelligent robots—can modify their own actions by responding to data received from sensors and by using the ability to process that sensory information.

This definition of a robot describes the current state of the technology and is generally accepted by the U.S. industry.

ROOTS OF ROBOTICS

Around 1923, the word "robot" came into general use following the publication of Karel Capek's play *R.U.R.* (Rossaum's Universal Robots). In 1926, robots first appeared in the movies in *Metropolis,* the most celebrated science fiction film of the silent period. The story, set in the year 2000, showed the masters of Metropolis exploiting the workers, who, like the Luddites in early nineteenth-century England, ultimately rebelled against the masters, the machinery, and the robot Maria.

Isaac Asimov, in his first robot story, "Strange Playfellows," published in 1940, featured a friendly robot named Robbie that saved a little girl. Asimov continued to write positive robot stories, trying to counteract what he calls the "Frankenstein complex." Asimov, together with John Campbell, then the editor of the leading science fiction magazine *Astounding Science Fiction,* began to formulate the Three Laws of Robotics. With Campbell's help and counsel, Asimov developed the robot characteristics for which he is now famous. The Three Laws of Robotics are:

1. A robot may not injure a human being or, through inaction, allow a human being to come to harm.
2. A robot must obey the orders given it by human beings except where such orders would conflict with the First Law.
3. A robot must protect its own existence as long as such protection does not conflict with the First or Second law.

In his third robot story, "Liar," published in May 1941, Asimov introduced the first of the Three Laws of Robotics and in his fifth story, "Runaround," published in March 1942, outlined all three laws for the first time. It was in this story that Asimov coined the word "robotics."

The technology of teleoperators received a boost in 1948 when Ray Goertz and others at the Argonne National Laboratory built the first mechanical master–slave manipulator with force feedback, which enabled an operator to feel what was happening to the manipulator on the other side of a wall. While work was progressing to improve teleoperators, there was a trend in the United States, mainly promoted by the U.S. Air Force, to improve productivity of the machining of aircraft parts. The idea for the modern numerically controlled (NC) machine tool came from John Parsons, who, with the help of Frank Stulen, convinced the Air Force in 1948 that automatically controlled machine tools could greatly increase the productivity in small and medium lots. These lot sizes make up an estimated 70% or more of most manufacturing and almost all of aerospace manufacturing.

In 1952, a young Harvard MBA, John Diebold, wrote the pioneering work "Automation, The Advent of the Automatic Factory." Diebold was thinking on a theoretical level, and in this important work he wrote:

During the last decade . . . developments in the fields of electronics, communications and electrical network analysis have made possible the construction of a wide variety of self-correcting and self-programming machines. These machines are capable of automatically performing a sequence of logical operations, similar in many ways to the mental processes of humans; they can correct the errors which occur in the course of their own operations, and can choose, according to built-in criteria, among several pre-determined plans of action. These recent advancements have been of such importance that they will constitute the first stages of what coming generations will look upon as the second industrial revolution.

The pioneering groundwork for robotics was brought together by the inventive and creative technical expert George Devol. In 1954, Devol was issued a patent for the Unimate, an abbreviation for Universal Automation. The Unimate was a teachable manipulator for programmable part handling. Devol continued to invent and eventually was awarded over 40 robotics-related patents, which became the core of Unimation, the first and most influential robotics company.

Until 1956, no one had been purely dedicated to robotics. This changed when George Devol met Joseph F. Engelberger at a cocktail party in Connecticut. Engelberger was receptive when Devol told him of his idea for a programmable manipulator. Subsequently Engelberger played the role of entrepreneur, supersalesman, and spark plug, which, when combined with Devol's inventiveness and strong patent position, was sufficient to provide the catalyst for the birth of the industrial robot industry. Engelberger later became known as "the father of industrial robots."

Between 1956 and 1958, Engelberger, Devol, Maurice J. Dunne, and George E. Munson visited many automotive facilities of major U.S. builders and other manufacturing plants to better understand the market and the types of potential applications that were best suited to the new concept of the industrial robot. Although Unimation is considered to be the first robot company, in 1959 the Planet Robot Company was selling pick-and-place robot devices. Planet's simple machines performed useful functions in industry and were the first commercially available industrial robots.

In 1957, the original company Consolidated Controls, supporting Engelberger and Devol's early efforts, decided not to pursue the business and decided to sell off its interests. At this time, Engelberger went to a variety of other companies and tried to interest them in the business and the robotics technology. At the same time, James Harder at Ford Motor Company, who was aware of Engelberger's difficulties, was pushing for automation at Ford and said that he could use 2000 of the robots immediately. He was worried that the fledgling robot industry would be set back with the loss of Unimation. Therefore, he circulated the specifications for the Unimate robot to other U.S. manufacturing and industrial companies, asking them to bid on producing such a machine for Ford. The net result of this twofold action—the pull from the marketplace (Ford) and the push from Engelberger—was that a number of large corporations entered the robot business, including AMF, Hughes Aircraft, IBM, Sunstrand,

and Western Electric. From that group, the most viable product, the Versatran robot used by AMF, became Unimate's leading competitor.

In 1958, with enough information in hand and confident that a machine could be produced that would sell, work on the Unimate began. The first Unimate was hydraulically powered, had a digital control and a magnetic drum memory, and used all discrete solid-state control components. This design was extremely innovative at the time. Much of the advanced controller design relied on Devol's early work with computers, memory devices, and electronics.

In 1961, the first of three prototype machines was installed in the General Motors Turnstedt plant in Trenton, New Jersey. The robot was to perform die casting work, and was taught by being led through the various steps of the operation, which it then recorded. The robot contained a memory of approximately 180 steps, 5 inputs, and 5 outputs. The market price was about $18,000. It was hoped that the Unimate would be applied for machine-tool loading and unloading, but 12 years passed before Unimates actually began to perform this work. In 1964, however, General Motors, as a result of their own internal studies, decided to use Unimates on their Norwood spot welding line, and placed an order for 66 robots to be used in their new Lordstown, Ohio plant, which was to be a showcase of modern manufacturing technology. This was an enormous order, as Unimation was then building only 3 or 4 machines per month. After the GM order was filled, Unimation went back to its previous productivity.

The industrial robot turned out to be a solution looking for a problem. Engelberger came to realize that nobody needed a robot. Manufacturers were only motivated by saving money, and a motivated human worker could usually outperform an industrial robot. Industry was uninterested in going through the difficulties inherent in installing this new technology; only when foreign competition, mainly from Japan, started to employ the machines did U.S. management become willing to invest the necessary time and money. While U.S. industry hesitated to buy robots, in the mid-1980s the Japanese were showing tremendous interest in robotics. For example, whereas Engelberger might talk before a dozen managers and engineers in the United States, in Japan he would speak before hundreds of enthusiastic professionals, all eager to learn about the new technology. Engelberger appeared on Japanese television and was often introduced as "the father of robots."

In 1968, Engelberger's Unimation granted Kawasaki the right to build the Unimate industrial robot line in Japan in exchange for royalties. Many other large Japanese companies were ready to jump into the market at the same time, and "robot fever" was beginning to spread throughout Japanese industries. The Japanese were quick to apply the technology because of a labor shortage, a good relationship between the workers and management, and, most importantly, the managers' long-term view on market share and industrial competitiveness based on manufacturing productivity. Joseph Engelberger has been tireless in his promotion of the increased productivity that is possible when robots are employed in manufacturing.

The first generation of modern roboticists and the first generation of modern robots reached their peak at the ROBOTS 6 Trade Show held in Detroit, Michigan, in March 1982. The press heralded the 1980s as the "decade of the robot;" predictions of fully automated, unmanned factories of the future abounded. The usually conservative financial community flocked to invest in robot and sensor companies based on forecasted sales and revenue figures. Most importantly, by 1982 the U.S. business leaders were finally making the long-term commitment to rejuvenate their factories by using advanced technology that would enable them to be competitive in the international marketplace. Automotive industries, which have always been the largest users of industrial robots, were widely seeking robotic solutions to production problems.

Major corporations such as IBM, General Electric, and Westinghouse entered the robot business at this time; the Detroit show and conference attendance set an all-time record, and the halls were filled with an eager public hoping to catch a glimpse of the near future. Robot vision systems were introduced at this show, and new companies were being formed to market this technology. Also on the horizon was the shining star of artificial intelligence, which was once again on the rise and holding great promise for robotics.

Another significant occurrence in 1981 was the formation of GMF, a U.S.-based joint venture between General Motors and Fanuc Limited that would design, manufacture, and sell robotics systems. Eric Mittelstadt was elected President and C.E.O. of the new company, in which GM and Fanuc shared a 50–50 equity interest. The robots sold by GMF are manufactured at the Fanuc facilities in Japan, with the exception of some machines built in the United States. Dr. Sieuemon Inaba, President of Fanuc, sits on the GMF board of directors.

When IBM, GE, Westinghouse, and GM entered the robot business, the overall robot market changed: past customers of the existing robot companies suddenly became competitors. A realignment of market share and market domination was soon under way. Between 1982 and 1986, GMF came to dominate the robot market in capturing more than 30% market share, largely because General Motors is the single largest user of industrial robots. From 1982 on, the large corporations began buying robot and machine vision companies and incorporating them as part of their internal plan to increase productivity by using advanced manufacturing technology, thereby gaining a foothold in the factory automation business.

There is still an enormous amount of work to be done. The next generation of roboticists are those future engineers, managers, and researchers who are still attending universities and working in their research laboratories. Those who join the manufacturing industries will apply the latest technology and push productivity levels to a new high. All of these workers will be the pioneers of the second generation.

ROBOT TECHNOLOGY

Robotics has a dual technological ancestry that has an important influence on discussions about what they are, what they can do, and how they are likely to develop. The two ancestral lines are (1) industrial engineering automation technology, a discipline that stretches historically over a century, and (2) computer science and artificial intelligence technology, which is only a few decades old. Ideas about the nature of robots differ according to the importance given to these two technological roots.

Most modern industrial robots are extensions of automated assembly-line technology. This form of automation historically has not depended on computers, although microelectronics provides a powerful new tool for extending its capabilities. In this industrial automation view, modern industrial robots are closely related to numerically controlled machine tools. From such a perspective, robotics is already approaching the state of a mature technology. Over the next decade, the most important impacts of robotics on the economy and work force cannot be considered separately from the impacts of industrial automation in general.

On the other hand, modern computer technology may provide future robots with new "intelligent" capabilities such as visual and tactile perception, mobility, or the ability to understand instructions given in a high-level natural language, such as "Assemble that pump!" The commercial availability of such capabilities may be one or two decades away.

In the view of some computer science researchers, robotics will have little significant social impact in the near future. They estimate that, given sufficient research support, a flexible, intelligent robot could be produced for the market within this decade. A robot of this type will be able to move freely about an unstructured environment and perform a wide variety of tasks on command with minimal reprogramming time. This view stresses continuing basic research in computer science related to robotics, particularly in artificial intelligence. Robots are seen as "stand-alone," reprogrammable devices capable of performing many tasks other than large-scale, assembly-line applications, for example, small-scale batch manufacturing, mining, or equipment repair.

Which of these views is most pertinent in terms of current policy issues will depend in part on whether such an "intelligent" robot would be economically feasible in the near future and whether it would meet a significant need in the industrial sector. In fact, it seems likely that both types of robotics technology will eventually become important, but that their economic and social impacts will differ to the extent that they are used for different purposes in different environments. Furthermore, the time scale for widespread adoption will be significantly later for the "intelligent" machines.

Robots are only one component of a large collection of related devices and techniques that form the technological base of industrial automation. Mechanical devices that perform tasks similar to those done by modern industrial robots have existed for centuries. The principal difference is that, whereas so-called "hard automation" is custom-designed to a particular task, robots are standardized but flexible and programmable units that can be installed in different environments with much less customization. There is a trade-off between the efficiency of hard automation and the flexibility of robots.

Since machinery will be integrated with the total design of a factory, it may not be useful to distinguish robotics as an independent technology. A fully automated factory of the future might include the following components:

- A computer-aided design (CAD) system that provides a tool for engineers to develop new products on a computer using an electronic display screen. The data base generated by the computer during the design phase is then used by other computerized parts of the factory.
- Numerically controlled machine tools and other automated devices that fabricate components of the product and transport and assemble them following instructions generated by the CAD system.

- Robots, also operating under computer-generated instructions, that transfer materials from station to station, operate tools such as welders and spray painters, and perform assembly tasks.
- Computerized information systems that keep track of inventory, trace the flow of material through the plant, diagnose problems, and even correct them when possible.

All of these technologies are currently under development and are being used in some form. They will likely evolve into components of a fully automated, flexible manufacturing facility. Thus, there appear to be two parallel technological tracks along which industrial robots are likely to develop: (1) stand-alone standardized units that will have varying uses in many different environments and (2) robotics technology that is integrated into complete factories that will themselves be flexible.

TYPICAL APPLICATIONS

Identifying the applications in which robots are most appropriate will be the key to the productivity of our factories of the future. A robot can be the better choice where a tool or product must be moved independently or in conjunction with another machine. The categories of manufacturing activities that fit this definition are:

- Manipulation or transport—movement of parts from one place to another.
- Processing—parts are altered by a tool, that is, drilling, routing, machining, welding, painting, soldering, or glueing, or are handled by a robot to install components in light manufacturing assemblies.
- Inspection—parts are transferred from one place to another for inspection and the robot awaits decision from some form of inspector or machine for instructions for its next move.

Several of the many areas in which robots are being applied will be examined in an attempt to show the versatility and potential for robots.

Material Handling

The technological issues involved in current material-handling applications range from the routine to the very complex. In the simplest cases, the "pick-and-place" processes, the robot needs only to move to a prescribed location, grasp an object, move to a second prescribed location, and release the object. In the more advanced implementations, the robot may use any combination of specially engineered grippers such as magnetic or vacuum grippers, some method of smooth path control, or various sensors to locate and verify acquisition of the workpiece. The level of sophistication, then, generally depends on the specific needs of each individual implementation.

The driving factor for robotization of material-handling applications depends heavily on the work volume. If the batch size is very large, then hard automation is generally more economical than robots. Conversely, if the batch size is very small, then human labor is usually more economical than robots.

However, there may be overriding reasons for using robots in applications where they would be less economical than other methods, including work in an unpleasant or hazardous environment, such as a foundry, or highly repetitive or difficult work that would cause fatigue or injury in human laborers.

Assembly

Robotic assembly operations may be performed at a variety of sophistication levels. For easy-mating assemblies, low levels of sensor and path control sophistication are required, while for the more critical assemblies, complex force sensing and machine vision may be necessary. In addition to advanced sensing requirements, critical path control may also be required. The geometry of assembling two closely fitted workpieces is not trivial; although a human can easily compensate for slight misalignment, a robot cannot always make the minute corrections in position and angle of attack to properly assemble two workpieces. Although completely accurate and efficient assembly control methods are not yet available, partial solutions to this problem are available and are being used in production.

The driving force for robotic assembly, as for robotic material handling, depends on throughput volume. For very large volumes, hard automation with fixturing systems is more economical than robotics, while for very small batches human labor can be more economical than robots. For those volumes of work where robots have the potential for being economical, robotic assembly has the advantage of increased consistency over human labor. Just as for inspection, the high repeatability of the robot affords a higher and more predictable level of quality control than with human systems. A secondary incentive for using robots for assembly involves clean room and hazardous or unpleasant environments. Using a robot for an operation that must be performed in a clean room eliminates the complications of human preparation for the clean room.

Welding

Welding is a process that joins metals by fusing them. The process of spot welding includes the compression of the two metals at the point of weld, the weld itself, a short period of cooling, and finally the release of the welded area. To sustain the welding electrodes over a long period of successive welds, they are water-cooled. Much of the process time is spent moving from one weld point to the next. In the auto industry, robots are generally synchronized to perform the same welding sequence over several chassis at one time.

Where welding must be done on heavy metals and over long seams, arc welding is more appropriate. In the arc welding process an inert gas floods the area to be welded and the arc is then struck and sustained between the welding rod and the workpiece. The temperature at the arc rises to sufficient levels to melt the metals and fuse the joint. This form of welding has found application in the joining of aluminums, coppers, magnesiums, and stainless steels.

The robot is strongly entrenched in welding processes, and with the automobile and aircraft industries as strong supporters and innovators, the applications will increase in other areas. Not only can robot welders perform more precisely and more repeatably than a human welder, but they also do it faster—some estimates indicate a three-to-one saving in time. And once again, the hazardous environment makes robots especially useful.

Spray Painting/Coating

In general, robotic painting and coating operations require a very low level of technological sophistication, for example, sensors are not widely used in painting applications. The most critical aspect of the robot technology for painting tasks is smooth path control. In some of the more recent painting applications, however, the robot controller is called on not only to direct the path of the robot and control the painting apparatus, but also to coordinate the painting with the movement of an assembly line and with other concurrent operations such as door opening.

Because robotic painting and coating operations require a minimum level of technology, in combination with the fact that this technology has been available for some time, robots have shown a heavy penetration into the painting industry, especially in automobile paint-spraying applications. In fact, several different robot manufacturers have built reputations solely on their paint-spraying robots.

Die Casting

Die casting involves the production of parts by injecting metal alloys under high temperature and pressure into metal molds or dies. This was a pioneer application for robot use, and the die casting industry now uses robotics to load the machine, quench the part, unload the machine, and perform rough trimming. Each of these operations is within the capability of the robot. Some are used in 24-hour operations, 7 days a week, with an extremely high degree of success and few downtime problems. The die-cast operation is an excellent example of how robots can replace workers in a hazardous environment on a 24-hour basis.

Press Operations

Presses are used to shape metal into a variety of shapes, from body panels of cars to appliances, and robots are now performing the basic operations. The pick-and-place robot can pick up a stock metal, place it in the press so that it registers correctly, remove the finished part, and then either stack it or pass it to the next operation.

Press operations are considered to be among the most hazardous in the factory, and safety regulations require sophisticated devices that make the press inoperative when humans inadvertently enter the machine safety zone. Over the years, as a result of human ingenuity, there have been many attempts to defeat these safety measures, and accidents have occurred.

Robots are best employed in those press operations where the cycle is relatively slow. Some presses work at a rate beyond the robot's capability to be useful in performing the supply and transfer functions. Some of these faster operations are now serviced by automated stacking equipment.

Inspection

Robotic inspection generally requires the most technologically advanced equipment available. As sensor technology improves, inspection applications are becoming more varied. Sensing systems currently used for robotic inspection include two-dimensional and lightstripe machine vision, as well as force sensing and tactile sensing. In addition, other types of sensing are being implemented as advances in infrared, ultrasonic, and eddy current sensing technologies have reduced the price of these sensors to a cost-effective level.

Until recently, sensing technology has been either unavailable or uneconomical. For this reason, robot penetration into inspection processes has been slower than expected. As the technologies improve and the prices drop, robotic inspection will become more common. Also, because inspection processes are increasingly coupled to assembly tasks, robotic inspection will be employed more with the increase in robotic assembly.

The primary reason for using robots in inspection tasks is quality control. The consistency and repeatability of the robot and the control algorithms that compare the workpiece to a model allow for not only greater but also more consistent levels of quality. One of the most important factors that could increase the use of robotic inspection is not availability of new technologies but rather the need for decreasing the cost and increasing the speed of current technologies. Additionally, three-dimensional real-time vision and precision tactile sensing arrays are very active research areas that, when fully developed, will expand the scope of robotic inspection.

THE ROBOT INDUSTRY

The principal uses of robots today are welding, spray painting, and a variety of so-called pick-and-place light assembly operations that involve simply picking up an object and putting it with a specific orientation in a predetermined spot. The automobile industry (Fig. 1-5) has been the largest user of industrial robots, in terms of the value of equipment installed. The following discussion considers the industrial robot to be an extension of manufacturing automation. We do not address possible new robot applications outside of manufacturing, such as underwater or nuclear equipment repairs.

Domestic robot manufacturers appear to fall into four groups:

1. Traditional machine tool manufacturers, such as Cincinnati Milacron, that have developed a broad state-of-the-art robot product line.
2. Firms such as Adept that have specialized in vertical robot markets, such as the SCARA light assembly robot.
3. Large manufacturing firms, such as IBM and General Electric. Some of these firms may choose either to retain the technology for their own use or to market their robots to other companies.
4. Small entrepreneurial firms (TRC) that develop new, innovative robots. This type of firm has been important in developing new systems and could play an important role in robotics.

The relative importance of these different types of firms in the market place will depend on and, in turn, influence the evolution of robotics technology. The history of the microelectronics market suggests that many innovations in robotics will come from the entrepreneurs. Significant in this regard is the trend among many larger industrial firms to acquire small, innovative firms to either diversify or integrate their traditional product lines with new technologies.

Despite improved growth in robot sales this year, the U.S. robotics industry

Figure 1-5 Robots spot-welding the Sentra passenger car and/or truck cab. (Courtesy of Nissan Motor Manufacturing Corporation U.S.A.)

remains a small, low-volume industry, largely dependent on the automotive and light manufacturing electronics industries for the majority of its revenues. The industry is currently in a flat growth/sales mode because the automotive industry cut back on their capital spending plans in 1989. At present the automobile industry's share of annual robotics orders runs about 50 percent, which is down substantially from the beginning of the decade. As a result of the decline in automotive-related capital expenditures between 1985 and 1989, the robotics industry has increased research and development in vertical applications that will allow other industries, such as light manufacturing, to apply robotics technology to their manufacturing processes.

Application advancements in light manufacturing, such as those made during 1989 in surface-mount and through-hole technologies, will reduce the robotics industry's dependence on orders from the automotive industry. These types of applications particularly suit the revitalized U.S. electronics and appliance industries. Also, the flexibility, quality control, productivity, and automation requirements of modern manufacturing ensure the expanding use of robotics in the factory of the future. The robotic industry's recent profitability will enable U.S. producers to devote more time, energy, and funding to application research.

The fastest-growing markets for robotics are in light manufacturing assembly operations. Recently the electronics industry has seen significant growth, which is influenced partially by developments in robot sensors, artificial intelligence, network communications, enhanced accuracy, and system integration.

Between 1987 and 1994, U.S. robot revenues are projected to show a compound annual growth rate of 9.7 percent and may reach $879 million by 1994. Revenues for light industrial robots alone are expected to exceed 50 percent of the total U.S. robot market by 1994. Internationally, the world market for robots was $2.83 billion in 1987 and may reach $4.93 billion by 1994. Imports of robots into the United States are estimated to account for at least 30 percent of domestic consumption. Eighty percent of these imports are from Japan, which is the dominant force in the world in robot manufacture producing more than half the total. In contrast, the United States and Europe each produce about 20 percent of the world total. There are about 300 firms producing robots in Japan, and one-third of this output is for in-house use only.

The growth of robots in American industry is tied to the level of long-term investment in new manufacturing methods and automation in general. In comparison to other leading industrial nations, investment has been dismally low in the United States. Assuming that American corporate management makes a long-term commitment, the U.S. robotics industry could change markedly over the next decade in response to demand shifts. As mentioned earlier, the spread of robots to a wider range of light manufacturing industries will make the industry less dependent on the capital spending cycles of the automotive sector. Furthermore, the rise in assembly and materials-handling applications for robots will bring an increase in demand for robot systems as opposed to standalone machines. Future success in the U.S. market will go to the supplier who can provide a complete turnkey system to meet users' needs. The application of peripherals and systems software for the more complex factory automation solutions will become an increasingly important focal area for domestic producers.

Robotics firms in the United States will remain dependent on offshore components in the manufacture and assembly of robot systems. However, the source for these imports may well shift, as the European Community appears ready to challenge the Japanese share of the world market. The Western European nations have also recently worked out agreements to share the cost of research and development. This type of joint effort will expedite the development of new technology and the closing of gaps where they exist. More importantly, it will reduce the costs associated with research and development for a number of companies and allow them to spread their research over a wider base.

IMPACT ON JOBS

In addition to the potential applications of new robotics technology, a number of impacts that the expansion of robotics will have on jobs have been identified. Each of these issues is discussed briefly in this section.

- Productivity
- Labor
  - Unemployment, displacement, or job shifting
  - Positive or negative effects on the quality of working environment (such as exposure to hazards, job boredom, and employer/employee relations)
- Education and training
  - Need for technological specialists
  - Need for a technologically literate work force
  - Need for retraining workers

Productivity

Much of the literature on robotics refers to the contribution that robotics will make toward improving industrial productivity. Since a major national concern is the strengthening of the productivity and competitiveness of U.S. industry, it is important to examine this issue.

Some experts warn about exaggerating the importance of robotics in improving productivity. Two reasons are offered:

1. Robotics is only one tool in a wide array of technologies available to automate manufacturing and enhance teamwork in order to increase industrial productivity.
2. Productivity is a subtle and complex concept with numerous definitions and measurements. Furthermore, even after a specific definition is chosen, industrial productivity depends on many factors that interact with one another. Hence, it is difficult to attribute productivity improvements to any single technology.

These warnings do not suggest that robotics is an unimportant production technology. Most experts believe it is important; however, they are cautious not to take a narrow view of all technologies when assessing impacts on industrial productivity.

Although most applications of robots to date have been made by large firms, the future diffusion of robotics and related technologies will also affect small- and medium-sized businesses in several ways. For example, there are likely to be many new business opportunities for small firms to develop and produce software and specialized types of equipment and to provide system integration services. Second, it can be argued that robotics and flexible automation may in some cases lower the minimum economy of scale for efficient production, and therefore new manufacturing opportunities for small firms will become available. This situation frequently arises when major equipment technologies change.

Capital formation is another issue that has been raised regarding robotics. The important question seems to be whether there is adequate capital to buy the appropriate robot technology that will enhance a company's productivity in three areas:

1. To fund the modernization of industrial plants for the use of automation technology. The financial need would be particularly great if we rebuilt entire plants to make the most effective use of robotics, rather than incrementally improve the existing plant.
2. To fund the construction and evolutionary expansion of U.S. plants to produce robots in the quantities necessary to have a significant economic impact.
3. To fund entrepreneurs who wish to develop new types of robots. The importance of the availability of capital for this purpose depends on the demand and desirability of increasingly efficient and economical technology.

The lack of capital is a very serious impediment to the growth of the robotics industry and to the expansion of robot use in manufacturing. Some experts believe that a tax policy, such as an investment tax credit, that encourages such investment would be an important stimulus.

Labor

Unemployment is an issue that is constantly raised in discussions about the impact of robots, but the relationship between robotization and employment is commonly misunderstood. Productivity improvements resulting from the use of robotics and related technologies can affect labor in a number of ways. These effects depend on factors such as:

- The effects of new technology on the relative proportion of machinery to workers (the capital–labor ratio) in a given industry.
- The extent of change in prices and production volumes for U.S. firms once the new technology is in use.
- The supply of qualified workers with specific job skills in a given industry.

United States employment in a given industry may fall because of productivity improvements, which by definition enable fewer workers to produce a given volume of product. Employment in a given industry may remain constant or rise, however, if productivity improvements are combined with increases in production volume. Effective labor compensation may also rise or fall if productivity improvements lead to shorter work weeks or new product prices or both, depending in large part on production volume and profitability. Finally, average wage levels will change with adjustments in the necessary mix of worker skills resulting from the implementation of robotics and related technologies.

Definitions of unemployment, like those of productivity, require distinctions between short-term and persistent job loss, and between true unemployment (job loss) and displacement (job shift). For some time, most experts in the United States have argued that more jobs are created by new technology than are eliminated. However, if these jobs are in different industries and/or require different skills, the effect on an individual who would be replaced by automation could be traumatic. In general, if they have been replaced in a union organization, they will in turn displace someone else, a process that ripples through the job structure. Even though the replaced workers may be employed, the opportunity for "new hires" is lost as a result of the job reduction impact.

On the other hand, new jobs will be created in the production and servicing of robots and related technologies. The number of jobs created and the rate at which they appear will depend both on growth rate of the robot industry and on the degree to which robot manufacture and repair are themselves automated.

To assess the effects of automation on future employment levels, a baseline must be established against which job loss or gain can be measured. This baseline could be a simple extrapolation of current trends, but it also may need to be adjusted to reflect two other effects:

- Virtual employment—domestic jobs that were not explicitly eliminated, but that would have existed if robots were not installed.
- Virtual unemployment—domestic jobs that would have been lost if the plant had not responded to domestic and international competition by automating.

As with productivity, it is difficult to attribute employment effects to any single component, such as robotics, as part of an entire range of improvements in the manufacturing process. Any examination of the effects of robots on jobs would need to consider robotics in the much broader context of automation technology in general. There are two principal sets of questions concerning unemployment. These questions differ in their focus, in their implications, and in the data collection necessary to analyze them:

1. Will the United States experience a long-term rise in the real unemployment rate because of the introduction of robotics and other automation? If so, will these effects be differentially felt by geographical location, social class, education level, race, sex, or other characteristics? What might be the employment penalty of not automating?
2. Will the use of robots create displacement effects over the next decade? How will these effects be specific to particular industry classes, geographical locations, or types of jobs? How will labor/management negotiations be affected?

The quality of the working environment is another issue that needs to be addressed. If robots are employed principally for jobs that are unpleasant or dangerous and if the new jobs created by robotics are better, the quality of work life will improve. In the longer term, productivity increases may also result in a shorter, more flexibly scheduled work week.

New forms of advanced manufacturing technology may in many cases relieve job boredom and resulting worker dissatisfaction that many management experts have been concerned with. Workers may be able to use more complex skills and perform a greater variety of tasks. For instance, they may be able to follow the assembly of a product from beginning to end and assume greater individual responsibility for the quality of the final product. The human working environment can also be improved by segregating processes that create hazardous working conditions (such as heat or exposure to chemicals) from the section of the factory occupied by humans. Furthermore, equipping a worker with a robot helper for strenuous activities not only eases job stress but also creates employment opportunities for those who have physical handicaps or other limitations.

Whether these benefits are realized depends in part on how industry uses robots. Many labor experts are concerned that some uses of robots will not be so salutary. For example, some argue that one long-term effect of robotics may be to "deskill" labor, requiring less ability on the part of humans as they are incorporated into a mechanized environment. Other experts have pointed out the increased opportunities for employer surveillance of employees. Some unions also fear that automation could be used by employers to "downgrade" jobs that require working with automated systems, or that robots might be targeted to replace unionized jobs first.

Education and Training

A number of education and training issues are raised in the areas of robot installation, programming, and maintenance. There is still a shortage of trained technical experts in the field of robotics, and if there is to be any significant expansion in the pace of robot-driven automation, many more computer scientists, engineers, software programmers, and technicians will be required in the next decade. A shortage already exists in many fields of engineering and science, and it seems to be particularly critical in areas of computer software design and programming. Hence, the lag in education and training is not unique to robotics technology, at least in the case of highly skilled jobs.

At the same time, the use of robots has already created some new technical jobs. Programs have been started at the community college level to train workers in robot installation, programming, and maintenance. There is also a need for a more technologically literate work force, one that has a basic understanding of technology and mathematics. Improved technological literacy would provide the following benefits:

1. To the extent that workers would be expected to instruct, oversee the maintenance of, or repair robot units, they would need some basic understanding of computers and systems, both mechanical and electrical.
2. A technologically literate work force would be less likely to resist the introduction of robots and other advanced manufacturing technology.
3. A knowledgeable, technologically skilled worker would be easier to retrain for another job somewhere else in the plant.

One reason the Japanese work force seems to welcome robots in their plants is the high level of technological literacy reported for the average Japanese employee. This would give employers greater latitude in finding another and possibly more skilled job for a displaced worker. If the introduction of robotics into a plant is not to result in unemployment, a program of retraining displaced workers for new jobs is necessary. Retraining also will be required for those workers who remain, for their existing jobs will change in form and function even if their job titles remain the same.

SAFETY

Industrial robots have a remarkably good safety record. However, additional precautions (safety sensors, guard rail/cage, systems, operator training) could increase the safety of robots still further. Industrial robots also eliminate some of the hazards involved in working in many factory environments, such as machine safety guards, heat, noise, fumes, and lifting of heavy loads that are encountered in using metal presses and painting. The importance of robots for risk control has been especially great since the Occupational Safety and Health Act went into effect.

There are several opportunities for enhanced robot system safety, including improvements to protect against software and hardware failures, fail-safe design, and the enhancement of operator training. These are briefly described in the following sections.

Protection against Software Failures

Redundancy, though expensive, offers the best protection against software failure. A double-redundant system can shut itself down when its two components disagree, and a triple-redundant system can use majority logic to override one failed component and continue operation. Both hardware and software redundancy are useful.

Hierarchical and multiprocessor systems can be made more reliable by data redundancy. Time-outs are another simple and effective failure test; for example, a time-out could be used in the interface hardware between a robot and its controlling computer. If the computer fails to send the robot interface a keep-alive signal, the interface halts the robot. A status check is a third way to detect software failure. In a status check, one computer sends specific data to a second computer, which can tell if the data are self-consistent. The safest way of checking status is to run two identical computers in parallel and compare their actions.

Protection against Hardware Failures

The servo valve is a weak point in a hydraulic system since dirt in the hydraulic fluid can cause the spool to stick in an open position and result in uncontrolled motion of the arm. A precise servo valve is a very complex and expensive device, but it could still be improved by rotating it continuously or back and forth around its axis independent of its normal control motion along that axis. This would improve valve operation by reducing static friction in the valve to zero and make the valve more sensitive to small control signals, as well as make it possible to detect a valve clogged by dirt in the fluid since the rotation would stop.

Sensors that detect loss of line voltage, pneumatic pressure, or hydraulic pressure, as well as excessive temperature, speed, acceleration, force, and servo errors, could also be included in the system. Either hardware or software could monitor the signals from such sensors. Redundancy in the individual components of robotic devices and safety systems can make the entire device or system more reliable. Component redundancy can be applied at many levels in a robot system; for example, a robot might have multiple actuators on each joint so that one could fail without making the robot drop what it is carrying. Of course, this increases the cost of the system, so it may not always be economically justifiable.

Fail-Safe Design

Hazard detection sensors, electrical circuits, and other components in a safety device can fail. Equipment that simulates whatever condition the sensor is supposed to detect can be added to guard against this, and this equipment would challenge the detection system automatically. If the sensor should fail to respond to a challenge, a warning signal would be generated by the safety device.

Operator Training

Accidents cannot be prevented by safety devices alone. Those who work with or around robots must also be trained in the precautions necessary for their own safety. For example, it is educational for workers to see a robot snap a 3/8-in. steel rod in half. Some of the mistaken assumptions include:

1. If the robot arm is not moving, they assume it is not going to move.
2. If the robot arm is repeating one pattern of motions, they assume it will continue to repeat that pattern.
3. If the robot arm is moving slowly, they assume it will continue to move slowly.
4. If they tell the robot arm to move, they assume it will move the way they want it to.

In summary, workers must use good common sense in all aspects of the robot application and should check each part of the robotics equipment safety as with any other piece of automated equipment.

INTERNATIONAL LEADERSHIP

Substantial investments in Europe and Japan for encouraging the use of robots is increasing the competition in robotics technology development. This competition exists on two levels: (1) developing and selling robotics technology itself and (2) using robots to produce goods more competitively (e.g., automobiles and in light assembly manufacturing). Some analysts believe that the directions of robotics-related research are significantly different between the United States and other nations, notably Japan. American researchers emphasize software and highly flexible larger systems, while many international laboratories are concentrating on vertical market hardware solutions. Other analysts maintain that the international state of the art in robotics is superior to that in the United States. In general, such "technological leads" are hard to either prove or disprove. However, there is a consensus that the utilization of robots is more advanced in several other nations, such as Japan and Sweden, compared to in the United States.

Although the international interdependence of robot producers facilitates the spread of new technology, gaps exist in several areas between the United States and its foreign competition. American firms lead their foreign competitors in a number of areas associated with robot peripherals and applications of the more complex robot functions. However, it appears that as a whole American business has been slow to apply these technologies in the production arena. Producers in Japan and Western Europe are concentrating on closing any technological gaps in areas where they lag behind U.S. producers, whereas they are extending their lead over U.S. suppliers in other areas of technology. In general, our international competitive position is partially driven by the application of robots, continued research and development, acceptors of U.S. and industrial standards, and fair international trade agreements.

The issue of international competition creates conflicts in import/export policy. Further controls might be placed on import/export of robots either for national security reasons or to limit foreign access to domestic high technology that increases the competitiveness of U.S. firms. However, such controls also deny U.S. robot manufacturers access to foreign markets. Even if the total international market in robots were to remain relatively small, robot technology would be a vital component in the much larger international market for sales of complete computer-integrated advanced manufacturing factories.

No country has pursued robotics with as much vigor as Japan. In the mid-1960s, when Japan imported the first industrial robots, Japanese industry and government were gaining in industrial strength and making a worldwide push in the automotive, motorcycle, and consumer electronics industries. Japan appeared to be ideal for the successful introduction of robots: a shortage of laborers to perform the work; good management/labor relations; stable, far-thinking management, not driven by a need for short-term returns on investment and equity; an industrial base that had been largely rebuilt after World War II; cooperative efforts among the universities, government agencies, and industrial giants; a basically clean, rational, and harmonious practice of manufacturing, which leads to an easier implementation of robotic technology; and an emphasis on efficiency and productivity using the simplest technology appropriate. In addition to these factors, Japanese corporate management views domestic competition as a continual threat to the corporate family's well-being.

As a result of the market environment and motivation, the Japanese captured the lion's share of the world industrial robot market and were far ahead of any other country in the application of industrial robots. Unlike the U.S. robot industry, where about a dozen companies dominate the robot business, in Japan there are 300 manufacturers of robots.

In the early 1970s, Japan's Ministry of International Trade and Industry (MITI) recognized that industrial robot technology would be important to Japan's movement into the international marketplace as a dominant manufacturer. Thus, MITI sponsored robotic technology research and encouraged the application of robots in various leasing programs by stimulating cooperative ventures between Japanese universities, government, and industries. In 1971, the Japanese Industrial Robot Association (JIRA) was formed. It was the first professional robot association ever formed, even though the United States had been using robots for a decade. This cooperative trade organization consisted of industrial robot builders and its main goal was to disseminate information on industrial robot technology. JIRA was organized with the help and leadership of many Japanese companies, particularly Kawasaki Heavy Industries and its executive vice-president and director, Usuneo Ando.

Research was subsequently conducted at many universities throughout Japan, including Waseda, Tokyo, Nagoya, and Kato. Tokyo University and many of Japan's large companies have their own research organization, among them Matsushita, Hitachi, Kawasaki, Yaskawa, Mitsubishi, Seiko, and Fanuc, under the farsighted management of Seiumon Inaba, President of Fanuc.

Until this time, Japan's strength was in the application of robotic technology; however, Japan has recently also taken leadership in technology design. Many of the robot arms used throughout the world are manufactured in Japan, as are an increasing number of the controls. One of the most popular robot manipulator designs, the SCARA robot, was developed under the leadership of Hiroshi Makino, professor of precision engineering at Yamanashi University. Work in undersea robotics is being conducted by the Japan Marine Science and Technology Center (JAMSTEC) in Yokosuka. The Japanese will surely continue their efforts in the application and development of robotic technology.

NOW AND THE FUTURE

The robot has existed as a tool for little more than 25 years. The technology evolved from early developments in servo mechanisms for remote control of naval weapons and aircraft control systems, teleoperator manipulators used in the nuclear industry, and machine tools. These developments began in the United States in the early to mid-1950s by George Devol and led to the founding of Unimation, the world's first robot producer.

Today's U.S. robotics industry is a mix of established robot producers, a few venture capital groups, and major robot users (such as IBM and Fanuc) who have moved into robot production. Although over 56 U.S.-based firms participate in the domestic robot market, most industry revenue is shared among the top 5 producers, who control more than 80 percent of the market. The majority of sales are made to firms in the automotive, electronics assembly, and aerospace industries.

The structure of the U.S. robotics industry has changed dramatically over the past decade. Beginning in the late 1970s, inflated market growth projections, stimulated by intense media coverage of robots as the technology of the future, fueled rapid growth in the industry. Overly optimistic projections of U.S. demand for robots encouraged Japanese and European industrial robot producers to establish footholds in the U.S. market, either independently or through established U.S. firms. Many U.S. producers, under heavy competitive pressures, looked offshore for suppliers from whom they could purchase existing technology and hardware at lower cost to them than by using domestic production. Several large firms sought to establish themselves as producers for general sale as well as for their own use. The entry of these companies, notably General Motors, IBM, and General Electric, had a significant impact on the structure of the U.S. robotics industry and on the market strategies of existing firms. The top three U.S.-based robot producers—Cincinnati Milacron, Adept, and GMF—illustrated the variety of firms in the industry. Cincinnati Milacron is a machine tool producer that has diversified into robotics. The company derives a comparatively small portion of its total revenues from robot sales. Adept, a spin-off from Unimation, derives most of its revenue from the sale of robots. GMF is a joint venture between General Motors and Fanuc Limited of Japan that was created in 1982, under which Fanuc shares its robot design technology with GM; only part of the GMF product line is manufactured in the United States. GMF has been one of the sales leaders in the U.S. robot market since 1984; its market share for 1989 is estimated at 31 percent.

The creation of GMF had a substantial impact on established robot producers such as Cincinnati Milacron and Unimation, who had focused their marketing strategies on large-volume sales of robots to the automotive industry, particularly spot welding robots. General Motors, the largest U.S. robot user, now purchases most of its robots from GMF. Several competing suppliers have been forced to move into less profitable lower-volume market segments and have suffered a reduction in their overall sales volume and market share as a result.

At present, the U.S. robotics industry is supported by a substantial level of technology transfer from foreign robot producers. Many U.S. firms have purchased exclusive or nonexclusive marketing rights from Japanese and European robot producers or have obtained licenses to manufacture these robots in the United States. Others have entered into joint ventures or technology exchange arrangements with one or more foreign firms. A majority of U.S. firms marketing robots simply add value to a basic robot manufactured offshore by enhancing its capability through the addition of end effectors, various forms of sensing devices, communications packages, and system integration services.

The utilization of robots in manufacturing will be the driving force if the trend for factory automation is to continue in the 1990s. We now have the technology to fully automate our plants; however, America does not have the funding and management vision to move aggressively. Our worldwide competitors will force us to apply robotics as one of the key manufacturing tools of the next generation.

2

COMPONENTS OF A
ROBOTIC SYSTEM

This chapter provides a description of the basic system elements of a robot and how they work.

ELEMENTS OF A ROBOTIC SYSTEM

Robots are available in a wide range of capabilities and configurations. The robot system consists of the following major subsystems:

- Manipulator system—the mechanical arm mechanism, consisting of a series of links and joints that perform the motion by moving the end-effector tooling through space. It closely resembles a human arm and consists of a base, shoulder, elbow, and wrist.
- Actuator power drive—provides electric, hydraulic, or pneumatic energy to move the manipulator arm and end-effector.
- End-effector tooling—a gripper or tooling that performs the robot's intended production task(s).
- Fixtures and tooling accessories—the accessories that integrate the robot system with the production task.
- Controller or computer—provides the logical direction for the robot.
- Sensor—provides enhanced robot system control feedback.

Robots can be classified according to the coordinate reference system defining their three axes of motion (x, y, z). These axes will produce vertical, horizontal, and in–out motion about the robot center of motion, which is normally its fixed base.

There are five basic geometric coordinate reference configurations used for robot motion (Table 2-1), each of which offers more or less freedom of activity with a corresponding cost dependency, with the more agile and flexible being the more costly. The job will determine the most suitable choice.

Table 2-1
Robot Arm Geometry Usage

Arm geometry	Usage (%)
Rectangular or Cartesian	18
Cylindrical or rotational	15
Polar or spherical motion	10
Revolute or jointed arm	32
SCARA	25

- Rectangular or Cartesian motion—characterized by moving in the classical up–down, left–right, or in–out directions (see Fig. 2-1). The wrist can be controlled in height, width, and depth of operation with a great degree of accuracy.

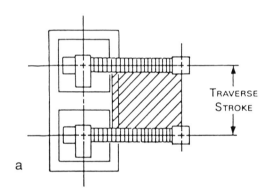

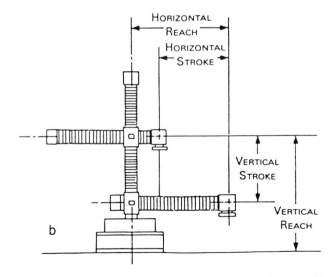

Figure 2-1   Illustration of rectangular or Cartesian motion. (a) Top view, (b) side view.

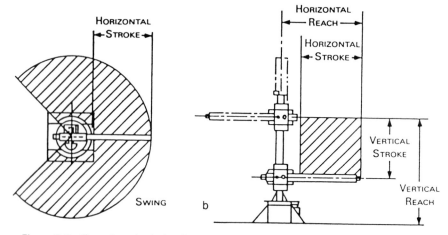

Figure 2-2   Illustration of cylindrical or rotational motion. (a) Top view, (b) side view.

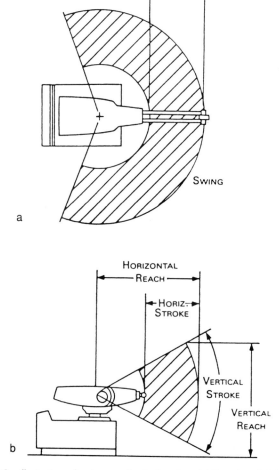

Figure 2-3   Illustration of polar or spherical motion. (a) Top view, (b) side view.

- Cylindrical or rotational motion—characterized by an extendable arm that moves up and down as well as in and out from a central pole, and swivels angularly around the pole (see Fig. 2-2).
- Polar or spherical motion—characterized by an extended arm mounted on a central pivot and can reach above and below its pivot point and rotate angularly around the pivot (see Fig. 2-3)
- Revolute or jointed-arm motion—characterized by a humanlike arm that can bend and swivel at the shoulder and bend at the elbow (see Fig. 2-4) This motion allows the arm to move back close to the base, extending the work area of the robot.
- SCARA arm motion—a SCARA robot is an anthropomorphic or jointed-arm structure that operates in a horizontal plane, as shown in Fig. 2-5.

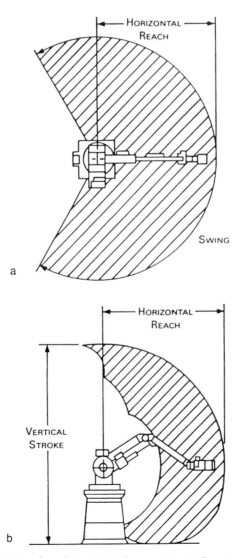

Figure 2-4   Illustration of revolute or jointed-arm motion. (a) Top view, (b) side view.

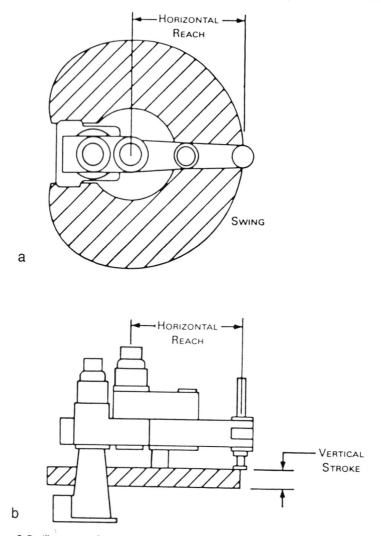

Figure 2-5   Illustration of SCARA horizontal jointed-arm motion. (a) Top view, (b) side view.

SCARA is an acronym for Selectively Compliant Assembly Robot Arm. The SCARA robot was developed for two-dimensional assembly operations, and this configuration can provide a highly rigid structure for excellent positioning repeatability. It is also possible to remove power from the SCARA robot's major axes without gravity causing the axes to move. By "relaxing" one or more axes, the arm becomes compliant to external forces, which facilitates close-tolerance insertion tasks.

Pitch, yaw, and roll are the basic motions referred to as degrees of freedom. The human arm has six degrees of freedom; two in the shoulder, one in the

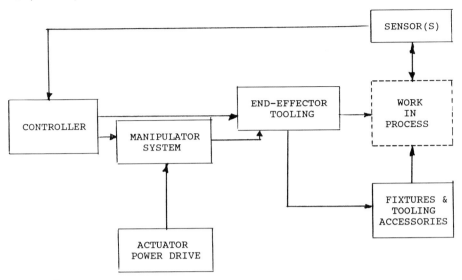

Figure 2-6 Functional block diagram of robot system.

elbow, and three in the wrist. Each of the joints must provide full 360-degree rotation to be a true degree of freedom.

Selection of the most desirable form of motion is based on the given task. A revolute geometry would appear to be appropriate for reaching to a weld inside a chassis. Simpler motions like a drill function could be easily handled by a cylindrical motion. In all cases the wrist must reach the work area in the proper orientation and be capable of the required movement associated with the task.

The major subelements of a robotic system, including controller, manipulator system, actuator power drive, end-effector tooling, fixtures and tooling accessories, and sensors, are described in detail in the following material and a block diagram is shown in Fig. 2-6.

MANIPULATOR SYSTEM

The manipulator is a series of mechanical linkages, arms, and joints capable of movement in various directions to control the end-effector. The manipulator/end-effector is driven by a power drive actuator that may use pneumatic or hydraulic cylinders, hydraulic motors, or electric motors. The actuators may be coupled directly to the mechanical links or joints or may drive indirectly through gears, chains, or ball screws. In the case of pneumatic or hydraulic drives, a flow of air or oil to the actuators is controlled by valves mounted on the manipulator. Sensor devices are installed to sense the positions of the various links and joints and feedback this information to the controller. These feedback devices may simply be switches actuated by the robot's arm or position-measuring devices such as encoders, potentiometers, resolvers, and/or tachometers to measure speed. Depending on the devices used, the feedback data are either digital or analog.

Manipulator Dynamic Performance

The quality of the manipulator can be described in terms of four parameters, combining the effects of the arm geometry, accuracy, and quality of the point servomechanisms providing location feedback and the computer programs written to direct the robot through its desired tasks. These are:

- Accuracy
- Repeatability
- Stability
- Spatial resolution
- Compliance

The dynamic performance of the manipulator is the ability to start, move, and stop with well-defined and predictable operation under all conditions of arm length and weight loading. This performance will be measured using the quality factors previously mentioned under both static and dynamic conditions.

The human body is a good analog to study the effects on the manipulator as weight is moved from one point to another. It is easy to visualize the areas on the skeletal frame where the forces will be most felt—the knees twisting under the load, the waist bending, and the shoulder, elbow, and wrist joints all taking part of the stress. The human control system is extremely well damped and approaches its rest points smoothly and surely compared to a loaded manipulator, whose ability to stop on target will be some form of damped oscillation around rest until stop occurs.

As with the human skeleton, loads are handled best with the least strain when the arms are bent close to the body, and loads are most difficult to lift and control at arm's length. Like the human, the manipulator will find it impossible to perform some tasks at arm's length. Unless directed otherwise, the robot may try to do the impossible with catastrophic consequences. Manipulator performance, as stated earlier, is a complex variable and needs considerable study and attention.

Accuracy and Repeatability

It is very difficult to define accuracy without bringing resolution into the discussion. Accuracy implies the capability to hit the mark, or reach the point in space, or get the correct answer. Repeatability is the act of duplicating an action or a result (see Fig. 2-7).

A repeatable act does not have to be an accurate one. A target shooter may have a tight group of shots at the six o'clock position on the target and have excellent repeatability but not accuracy, since the pattern missed the bulls-eye.

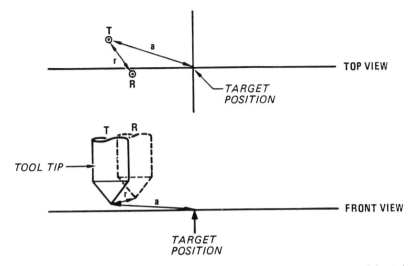

Figure 2-7 Accuracy/repeatability relationship (exaggerated) showing that repeatability is better than accuracy. a, Accuracy; r,repeatability; T, closest initial position; R, repeated position.

The shooter can achieve both repeatability and accuracy if the shot pattern remains clustered as before but shifts to fall accurately within the bulls-eye. Without repeatability one may occasionally achieve accuracy, but it will be unpredictable and therefore undesirable for a manipulator, whose job is to faithfully repeat an action over and over.

Repeatability for the robot applies to its ability to return faithfully to the position where it is sent. The accuracy of that position, that is, the precision of that measurement, will depend to a great degree on the resolving powers of the servo mechanisms. In the short term, temperature variations that may contract or expand the robot components will not be a serious concern, but in the longer term, they will affect ultimate performance. One might expect these types of variations to be most critical in precision operations requiring extremely high accuracies. To achieve the accuracies required may necessitate some form of temperature control in the work area.

Accuracy of the machine is achieved (or lost) by three elements of the robot system: the resolution of the control components previously mentioned, the inaccuracies or imprecision of the mechanical linkages, gears, and beam deflections under different load conditions, and the minimum error that must be tolerated to operate the arm under closed servo loop operation. Table 2-2 provides accuracy and repeatability tolerances for the most dominant robot types for today and projections for the future.

Stability

Stability is a quality referring to that feature of the robot that keeps it from breaking into oscillation (or vibration) as it moves from point to point or when at rest. An undamped system will oscillate in an unbounded manner until the

Table 2-2
Average Accuracy by Robot Type

Robot application	1990	1995
Machine tending	0.005	0.005
Spot welding	0.004	0.002
Arc welding	0.004	0.002
Spray painting/coating	0.01	0.01
Processing	0.004	0.002
Electronics assembly	0.001	0.0005
Inspection	0.001	0.0005

servo mechanism or part of the manipulator is damaged, as it is forced through severe angular accelerations in trying to react to the commands of the controller. An overdamped system, however, causes the arm to follow the commands of the controller in a sluggish way. A critically damped servo system will provide an optimum situation in which the arm will be steady at rest but respond to command with a minimum overshoot when moving from point to point along the work trajectory.

A servo sensor must detect an error between the present position and the next position on the path. An optimum approach to movement would be one where the servo responds to large errors with faster movements and as the error is reduced, that is, as the arm is nearing its next point, the arm moves more slowly to the next desired point.

Spatial Resolution

Spatial resolution, another significant parameter in robot design, refers to the minimum or smallest dimension to which the system can define the work space. This resolution determines the smallest error that can be sensed by the robot. This limit can be placed by the minimum resolution of the controller or the minimum resolving increment of the servo system, whichever is less. A microprocessor using 8-bit words can resolve to one part in 256, while a 16-bit machine can resolve to one part in 65,336. Of course, resolution is selected to match the need. To use a 16-bit controller to move pallets would be serious overkill, like measuring mileage with a ruler instead of an odometer.

Compliance

Manipulator compliance is an indication of displacement in response to a force or torque exerted on it. A high compliance means the manipulator moves a good deal when it is stressed and therefore would be termed spongy or springy. Low compliance, the other end of the scale, is characterized by a stiff system. Compliance involves a complex set of variables that are dependent on where forces are applied, the sticking and sliding frictions of couplers and gears, the effects of the power source, and even the frequency of the force exerted. Compliance can be theoretically calculated but can only be accurately measured after the robot has been put in place and is put through its paces. Like the other variables affecting accuracy and precision, each becomes more important as more stringent repeatability and accuracy requirements are imposed.

Compliance is a feature that can be good or bad depending on where it occurs and whether its sequence is desirable. A spongy, compliant robot arm would not be desired if it were grinding or milling since the part would oppose the grinder and would essentially try to hold the robot back from the part being serviced. On the other hand, in a situation where the robot was meeting some unpredicted opposition, the robot could destroy itself if it were to remain uncompliant and oppose this force. Clearly there are conditions where both high compliance and low compliance are appropriate responses.

COMPUTER/CONTROLLER

The computer/controller system (Fig. 2-8) has a threefold function: to start and terminate motions of the manipulator in a desired sequence and at desired points; to store position and sequence data in memory; and to interface with other advanced manufacturing technology systems. The heart of the control system is the controller. Robot controllers run the gamut from simple step sequencers through pneumatic logic systems, diode matrix boards, electronic

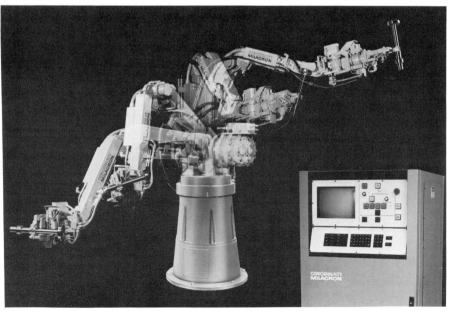

Figure 2-8 Cincinnati Milacron T³ industrial robot computer/controller. (Courtesy of Cincinnati Milacron.)

sequencers and microprocessors, minicomputers, and personal computers. The controller may be an integral part of the manipulator or may be housed in a separate cabinet. The controller initiates and terminates the motions of the manipulator through interfaces with the manipulator's control valves and feedback devices and may also perform complex arithmetic functions to control path, speed, and position. Other interfaces provide two-way communications between controller and ancillary devices. These interfaces allow the manipulator to interact with whatever other equipment is associated with the robot's task.

Depending on the complexity of the robot, the control mechanism can range from electromechanical stops and limit switches to more sophisticated microprocessor-driven, programmable devices. As always, complexity is based on the operating scenario planned for the robot. The levels of sophistication, described next, cover the range of industrial robots.

Fixed-Sequence, Nonservo, Point-to-Point Robots

Fixed-sequence, nonservo, point-to-point robots perform a series of operations in a predetermined sequence. Fixed-sequence robots are run in what is called an "open loop." The robot is driven to certain sequenced points, and the controller receives no information or feedback on how well the command was followed. The robot relies on mechanical stops or electromagnetic switches to ensure compliance with commands. Only the end points of the motions are sensed.

Point-to-Point, Servo-Controlled Robots

Point-to-point control robots are servo-controlled and use a memory to recall a series of locations and operations previously located under manual control. These robots, instead of being driven to mechanical stops, are driven by electrical signals to each point along the path of motion. Theoretically the servo can stop the arm at a series of points along the path, but the real resolution of the path length is controlled by the resolving power of the servo and the signal that drives the servo.

Servo-controlled robots are run in a "closed loop." This means that the servomotors drive the arm to a point determined by an error signal created by the difference between the arm's current location and the position to which the arm is being directed. The closed-loop servo system will try to minimize this error signal at all times and will drive the arm to keep the error as small as possible. Point-to-point robots are programmed by walking the robot through the operational mode and storing a series of coordinates along the path. Upon completion, the robot will then repeat the operation automatically under closed-loop conditions.

Continuous Path, Servo-Controlled Robots

Continuous path control robots (Fig. 2-9) are also servo-controlled and learn the path speed and operation required either on- or off-line. The operator actually teaches the robot by taking it through the operation desired. Like the

Figure 2-9 Continuous path, servo-controlled welding robot.

point-to-point robot, the continuous path robot is also run closed loop, but the two differ in how they are programmed and how data are stored for future use. An operator leads the continuous path robot's arm through the pattern exactly as if the operator were performing the task (e.g., welding or painting). While the operator teaches the robot, a continuous recording is being made of all the servo voltages. The voltages that are recorded on magnetic tape or disk can be replayed through the robot, which will duplicate the task it was previously taught.

The controller functions as the brain and nervous system of the robot and consists of any programmable device from a rotary drum switch to a full computer. The controller not only directs the robot through its programmed moves, but in smart robot systems with artificial intelligence it also integrates the robot with ancillary machinery, equipment, and devices. In addition, the controller can monitor processes and make decisions based on system demand, while at the same time reporting to a supervisory control. There are three types of controller programming: walk-through, lead-through, and plug-in. The major factors utilized in determining which type of programming to use are cost, operational environment, task variance, and the utilization of single or integrated units tied to a specific controller.

Walk-Through Programming

Walk-through programming requires the operator to physically manipulate the unit through the desired sequence of events. The robotic unit records each motion and joint position. Upon program execution these motions and positions are replicated in sequence. Ease of programming is an obvious advantage; however, operator errors and subsequent reprogramming may offset this apparent advantage.

Lead-Through Programming

Lead-through programming requires the operator to utilize a teach box (Fig.2-10) or remote programming unit to guide the manipulator through the desired sequence of events. Various motions and positions are again recorded and, upon program execution, are replicated. Ease of programming by remote control has advantages when working with units located in hazardous environments such as radioactive materials handling, space systems, and remote undersea systems. However, operator errors and subsequent reprogramming are disadvantages.

Plug-In Programming

Plug-in programming consists of placing a prerecorded program into the smart robot unit. This method is by far the fastest and easiest programming method available today. It also tends to be the most expensive.

ACTUATOR POWER DRIVE

All the motions that we take for granted in moving our arm from one point to another are, for the robot, an additional need for power (Fig. 2-11). Each joint that the robot performs with will require a motor or actuator to move it. Even the acts of holding and letting go will require actuation power and drive mechanisms. The three primary sources of actuation power drive for industrial robots are electric, hydraulic, and pneumatic.

- Electrically actuated robots are almost all driven either by stepping motors or dc motors. They tend to be less powerful than the other types but have excellent accuracy and repeatability. They are generally quiet and take up less space than the other types of robots, and are also more expensive. They are the most used power drive actuator.

- Hydraulically driven robots are mechanically simpler than their electrically driven counterparts and have both the physical strength and high speed that are essential in heavy duty robots. While the robot uses hydraulic servo valves and analog resolvers for control and feedback, digital encoders and modern resolvers can provide a very high repeatability and accuracy.

- Pneumatically driven robots are used for limited-sequence activities, such as pick and place, where speed and precision are not critical. They use compressed air to drive the mechanical arm and tend to be lightweight, fast, and the least expensive alternative, partly because of the limited capability. Their corresponding simplicity keeps the reliability high and the maintenance cost down. They can only be used where there is already a source of compressed air available.

Which power source is best is a question of what is most important in the installation. Table 2-3 ranks the advantages for each of these systems.

Figure 2-10   ADEPT teach box (upper left corner) used for lead-through programming.

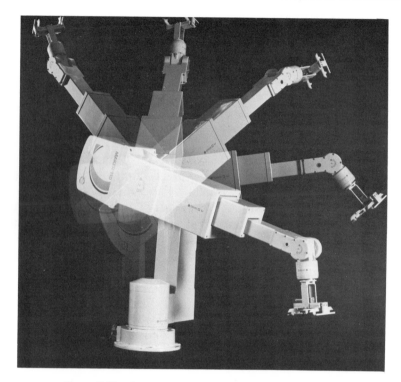

Figure 2-11 Actuator power drive system moves robot arm.

The function of the actuator power drive system is to provide energy to the manipulator and end-effector. In the case of electrically driven robots, the power supply functions basically to regulate the incoming electrical energy and to provide the ac or dc voltages required by the electronic circuits internal to the robot controller and also by the drive motors. Hydraulically actuated robots normally include a hydraulic power supply either as an integral part of the manipulator or as a separate unit. The hydraulic system generally follows straightforward industrial practice and consists of an electric motor-driven

Table 2-3
Ranking of Actuator Advantages (Rank Order 1 to 10, Least to Highest, Respectively)

Advantages	Hydraulic	Electric	Pneumatic
Initial cost	5	8	1
Maintenance cost	6	6	3
Load capability	1	10	6
Energy usage	10	9	9
Floor space	10	9	8
Use in flammable environment	9	10	2
Spatial resolution	8	3	10
Accuracy	4	1	9
Compliance	7	9	10
Repeatability	3	2	10
Speed	2	5	4

Table 2-4
Robot Actuator Power Drive System Usage

Robot actuator power drive	Usage (%)
Electric	55
Hydraulic	34
Pneumatic	11

pump, filter, reservoir, and usually a heat exchanger. Power for pneumatically actuated robots is usually supplied by a remote compressor that may also service other equipment in the factory.

The majority of the industrial robots currently in operation in the United States are powered by electric drives, due to the increased use of light manufacturing assembly robots. Robots with hydraulic drives are the second most common type, commonly used in the auto industry, whereas robots powered by pneumatic drives are relatively rare. Table 2-4 shows some statistics on the percentages of actuator drive mechanisms in use today.

END-EFFECTOR TOOLING

Four elements make up the total cost of a robotic installation:

- Base price of the robot
- Installation-related costs
- System engineering and integration costs
- Tooling cost

This section examines end-effector tooling as one of the critical elements of a robot system.

Just as a purchaser of stereo equipment would be ill advised to spend lots of money to improve a sound system and then ignore the speakers that funnel all the new sound into the room, the purchaser of a robot would also be unwise not to pay strict attention to the importance of end-effector tooling for an optimum robot system configuration. Tooling consists of a variety of peripherals that should be reviewed since they are so important and are generally unique for any installation.

Tools serve a variety of roles in the manufacturing process. Some of the more significant robot end-effector tool applications include:

- Metal working
    Cutting
    Drilling
    Grinding
    Chipping
- Welding
- Adhesive application
- Surface treatments
    Painting

       Finishing
       Cleaning
       Sealing
     • Identification
       Marking
       Stamping

Manipulator end-effector tooling consists of a variety of unique peripherals for each installation:

- Hands or grippers that are required to do specific tasks. These end-effectors can include material-handling grippers (Fig. 2-12), welding torch holders, grinding and drilling tools, and spray paint adapters.
- Fixtures to perform special holding of the work item but separate from the robot. Clamp fixtures to hold joints to be welded or holding fixtures for spray painting applications are typical examples.
- Material-handling equipment to move the work within the work space of the robot. This includes conveyors, slides, part feeding devices, and transfer devices.

Classification of End-Effector Tooling

In the following discussion, tooling is classified as either fixed or movable and either passive or active. Fixed tools always sit in one place, whereas

Figure 2-12   Material-handling gripper used to install glass auto windshield. (Courtesy of Cincinnati Milacron.)

movable tools can be carried around by a manipulator. Passive tools contain no actuators or sensors and exchange no signals with the workstation control computer, whereas active tools do. This breakdown gives the four classes of tooling shown in Fig. 2-13. Each class poses significantly different control problems.

- Fixed active tooling includes all items that require or produce control information signals, but are stationary and not moved from place to place by the manipulator. These tools might include conveyors, numerically controlled equipment, part feeders, vises, clamps, part orienters, and glue

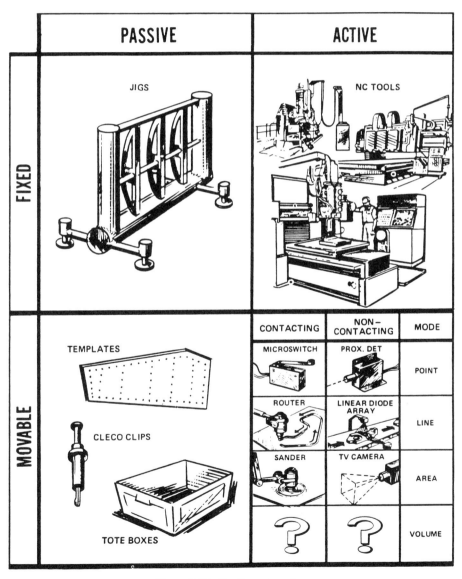

Figure 2-13 Tooling categories.

dispensers. The sensors mounted in place on the tool, such as photocells, proximity sensors, force-sensing tables, and machine vision cameras, are considered part of the tooling.

- Fixed passive tooling, such as jigs and work tables, includes all tools that support the station and contain no active actuators or sensors.
- Movable active tooling includes all objects that the manipulator carries from place to place and that either require control signals or produce information. Examples are grippers, including any sensor attached, and all power tools. Some sensors are mounted on the manipulator.
- Movable passive tooling includes any unpowered items that the manipulator carries from place to place. Included in this class are items such as tote boxes, templates, rivets (but not the riveter), jigging components, and the workpiece itself.

Two other factors of active tooling, both fixed and movable, determine the difficulty that the workstation controller will have in operating the tooling. These factors are whether the tool makes contact with the workpiece and the dimensionality of the region over which the tool interacts with the workpiece. This distinction leads to the contacting and noncontacting classification scheme under movable active tooling shown in Fig. 2-13.

Tooling that touches the workpiece includes grippers of all kinds as well as most kinds of tools that remove material from the workpiece or change the shape of the workpiece. Tools that do not contact the workpiece include most tools that deposit material. A sensor can be used as a special kind of tool that has no effect on the workpiece. Sensors often are included as components of multiple-purpose tools, and the sensors themselves may be either contacting or noncontacting.

Robot/End-Effector Tool Interface

One of the most important decisions in robot system design is the interface between the manipulator and the tool end-effectors that the robot carries. The interface must support the end-effector structurally, provide it with power, and convey information to and from it. The interface must be reliable and designed to permit quick connection and disconnection, and the manipulator should not have to be positioned with extreme accuracy to make the connections. The interface equipment should be impervious to whatever environmental conditions are likely to occur in normal operations, such as moisture, oil, metal chips, and occasional collisions.

Power and information can be transmitted in several different ways, some of which may offer advantages over others in certain situations. For example, in fully automatic spray painting, operating the end-effector in an atmosphere whose solvent concentration is above the explosive level may be cost-effective. In that situation, selection of nonelectrical power transmission methods would be advisable to avoid the possibility of sparks. In a radioactive environment, avoidance of power transmission methods that are based on hydraulics would be advisable, because this method would pose the additional problem of cleaning up radioactive contaminated hydraulic oil in the event of an accident.

Structural Elements

Three major aspects of the mechanical connection between the end-effector and the manipulator are the strength and compliance of the wrist socket (Fig. 2-14) and the protection that the socket affords against excessive forces on the end-effector. "Wrist socket" refers to the portion of the manipulator that comes in contact with the end-effector.

Strength The wrist socket must be able not only to support the weight of the end-effector but also to withstand any inertial forces arising from rapid accelerations. If the end-effector happens to be a gripper, then the mass of any object that it carries also must be included in calculating loads.

Compliance Most manipulator wrist sockets are rigid structures that provide no compliance at all. In some applications, however, much of the manipulator's work may require some form of accommodation in response to forces arising from contact with solid objects. In such cases, it may be economically advantageous to provide an appropriate compliance in the wrist socket that either will aid in performing the required accommodation motions or will perform them automatically. The best kind of compliance and the appropriate way to obtain it will certainly differ from application to application. Some possible advantages of placing the compliance in the wrist socket include the opportunity to use it with many different end-effectors and a reduced moment of inertia in the manipulator. This reduced moment of inertia may make higher accelerations possible and improve production rates.

Overload Protection Having the wrist socket provide breakaway protection for the end-effector is extremely desirable. Excessive force on the end-effector should cause two actions to occur: (1) the mechanical connection should become compliant and (2) the sensor(s) in the wrist socket should signal the workstation control computer that an unexpected condition has occurred. That computer should immediately take action to prevent damage to

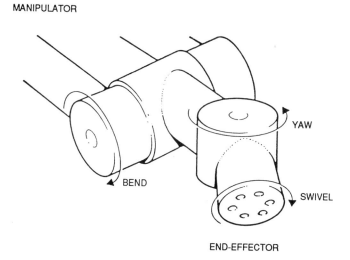

Figure 2-14 Typical wrist articulations.

the manipulator. Many different designs for breakaway wrists have been developed on the basis of a variety of simple mechanisms:

- Mechanical fuses—These are cheap, replaceable structural elements, such as shear pins that break or thin-walled tubes that buckle under excessive stress. Honeycomb structures are also good fuses.
- Detents—These consist of two or more structural elements that are held rigidly in position with respect to one another by spring-loaded detent mechanisms. For example, a disk fits into a cylindrical tube, and inward-facing ball detents at three places around the cylinder wall mate with matching depressions in the rim of the disk.
- Preloaded springs—In the mountings, one or more pairs of structural elements are held in contact by springs. A force or torque acting in any direction on the end-effector will tend to separate one or more of these pairs of elements to provide the breakaway action. The spring force establishes the level of stress on the end-effector at which the breakaway action will occur.

Preloaded spring mountings are the most desirable because they will reset themselves automatically when the force on the end-effector is removed. The ball-detent mountings are the next most convenient because they require manual intervention to reassemble the structural elements. The least convenient to use are the mechanical fuses because they require not only manual intervention but also replacement of the used fuse.

The breakaway action should not leave the end-effector unsupported. Mounting methods based on mechanical fuses and detents usually allow the end-effector to fall a short distance and dangle from the wrist socket; this can be dangerous. Attaching the end-effector to the wrist socket by a steel safety cable may or may not be advisable. One must decide whether the damage that could result from a dropped or thrown end-effector would be worse than the damage that could result in its swinging from such a tether.

One must also ask what would happen if the breakaway action does not provide sufficient compliance to avoid damage. For example, if the end-effector becomes stuck in a workpiece that is being carried by a powerful conveyor and the wrist socket should fail in such a way that the various power and signal connections are not damaged on the manipulator side, the end-effector should be sacrificed to save the manipulator's wrist socket. Replacing a broken tool will not take the manipulator out of production for as long as it would take to repair its wrist socket.

A point that is often overlooked in designing a breakaway mounting is that it should break away in response to any single pure force or torque above a certain level on the end-effector. To verify this, one can displace the end-effector in any direction without rotating it and check to ensure that it breaks away. Pick an arbitrary point on or in the end-effector and rotate it slightly about that point without allowing the center of rotation to move. If it still breaks away, then the end-effector is fully protected. For example, in the disk-in-cylinder detent-style mounting described earlier, the end-effector cannot be moved parallel to the plane of the disk without the disk being moved also. Therefore, this mounting does not provide complete protection.

In some manufacturing, there will be a need for the robot workstation to operate on workpieces in motion on a conveyor. Therefore, the proper response to the breakaway exception condition is to simply stop the manipulator as quickly as possible. A large manipulator can be damaged easily by making it stop too quickly because of the excessive stress that the deceleration can place on components, such as gears and hydraulic lines.

Power Transmission

Most end-effector tools require power for operation. Power lines that dangle from the end-effector can easily catch on equipment, be severed, and present severe hazards. Placement of power conduits along (or better yet through) the links of the manipulator is much safer. Each power line must terminate in some sort of connector at the wrist socket. In the following we describe typical connector options for various types of power transmissions.

Electrical Electrical connections can be made through standard heavy-duty terminals if the mechanical design of the wrist socket enforces accurate positioning of the two halves of the connector. An alternative approach is to place exposed, compliant, conductive material on one or both sides of the interface. Connection of an end-effector to the wrist socket then presses these terminals together. Appropriate materials include woven-wire buttons and electrically conductive, silver-doped rubber.

Pneumatic Adequate pneumatic connections for either pressure or vacuum can be made by pressing two metal surfaces together with an O-ring as a gasket. Commercial pneumatic connectors may also be used if they can make and break connections reliably when simply pushed together or pulled apart. In designing the pneumatic interface, if the end-effector does not require an air or vacuum supply the connector should plug that supply line to prevent leakage. A small air or vacuum accumulator tank at the wrist can permit use of a smaller-diameter pneumatic supply while providing adequate short-duration flow capacity. Regulators at the wrist can provide multiple air pressures with a single supply line.

Hydraulic Hydraulic connectors are more difficult to implement. Again, connectors that can be operated by a simple push or pull should be used. If the manipulator is hydraulic, attempting to use its own fluid supply to operate end-effectors is inadvisable because of the danger of contaminating the former with grit. Grit in the manipulator's hydraulic fluid can cause a servo valve to stick and can result in a sudden, rapid, unpredictable, and dangerous manipulator motion. Although advanced manipulators monitor for such events and can shut down when they occur, prevention is still better.

Optical Power can be transmitted optically, and one method is to simply shine light on a photovoltaic cell array on the end-effector side. The light need not be coherent. Because of the difficulty of transmitting power in this way, this method is applicable only in special situations, such as when operating in an explosive atmosphere. The same beam of light, however, also can carry information, which obviously has advantages in some situations.

Mechanical Power also can be transmitted mechanically. For example, a motor on the manipulator side can rotate a splined shaft that mates with a shaft on the end-effector side. This method can reduce tooling costs by allowing one motor to be shared between several end-effectors. Transmitting the shaft rotation through a flexible cable from a motor that is mounted farther back along the manipulator can also improve performance by reducing the mass and weight at the wrist. If the manufacturing application demands it, limited amounts of mechanical power can be transmitted to a hermetically sealed tool through flexible elastomeric or metallic membranes. A variety of drive mechanisms for this purpose are commercially available (such as bellows, peristaltic plates, and wobble drives).

Control Signal Interface

Most end-effector tools require control information from the computer, produce information for it to use, or do both. Control information is usually transmitted at low-power levels. This procedure makes it easier to design connectors and conduits, but it also introduces the problem of noise susceptibility. Several different information flows may be multiplexed into a single signal channel. Multiplexing may be advisable if the cost of multiple connectors is too high or if their overall reliability is too low.

End-Effector Gripper Requirements

End-effector grippers are the most significant "contacting" tools. They are multipurpose and have the following characteristics:

- Used to pick up and/or put down objects.
- Hold the work so it cannot move within the gripper.

Grippers generally use one of four methods for holding an object in place:

- Friction
- Physical constraint
- Attraction
- By supporting the object

There are a variety of ways to grip a tool or workpiece, most of which are motivated by the nature of the item to be gripped. Some of these include:

- Mechanical gripping devices
- Hooks
- Electromagnetics to pick up metal objects
- Vacuum cups
- Adhesives
- Bayonet sockets that can be used to attach other tools

Friction grippers generally rely on soft material at the point of contact with the object to ensure sufficient force of friction for gripping. They apply pressure on the workpiece either by expanding within it or by closing on it from outside. Materials for grippers should be chosen to withstand repeated impact as well as the potentially harmful effects of the other work by-products, such as oil from a hydraulic system or machining residue and other hazards.

Physically restraining grippers may or may not exert pressure on a workpiece. Some grippers use loose-fitting fingers that are curled around the workpiece and then some form of pressure from air, hydraulics, or other power source expands into the gripper, causing the object to be held rigidly in place. For example, fluidized beds of sand or ball bearings can be used as vises or clamps in this method. There are a variety of approaches to gripping, but generally they can be identified as either a parallel jaw or multifingered configuration. The parallel jaw gripper will typically contact the work over the total area

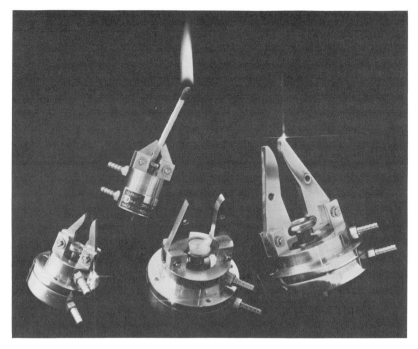

Figure 2-15   Typical robot gripper tools. (Courtesy of MACK Corporation.)

of the gripper, which will determine the desired pressure and ultimately the size of the gripper required. The finger grippers will make contact over a relatively small area. Several types of grippers are shown in Fig. 2-15. Adhesives are already being used in the work space to maintain the orientation of parts but so far not as part of the gripper. A hook is the most common support gripper. Gripping functions include:

- Handling and movement
    Pick and place
    Palletizing
    Stacking
- Loading and unloading
    Castings
    Injection molds
    Furnaces
- Manipulation
    Forging

Typical gripper tools include welding, grinding and deburring, paint spraying, and drilling end-effectors.

Welding Tools

The basic functional characteristic of a robot is its ability to work in hazardous places and to complete repetitive work accurately. Welding is one of the most recognized uses for a robot, and a variety of welding approaches and techniques are in use today:

- Spot welding guns weld by injecting high currents at the weld point. The sequence of this operation is: the workpiece is gripped tightly between two jaws, the manipulator positions the welding gun to the desired spot, turns on the gun, and waits the prescribed time for the weld to be accomplished. The jaws are opened and the part is released.
- Stick welding guns exert little pressure on the workpiece except if the electrode or rod should accidentally touch it.
- Plasma welders have no electrodes and are the choice where force on the workpiece needs to be minimized.
- Laser welders can weld by either delivering laser energy directly to the surface being welded or by deep penetration below the surface. Pulsed and continuous laser welders are in use and their numbers are increasing rapidly.

Each of the welders must be capable of following precise paths or the result will be incomplete welds. The speed of the welding tool must be accurately controlled as the weld moves through metals of different thicknesses to prevent distortion of the metal from the heat generated by the process.

Grinding and Deburring Tools

Grinding and deburring are considered low-precision processes in which a rotating abrasive tool is pressed against a workpiece, sometimes in response to a template guide. The manipulator should be insensitive to or resist side loading that can arise from the tool coming upon lumps of material on the surface being worked. Failure to prevent side loading can result in chattering and oscillation of the arm, which will cause damage to the piece being worked or to the work fixtures holding the piece in position.

Paint Spraying Tools

Painting, another of the hazardous functions of many manufacturing processes, is a natural job for robotics. Removing human workers from the operation can significantly reduce the air-conditioning cost of the painting facility, which requires that the air be breathable and therefore be exchanged regularly.

The spray gun end-effector attached to the manipulator will be directed over the surfaces in patterns designed to match each item and its contours. Some of the more sophisticated shapes require a complex pattern to get the uniform coat of paint required without any overlap problems from stroke to stroke. Several control problems are present in the spray painting process:

- Paint must completely cover the item.
- Minimum thickness is required.
- Uniformity or constant thickness must be controlled.
- Amount of paint used should be the minimum to do the job to limit waste.

Currently the patterns used to apply paint are generated by first recording the motions of a human painter and then replaying the moves through the robot controller. Of course, everything must be in identical orientation each time or the result will be less than desirable. The parts to be painted can be movable or stationary as long as the condition was the same as previously recorded when the human painter performed the job.

Drills

Drilling holes is one of the most common operations in manufacturing. The drill must be oriented normal to the work surface and the pattern can be best implemented by using a template method of guiding the robot end-effector tool.

FIXTURES AND TOOLING ACCESSORIES

Robot systems include many kinds of tooling other than end-effectors. The workstation may include tooling for calibration, measurement of tool wear, jigging workpieces and templates, feeding and orientation of small parts, and brush tables. Some general principles to keep in mind when considering auxiliary tooling are to:

- Provide access to the tooling for maintenance personnel.
- Protect cabling on the floor from objects that may be dropped by the manipulator/end-effector.
- Either design tooling to be sturdy enough to withstand the maximum force that the manipulator/end-effector can exert or equip them with breakaway mountings.

Templates

Templates are one of the most important kinds of tooling that will be used in the robot workstation until templateless machining techniques are fully perfected. Two kinds of templates most often used in manufacturing are (1) fiberglass layups containing bushings for robotic hole drilling and (2) perforated sheet metal panels for guiding manual semiautomated drilling operations. When the controller takes over the job of jigging templates in place on workpieces, then it becomes necessary for the controller to be able to identify templates to ensure that it is using the correct one. A variety of methods may be used to mark the templates in a machine-readable way, such as OCR characters, bar codes, perforation or notch patterns in its surface or edge, and patterns of embedded permanent magnets.

Tool Storage

In any workstation where a manipulator uses a multiplicity of end-effectors and other tools, storage must be provided for the tools that are not being used. The manipulator should be able to pick up an end-effector from the tool-storage area and put it back without manual assistance. Proper design of the manipulator's wrist socket will permit this.

It is desirable for the workstation controller to be able to distinguish one end-effector from another in some way, because a human operator could accidentally place the wrong end-effector in a tool rack. If a mishap during a production run should make it necessary to restart the workstation control computer, time will be saved and possible additional problems will be avoided if the computer can determine automatically whether or not the manipulator is holding an end-effector and which one it is. Some ways of identifying an end-effector include:

- A binary-encoded tool number readable through wires in an electrical information connector in the wrist socket.
- A binary-encoded tool number in a pattern of small permanent magnets that can activate magnetic switches.
- A bar code.
- A unique shape that can be recognized by the machine vision software.
- A unique weight that can be read by a force-sensing wrist.

Ideally, the end-effector identification information should be available to the workstation control computer through the wrist socket. If an unidentified end-effector has to be carried to a reading station in the work area for identification, there is the additional problem of knowing what its shape is before moving it to prevent hitting anything with it on the way.

Providing a wear sensor for drills, routers, grinders, and similar tools may also be worthwhile, and the tool-storage area may be a convenient place to locate it. A sensor in each slot in the tool rack will save production time.

Jigs

Jigs are a significant expense in manufacturing. These heavy, bulky objects must often be stored between production runs. With present-day manual fabrication techniques, the need to move one of these large jigs is only occasional, and cranes and manpower easily satisfy these needs now. In automated plants of the future, processing times at each station may shrink by an order of magnitude, and this shrinkage will aggravate material flow problems. Management should be alert to the possibility of identifying work centers in which automatic mechanisms would be cost-effective.

Current jigs position each part of an assembly accurately with respect to the other parts for fastening operations, such as drilling, countersinking, and riveting. For use with conventional industrial manipulators, however, the jig also must position the assembly accurately with respect to the manipulator because available commercial manipulator control software provides only very limited indexing capabilities for adaptation to an arbitrary workpiece position. This adaptation process is called automatic indexing. If available manipulator control software should be improved to support automatic indexing, the assembly would not have to be positioned accurately. This improvement would present an opportunity for cost savings in tooling; however, the assembly must still be held rigidly in place to withstand any contact forces that may arise during operations.

Part Orienters

Small parts can be oriented fairly well by vibratory feeders with specially designed tooling for each part. Orienting larger parts requires different methods because the energy required to orient them by vibration is excessive. Noise levels become dangerous and the parts themselves can be damaged by colliding with each other. The robot workstation will probably require automatic rivet feeders for rivets and other fasteners.

Part Presenters

Manufacturing involves the insertion of components and these components will have to be fed to the appropriate tools for insertion. The feeder equipment will be an important part of the robot workstation tooling and should be selected on the basis of its reliability. One of the most troublesome problems in the automatic feeding of small parts is that they jam in the feeder mechanisms. This jamming is not so serious in manual assembly, since people are so dexterous that they can clear those jams very quickly. Unfortunately, programming a workstation to correct any kind of part-feeding jam that might occur is difficult simply because of the enormous variety of failure modes.

ROBOT SENSORS

Sensors are to the robot what our five senses are to us as humans, providing independently unique information about the environment while working together to display the real world and guide actions to completion. A solution to the information requirements of the workstation is a sensory system designed to cue the robot. In fact, extreme precision in tooling can be replaced by sensors to determine the precise locations of elements in the work process. Except for machine vision sensors, most sensors are inexpensive when compared to the cost of electromechanical and mechanical components. Sensors used in a robot workstation fall into several categories:

- Proximity sensors
- Range sensors
- Tactile sensors
- Acoustic sensors
- Machine vision sensors

The use of sensors will affect the programming aspects of the robot workstation by setting boundary conditions and creating inputs to decision networks in the software. Signals received from the sensors may be used directly as controls or acted on with signal processing circuitry to extract the information content.

Proximity Sensors

Proximity sensors will detect the presence of, or the closeness of the manipulator to, a desired object. Some rudimentary sensors will sense only presence, while others can provide information on proximity. Several types of proximity sensors are discussed in the following material.

Optical proximity sensors measure visible or invisible light reflected from an object to determine distance. Light sources can be from incandescent lights, from light-emitting diodes (LED), or, for greater precision, from laser sources.

Eddy current detectors use small coils in the manipulator that are stimulated when in the proximity of metal. The smaller the coil, the closer the manipulator must approach to effect detection and, therefore, the more precise the location has become.

Magnetic detectors, which work in a similar way, can sense the presence of ferromagnetic material. Solid-state detectors with appropriate amplification and processing can locate a metal object to an impressive degree of precision.

Electrostatic sensors can sense proximity but are susceptible to background conditions, including the electrostatic body charge of the operator, which can vary considerably from day to day depending on humidity.

The capacitive effects of objects can also be detected by highly sensitive field effect devices, similar to those used in elevator buttons that are activated by touch, which react to the capacity of the human to ground.

Acoustic proximity sensors, which transmit acoustic energy and sense the standing waves generated by an object, offer another precise sensing technique. By measuring higher and higher harmonic standing waves, the distance to the object can be more accurately resolved.

Range Sensors

Range sensors are designed to measure the distance from the sensor to the object. If the sensor is located on the end of the robot arm, then the precise location of the arm has been specified. Range sensors can be useful in locating not only the manipulator but also other objects in the work area.

Light interferometers are used when a greater accuracy is required. They generally use a short-wavelength light source and, like the acoustic proximity system, sense interfering patterns that occur as exact harmonics of the transmitted light.

The use of two television cameras can likewise provide range sensing but at a greater cost. The cameras provide stereo vision on the work scene and recognize and identify random parts using pattern recognition techniques. Acoustic range finders have a relatively long wavelength, which does not permit significant accuracy for precision measurements, but they are useful for determining the presence or absence of objects.

Tactile Sensors

Tactile sensors respond to the contact forces that are generated between themselves and the object held. The presence of an object is unknown to the tactile sensor until contact has actually occurred. Tactile sensors can be either touch or stress sensitive. Touch sensors provide a signal on contact only, whereas stress sensors provide an analog signal proportional to the degree of pressure applied to the object. Combinations of single-axis stress sensors can provide multidimensional stress sensing.

The simplest of the touch sensors are the microswitches. These can be fabricated in a variety of ways and can be contact point sensing, as in the case of the conventional switch, or area sensing, in the case where arrays of microswitches are configured. Finally, strain gauges can provide both touch and stress sensing with a degree of accuracy limited only by the sophistication of the strain gauges used.

Figure 2-16   Machine vision sensor system.

Machine Vision Sensors

As the visual sensing capabilities of the television camera are integrated with modern pattern recognition algorithms, vast improvements will be realized on the assembly line (Fig. 2-16). Visual feedback on a line will free the robot from knowing precisely the status of parts on the line, and recognition of objects will add yet another degree of versatility to the automation process. Although the camera is currently only in rudimentary use in factories, it will eventually become as common as the other sensors. Furthermore, as microprocessor technology continues to become more capable and less expensive, the ability to reliably recognize and identify objects will also increase. Each of these types of sensor technology is described in detail in Chapter 3.

SYSTEM CHARACTERISTICS

In addition to the working elements of a robot system, several key system characteristics, such as work volume, load handling capacity, and optimizing the work volume configuration, are integral to its operation.

Work Volume

Figure 2-17 shows typical robot system work volumes. Sometimes the work space or the workpiece is defined such that some robot motions will not be

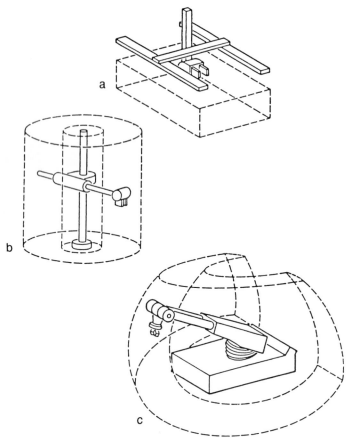

Figure 2-17 Typical work volumes. (a) Rectangular, (b) cylindrical, (c) spherical.

necessary. Fixed orientations known with respect to the robot will reduce its need to move in that axis and therefore reduce its complexity by one joint and all the corresponding actuators, sensors, and other controls that accompany that joint. Table 2-5 shows how robots are configured today and predicts no significant changes in the future.

From a purely theoretical viewpoint, by definition robots are programmable and regardless of the orientations, the workpieces, and the work space conditions, programming must account for all variations and provide for the correct path to accomplish the task. The optimal path will be the one that reduces the cycle time and therefore the overall cost of the operation.

Table 2-5
Percentage Distribution of the Number of Axes

Number of axes	1990 (%)	1995 (%)
4 or fewer	33	33
5	30	29
6	34	35
7	3	3
	100	100

The actual work limits will be determined by the manufacturer's specified reach and the tool length to be interfaced by the manufacturer. Other subtle variations in work volume will occur when the tool is considered since its geometry will in some cases enhance reach and in others reduce it. In some situations joints are driven to their limits and are unable to move the tool to the desired orientation and point in space. Although mathematical analysis would reveal these discontinuities, the simplest way is to ensure that the proper movements are within the work sphere of the selected robot. Simulation programs also provide excellent system integration tools for work-envelope analysis. The length of the rigid elements and the configuration of the joints will determine the shape of the work volume.

Load Handling Capacity

Considerations must be given to the load. Table 2-6 gives estimates of required load capacities for typical applications. The tool, the paint gun, the welder, or the items to be moved are at the end of the arm and their weights and torques will impact the work volume. Just as a human can lift more weight with a bent arm, so it is with a robot. Likewise, handling weight at arm's length is most difficult. These considerations will alter the theoretical work volume specified by the robot manufacturer.

Except for the Cartesian-coordinate (x, y, z) robot that operates with fixed arm lengths, the movement arm will be variable depending on the work location. This suggests that there will be optimal and conversely minimal performance areas within the robot work space. Large weights at greater arm lengths will create the greatest stress in the robot. Table 2-7 projects average velocities of robots today and in the future by application.

Table 2-6
Percentage Distribution of Load Capacities for Typical Applications

Load capacity (pounds)	Materials handling (%)	Finishing and processing (%)	Electronic assembly (%)
0–5	16	17	94
5.1–10	11	17	6
10.1–20	17	34	0
20.1–40	34	20	0
40.1–60	11	6	0
Over 60	11	6	0

Table 2-7
Average Robot Velocities

Robot application	1990 (in./sec)	1995 (in./sec)
Machine tending	40	50
Spot welding	40	40
Arc welding	35	35
Spray painting/coating	50	50
Processing	30	40
Electronics assembly	50	55
Other assembly	50	60
Inspection	40	40

Optimizing the Work Volume Configuration

Robot installations can be enhanced to increase the work volume in the following way:

- Work volume can be extended by installing a long tool.
- Some tools are capable of motion.
- 95% of today's manipulators have mobility and are mounted on a movable base, which allows for directed and determinable base locations; the remaining 5% normally move on tracks.

To achieve an optimum work volume, robots can be mounted on the floor, ceiling (Fig. 2-18), or wall. Smaller robots can be tabletop mounted. Approximately 65 percent are floor mounted, 20 percent are on tabletop, and the remaining are on ceilings, walls, or other equipment.

Figure 2-18   KUKA "Autoflex" systems with overhead-mounted robot at upper right.

The capability of the robot to perform any task is directly related to its sphere of influence, that is, the dimensions and overall volume that the robot can operate within or reach. A point on the wrist of the manipulator is generally accepted as that reference defining the outer reach of the robot. Since each manufacturer sells robots for a variety of uses, the tools that will be interfaced cannot be predicted and therefore this frame of reference is choosen. Like the mile per gallon fuel efficiency ratings for automobiles, everyone knows they may never get that performance with their car, but it is a useful number to compare product characteristics.

3

SENSORS FOR
ROBOTIC SYSTEMS

INTRODUCTION TO SENSORS

According to Webster's dictionary, a sensor is "a device that responds to a physical stimulus (such as heat, light, sound, pressure, magnetism, or a particular motion) and transmits a resulting impulse." Any discussion of robotics must address sensors and the role they play in robotic applications. This chapter provides a broad overview of sensors and their potential applications. The term "sensor" is defined and examples of typical types of sensors are provided.

A sensor responds to some external stimuli and then provides a useful output. Using the concepts of "input" and "output," one can understand how sensors play critical roles in both open and closed control loops, (Fig. 3-1). Of course, closed loops are the most useful, where sensor input from the environment can be fed directly back to a control or actuator. This input to the control portion of the system can then drive the actuators to change the sensor environmental stimuli to whatever values have been previously determined as correct.

Since the early days of the development of sensor technology, most sensors have been designed to respond to a variety of stimuli without being able to differentiate one from another. So, in any control loop situation, it is often very difficult to distinguish the presence, absence, or condition of the desired "sensed" phenomenon from background "noise" or other unwanted stimuli. Sensor technology is a necessary ingredient in any control-type application. Without the feedback from the environment that sensors provide, the robot system has no data or reference points, and thus no way of understanding what is right or wrong with its response.

It should be noted that "sensor technology" per se does not exist. Sensors, depending on their application, involve many diverse technologies based on their use to sense position, pressure, temperature, flow, or the presence of a vapor or gas. The environments in which sensors operate include a broad range of stimuli-producing phenomena, such as temperature, humidity, light levels, and change in position.

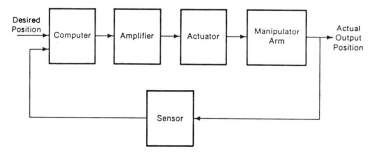

Figure 3-1   Closed loop control sensor.

SENSOR APPLICATIONS IN ROBOTICS

It is obvious that for a robot to do its work, it needs to be controlled by input provided by sensing changes in its actions. Even the most elementary robot doing a pick-and-place application is enhanced if some kind of sensor is provided to let it know when and where to pick and place.

Sensing Needs

To combine sensing technologies for robotic applications, we need to understand the five basic types of sensing needs for robot systems. These needs include presence/absence, positioning, inspection, condition measurement, and identification.

- Presence/absence: Detect if an object is there or not
- Positioning: Determine exact location within a set of parameters
- Inspection: Verify specific object characteristics (machine vision devices)
- Condition measurement: Monitor and predict machine and/or measurement system performance
- Identification: Tracking parts of lots to determine what operations must be performed on them

The presence/absence need is to detect whether an object is present. Sensors in this category usually deal only with an on/off or digital signal. Their application is relatively straightforward, but they are often used in large numbers in a system and play a critical role (Fig. 3-2).

Positioning goes a step further and involves determining not only if an object is there, but exactly where it is within certain specific tolerances. This need exists when the relative movement or position between two objects must be determined and closely controlled.

The inspection need goes a step beyond positioning and involves verification that a particular object's characteristic, such as solder bumps or a particular bolt, is present. This type of sensor is often intended to replace human inspection and is very important for enhanced quality control. Inspection-type sensors are usually "intelligent" in that they can be trained to recognize and distinguish color, shape, and size (see Fig. 3-3).

Identification is related to inspection in terms of the type of sensors that are often used, but the basic need here is to differentiate types of parts in order to

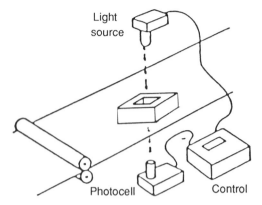

Figure 3-2   Example of presence/absence sensing application.

route them throughout the process rather than to deal with them in individual robot workstation operations (as is the case with inspection). Identification may range from a relatively simple sorting of a few types of parts to an elaborate identification of each part being assembled into one unique product in order to track and record the progress of its assembly path through the plant. In a fully integrated automated system, this function is very important because input from the sensors provides instruction to each robot workstation about functions to be performed on the workpiece at that location (see Fig. 3-4).

Sensors in the condition measurement category sense various types of inputs, conditions, or properties to help monitor and predict the performance of a machine or system. Their function in a robotics application may be critical, although they may not be directly involved with the workpiece. For example, temperature or current sensors could play a vital role in detecting the overheating of a critical machine or machine process (see Fig. 3-5).

Industrial robots are rapidly evolving as the need for improved productivity and quality continues to increase. For a robot to completely perform a task presently done by humans, it must be able to sense both its internal state and its environment. Sensors are being developed to meet this need by making robot systems adaptive and intelligent. This is accomplished by obtaining information about the robot's workplace and the object to be manipulated.

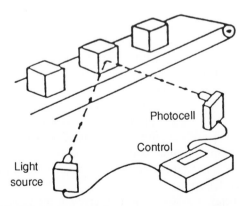

Figure 3-3   Example of inspection sensing application.

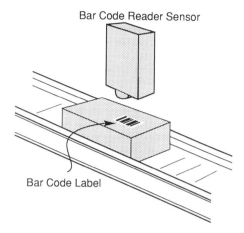

Figure 3-4   Example of identification sensing application.

Sensors can be classified into two major categories: contact and noncontact sensors. A contact sensor measures the response of a target to some form of physical contact. This group of sensors responds to touch, force, torque, pressure, temperature, or electrical or magnetic quantities. A noncontact sensor measures the response brought by some form of electromagnetic radiation. This group of sensors responds to light, X-ray, radar, acoustic, electric, or magnetic radiation.

Just a few years ago only simple sensors, such as strain gauges and microswitches, were used with industrial robots. Since then, the development of sensors for industrial robots has grown by leaps and bounds. Today there are so many types of sensors and applications available that it would take an entire encyclopedia on sensors to provide adequate information on all of them. Therefore, this chapter deals with fundamental sensors that will make industrial robot systems more adaptive and that will provide the information needed for the robot to respond to unexpected situations. A solution to the information requirements of the robot workstation is a sensory system designed to cue the robot. In fact, extreme precision in tooling can be replaced by sensors to determine the precise locations of elements in the work process. Except for machine vision sensors, most sensors are inexpensive when compared to the cost of electromechanical and mechanical components. Sensors used in a robot workstation fall

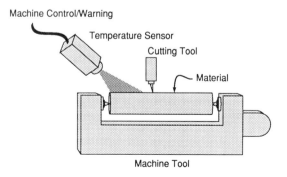

Figure 3-5   Example of condition measurement sensing application.

into five categories. Each of these major sensors is described later in this chapter.

- General Purpose
     Proximity sensors
     Tactile sensors
     Range sensors
     Acoustic sensors
- Machine Vision
     Machine vision sensors

SENSOR INTEGRATION

This section discusses some general principles to keep in mind when using sensors. The use of sensors in a robot workstation affects how programs to control that workstation are written. Signal processing techniques can improve the performance of certain kinds of sensors regardless of the principles on which they operate.

Programming

The task program for a robot workstation can use sensors at that station to obtain information on which to base decisions for choosing alternate processing steps. During normal production, most sensor readings will be for the purpose of verifying the correct completion of an individual processing step, such as drilling a hole or setting a rivet. The robot task program can obtain this information at run time after attempting the processing step, and the program can then take corrective action if something goes wrong. Present practice is to develop algorithms for this sort of in-process testing in an ad hoc way and to write fairly explicit task programs. The program-development process usually involves imagination and experimentation to determine whether the tests being made will detect enough of the processing errors that actually occur and whether the canned responses to those errors are adequate. In the future, as industry settles on standards of practice for robotic manufacturing, the problem of generating reliable task programs will become simpler because fewer choices will have to be made manually.

Teaching

Aside from obtaining decision-making information, the other major use of sensors in a robot workstation is to supply, either indirectly by intermediate computations or directly, the values of any deferred data items in the task program. The most common kind of deferred data in a robot task program probably is position information. Visual information is often the next most frequently trained kind of information. However, the actual amount of visual input information could be quite large. Force and torque levels may have to be trained only rarely. These levels more likely will be worked out during planning from known workpiece and tool weights and standards of practice and then supplied as predefined data values with the rest of the task program.

Position information is very easy to train because a robot manipulator is like a large coordinate measuring machine. A special end-effector shaped like a pointer makes it easier for the trainer to designate locations in the work space whose x, y, and z positions should be recorded.

Sensitivity

A noncontact sensor usually is susceptible to interference from equipment that emits the energy to which the sensor responds, for example, light, sound, or electromagnetic radiation. This poses the problem of separating a signal from noise. Three general principles are useful in increasing the sensitivity of such a sensor and reducing its susceptibility to noise and interference: filtering, modulating, and averaging. These principles can be used with sensors that respond to energy fields such as light, sound, magnetic, electrostatic, and radio frequency emissions.

The principle behind filtering is to screen out most of the noise energy on the basis of some property, such as its frequency, and concentrate as much as possible on the signal energy. The principle behind modulation is similar to that of filtering but more precisely to filter information that is carried by or encoded into the sensed energy field. Modulation varies some aspect of the field in a way that is unlikely to occur in the noise. Finally, the principle behind averaging is to screen out noise on the basis of its randomness over a period of time. The signal should have some nonrandom properties that will not average out to a zero value. These system integration sensor techniques facilitate robot operations that are enhanced by general-purpose sensors and/or machine vision sensors.

GENERAL PURPOSE SENSORS

General purpose sensors that are useful in robotic applications can be classified into four distinct categories: proximity, tactile, range, and acoustic sensors.

Proximity Sensors

A proximity sensor is a device (Fig. 3-6) that senses when an end-effector is close to another object. "Close" can mean anywhere from a few inches to a millimeter depending on the sensor. Most proximity sensors indicate only the

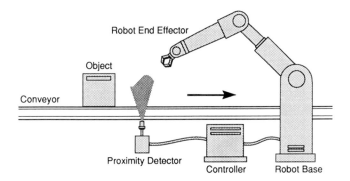

Figure 3-6 Proximity sensor diagram.

presence or absence of an object within their sensing region, but some can also give information about the distance between the object and the sensor. The following paragraphs describe several kinds of proximity sensors that could be useful in a robot workstation.

Optical proximity sensors now on the market operate on either visible or invisible infrared light and most measure the amount of light reflected from an object. A factor in their reliability is the type of light source that they use. The infrared-reflectance sensor with an incandescent light source is one of the most common. This sensor is widely available in a variety of convenient rugged packages and is not expensive.

Most optical sensors require a source of light. Incandescent filaments operated at reduced voltages can have multiyear lifetimes but are susceptible to damage from vibration. Light-emitting diodes have the reliability that is characteristic of other solid-state devices; they are insensitive to shock and vibration and are preferred over incandescent lights. Other light sources, such as electro-luminescence or radiation-induced fluorescence, are rarely used. Laser diodes can emit milliwatts of coherent light but are still expensive and their reliability is not as well established as that of other light sources.

Eddy-current proximity detectors produce an alternating magnetic field in a small volume of space at the tip of a probe. This field induces eddy currents in any conductive body that enters the sensitive volume, and the eddy currents produce their own magnetic field that opposes the field emitted by the sensor. Coils or solid-state magnetic-field sensors in the probe then detect any change in the flux density at the probe tip and signal the presence of an object. The sensitive volume usually is quite small so that eddy-current proximity detectors are appropriate for detecting the presence of objects only when they approach the probe tip to within about 1 millimeter.

Magnetic-field sensors are excellent proximity detectors. These sensors may be made from a reed switch and a permanent magnet mounted near the object to be detected. Alternatively, the magnet may be part of the sensor and the presence of the object can complete a magnetic circuit that operates the reed switch. Other forms of flex sensor, such as Hall-effect devices and magneto-resistive elements, are usually integrated with a solid-state amplifier for increased signal output. The combination of a reed switch and a permanent magnet is particularly attractive because neither device must be supplied with power for operation.

Proximity detectors that operate on the basis of electrostatic effects can also be built. The difficulty with these detectors is that they are quite sensitive to stray fields radiated by electrical equipment and to fields from static charges induced by friction or by paint-spraying operations. The signal conditioning and processing techniques described earlier might improve the performance of such sensors.

The familiar touch-sensitive capacitance button used in modern elevators also can be adapted for use as a proximity detector. In some of these devices, the capacitance between the person's body and his or her surroundings changes the resonant frequency of a tuned circuit. Usually these devices only react to contact with a large conductive object, such as a person. However, by attaching a conductive plate or rod to the contact point, the device can respond to objects at a distance by virtue of their self-capacity.

Fluidic proximity detectors usually operate on the back pressure created when the presence of an object blocks an exit orifice. These devices can provide surprisingly precise indications of extremely small clearances between the probe and the object and are routinely used as sensors in automatic noncontact gauging and inspection equipment.

Tactile Sensors

Tactile sensors respond to contact forces that arise between themselves and solid objects. Unlike proximity detectors, tactile sensors do not indicate the presence of an object until it actually touches the sensor. A useful combination of sensors in an end-effector is a proximity sensor that works in conjunction with a touch sensor. The proximity detector can detect the presence of an object still some distance away so that the workstation controller can safely move the end-effector quickly toward that object even if its position is not precisely known. The signal from the proximity detector would give the workstation controller the warning it would need to slow down and avoid a collision. Then the controller could monitor the touch sensor while moving the end-effector slowly toward the target.

For a robot to accomplish light, delicate assembly tasks, the end-effector must possess human handlike qualities and have a sense of touch. Touch is of particular importance for close-up assembly work and for providing the feedback necessary to grip delicate objects firmly without causing damage. The best and most developed sensor for this task is a tactile sensor that is a sophisticated force and pressure sensor. It usually consists of a two-dimensional array of force transducers that convert force and pressure readings into electrical impulses that can be analyzed by a microprocessor, which tabulates the voltage readings into a matrix.

Tactile sensors can be classified into touch sensors and stress sensors. Touch sensors produce a binary output signal, depending on whether they are in contact with something. Stress sensors produce signals that indicate the magnitude of the contact forces. Individual stress sensors usually respond only to force in one direction; however, combinations of two or more can report forces as well as torques in two or three directions. The simplest kinds of touch sensors require no specific sensor device at all if the objects they are going to touch are electrically conductive. Application of a small potential difference between them will cause the potential to go to zero when contact has occurred.

The tactile sensor is a contact sensor. It can be used in any application where there is a need to measure a force. Tactile sensing systems include table sensors and tactile sensors that are mounted on the fingers of the gripper.

Microswitches are probably the least expensive and most commonly used form of touch sensor. Microswitches should be mounted to protect against accidental collisions with objects in the work space. These devices can be equipped with feelers to protect them against excessive force and to extend the region in which they can sense contact. A simple type of tactile sensor is a gripper that is equipped with an array of miniature microswitches. This type can only determine the presence or absence of an object at a particular point or array of points.

Strain gauges often are used to make force sensors, torque sensors, and sensors that can measure both kinds of stress simultaneously. The sensors usually are constructed by attaching individual strain gauges to the roots of cantilever beams milled into solid blocks of aluminum. The orientations of the beams and the connections between them may be designed to partially resolve the applied force and torque mechanically into its six components with respect to a set of Cartesian axes fixed in the block. Alternatively, the beams may be positioned according to other criteria such as strength or convenience of manufacture. The various stress components may then be resolved by appropriate software. Transforming a set of forces and torques from one reference frame to another with software or appropriate analog computer hardware is a simple matter and is called remote moment sensing.

A more advanced type of tactile sensor uses arrays of pressure-sensitive piezoelectric material. This material conducts electrical current when stressed, and the more pressure applied to the material, the more electrical current is produced, which allows the sensor to perceive changes in force and pressure. Matrices of tactile sensors can range from $8 \times 8 \times 80$ to 80 two-dimensional arrays. Since the force can be determined at each point, the forces can be mapped and the shapes can be determined. The force data may then be used to display the shape of the object on a TV screen. The procedure for processing the image is similar to that used in gray-scale machine vision systems. The analog electrical signals are converted to digitized values, and these values can then be displayed using gray-scale processing. The various voltages, produced from different quantities of force applied to the sensor, can be related to different shades of gray. Thus, the shape and force distribution of the object on the sensor can be determined and displayed on a monitor.

Most tactile sensing systems use an 8-bit parallel out microprocessor, which can only handle 256 increments of digitized voltage readings, meaning that only 256 increments of a maximum force can be read. The sizes of arrays in current systems range from 8×8 to 80×80 pixels. The tactile sensor with an 8×8 array on 0.3-in. centers collects and outputs data from the full array of sites in 3 msec. The analog signals are digitized with 8-bit resolution, giving 256 increments. The typical deflection resolution for this sensor is 0.0005 in. per increment, and the force resolution is 0.0007 lb per increment. New systems will have an 80×80 array of sensitive sites on 0.080-in. centers, will have sensitivity of 0.0063 lb per increment, and will take 0.2 msec to scan the entire array. A reduced area scan can be used to speed up scan time; by using this feature, not every point is read, only the points that are in a particular pattern. Other tactile sensors under development for practical use in the near future include a pressure sensor that can exert pressures ranging from 0.0022 to 0.022 lb for delicate assembly work, a force sensor with a range of 0.0022 to 22 lb for inserting small parts, and a sensor with surface tension recognition to allow fragile materials to be grasped with humanlike robot hands.

Over the past few years, considerable development work has been done on using tactile sensors for object recognition. This has brought about many advances in tactile sensing, such as the elimination of cross talk between picture elements on the tactile matrix. The major drawback of tactile sensors is that they perceive an object in only two dimensions. Unless additional advances are made, tactile sensors will not replace vision sensors for object recognition applications, except in cases where there is a problem with lighting, line-of-sight obstructions, or overlapping parts. However, the integration of tactile sensing and vision sensing would greatly enhance adaptive robotic assembly tasks. An example of this sensor fusion would be to use a machine vision sensor to locate, identify, and position the robot, and then use a tactile sensor to find the force, torque, weight distribution, pressure, center of mass, and compliance of the material. An object can sometimes be identified just by weight or weight distribution alone. This hand–eye coordination for general-purpose manipulation would be extremely powerful in the industrial world.

The tactile sensor can also be used in force feedback applications. This is essential where the gripper is handling delicate, fragile objects so that the robot will not apply too much force and crush the object. Simple pressure sensing in two dimensions is just one aspect of human touch used for assembly tasks. For tactile sensing to be truly useful in adaptive assembly tasks, the sensor must be as capable of sensing physical qualities as the human hand. These qualities include pressure, direction of forces, temperature, vibration, and texture. As tactile sensors continue to develop in ruggedness and sensitivity, the robot must be able to process more quickly the information supplied to it by the sensor. This would allow larger tactile sensing arrays and higher resolution. The development of tactile sensors will evolve until truly adaptive sensors are able to obtain the information necessary for the evaluation of unexpected situations. Better software and estimation algorithms for tactile image processing will help make tactile sensors more useful in industry. Then, the robot will be able to accomplish tasks presently done by humans, because it will have a "human" sense of touch.

Range Sensors

The term range sensor identifies a device that can provide precise linear measurement of the distance from the sensor to an object. Range sensing has been used to perform robotic tasks such as object recognition, manipulation, and navigation. The main goal of any ranging system is to repeatedly obtain accurate range information of the surroundings. Ranging systems are usually used in automated guided vehicles or where the robot has a large work space. Range sensors are classified into two categories: passive devices, such as stereoscopic vision systems, and active devices, such as ultrasonic ranging systems.

The main problem with range sensing occurs when all objects in the work space are not sensed by the transmitter. The use of additional transmitters helps reduce this problem. In the case of a stereoscopic machine vision (Fig. 3-7)

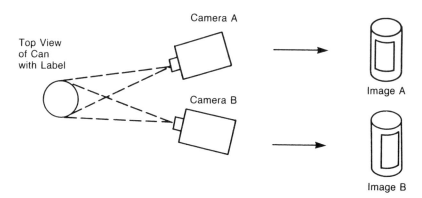

Figure 3-7 Stereoscopic machine vision range finding diagram.

Figure 3-8   Polaroid acoustic range finder.

system, a single projector with multiple cameras can view the target area from different angles. The system senses more data than a single-camera system but requires more hardware, software, and computing time to work.

Ultrasonic ranging systems (Fig. 3-8) like the one used on automatic-focusing Polaroid cameras are widely used to give environmental awareness to a mobile robot. An ultrasonic sensor determines the range by measuring the elapsed time between the transmission of certain frequencies and their detected echoes. Different discrete frequencies are used because surface characteristics could cancel a single waveform, thus preventing detection. Range sensors are still in the early stages of development, and further research will improve their capabilities and reduce the cost of implementing range sensor technology. A robot using a range sensor will eventually be able to sense its surroundings and navigate an automated guided vehicle in the factory of the future.

Acoustic Sensors

Animals such as bats use natural acoustic sensing for detection of objects, verification, measuring distances, communication, and other functions. Acoustic sensing systems have recently been applied to robotic and automated applications. They can be used for tasks like measuring flatness, depth of holes, bends in sheet metal, dimensions of odd-shaped parts, and part inspection and orientation.

The acoustic sensor system (Fig. 3-9) works in the following manner. A

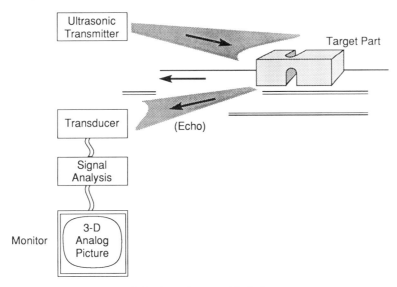

Figure 3-9   Acoustic sensor block diagram.

transmitter emits ultrasonic waves, all of the same wavelength, toward a part. Some of the waves echo from the part, return to the transducers, and form an analog picture. These pictures, like acoustic holograms, are three-dimensional, and the sensor can determine measurements in three dimensions. In sorting parts, the picture of the object being analyzed can be compared with a previously learned shape. Use of sound waves rather than light waves, which machine vision systems use, can have its advantages. Sound waves diffract around objects, so accurate measurement can be made of several sides of an object. Light waves, on the other hand, do not diffract much, so only one side of an object can be viewed and analyzed at a time. Acoustic sensors are best used at close range because sound waves are influenced by ambient noise in the environment. Even with the use of filters, inaccurate results are still obtained at greater distances.

At close range, however, acoustic sensors can be very accurate. Current systems, which use a frequency of 20–30 kHz, can be accurate up to 0.0001 and make 50 measurements per second. Generally speaking, the higher the frequency, the greater the resolution. Acoustic sensors work best at a predetermined distance from the object, usually less than 1 in. Current development is attempting to increase accuracy and reduce processing time when the distance from the object is unknown and may be greater than 2 in. Acoustic sensors will provide a unique alternative for presence/absence detection, measurement, and inspection, and they will allow the robot to sense with sound.

Today, most robots work on assembly lines, where they are programmed to perform repetitive motions at the same place in space. An object to be welded, for example, must be positioned precisely at a predetermined location or the robot will weld in the wrong place. In adaptive applications, a robot must be able to sense its environment. Most of the progress in obtaining flexible, adaptive robot systems will come from the development of vision, tactile, acoustic, and range sensors. The development of these sensors will allow an increase in accuracy, sensitivity, resolution, and ruggedness. Development will also provide ways to process the information faster and thus lower the cost.

There has been much discussion recently concerning the standardization of sensors. Standardization of some sensors could come in as soon as several years. Robotics and sensor technology, however, are still developing. Therefore, the sensor industry should not have rigid standards, but should let the companies compete with each other and allow better technologies to develop. In general, the robotic industry needs to seek a more diverse market, for currently 6 out of 10 robots are used in the automotive industry. Other manufacturers are also beginning to realize that to improve productivity and quality, they need to automate their plants with robot systems that possess sensors such as those discussed. The future looks very bright for sensors that will provide the information necessary for robots to perform adaptive applications.

MACHINE VISION SENSORS

Machine vision will be an essential part of robot systems of the future; existing robot technology is clearly in need of sensory feedback to extend its limited capabilities. Special-purpose machine vision systems are already appearing in increasing numbers on factory floors. Considering the premium that batch fabrication places on a plant's ability to respond quickly to managerial decisions and the vagaries of delivery schedules while processing a wide and ever-changing variety of parts, machine vision systems are urgently needed.

Visual feedback can minimize the need for jigs and fixtures and ease tolerances on parts. Visual feedback controlling a manipulator in real time can allow it to work on a moving line without requiring precise control of the line. The same machine vision system used for these purposes also can provide 100% process inspection capability for little or no additional investment.

Purpose of Machine Vision

Machine vision systems can be used for two different purposes: to recognize objects and to measure specific characteristics of the objects. The following discussion provides in-depth information on the purpose of machine vision systems.

The general goal of machine vision systems (see Fig. 3-10) is the development of mechanisms for effectively interpreting visual images. Interpreting images can be described as the process of going from a video signal to a symbolic description of it. The same image may, in fact, have many descriptions depending on the reasons for processing it. One goal may be to count all the objects in an area, another may be to describe them, and another may be to determine their exact location. Among the reasons for interpreting images with machine vision are:

- Identifying objects
- Locating objects
- Detecting changes
- Describing a scene

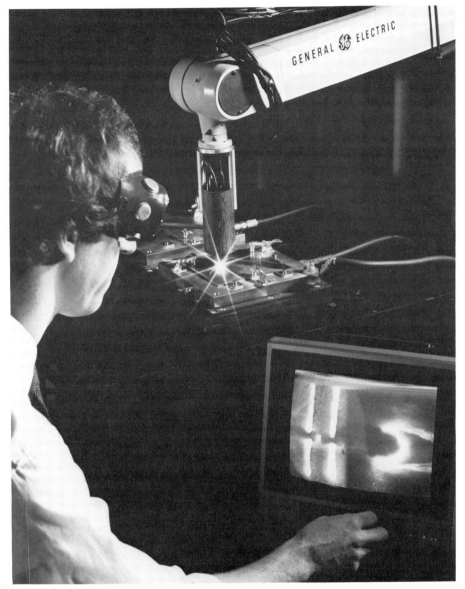

Figure 3-10 General Electric advanced machine vision and control system used for welding.

The commercial machine vision systems that are available are principally for industrial use, as shown in Table 3-1. These systems can identify and locate objects in a controlled environment with some restrictions such as:

- The number of possible objects that can be identified is limited.
- The number of objects in the scene is limited.
- The objects cannot overlap.
- The object must be viewed vertically.
- The image features of an object must be extracted from its silhouette binary image.
- The objects can be illuminated to obtain high dark-to-light contrast.

Table 3-1
Commercial Machine Vision System Developers

Industrial vision companies	Large diversified manufactuers[a]	Robot manufacturers
Machine Intelligence Corp.	General Electric	Automatix, Inc.
Robot Vision Systems	Chrysler Corp.	Cincinnati Milacron
Object Recognition Systems	General Motors	Adept Technology
Octek, Inc.	International Business Machines	Advanced Robotics
Cognex	Texas Instruments	ASEA
Spectron Engineering, Inc.	Navistar	GMF Robotics
Ham Industries	Westinghouse	RVSI
Image Recognition Systems	Hughes	
Everett Charles	Lockheed	
Inspection Technology	Fairchild Camera and Instrument Corp.	
View Engineering	Martin Marietta	
Automated Vision Systems	McDonald Douglas Automation Co.	
Perceptron, Inc.	Cheesborough Ponds	
KLA Instruments	Honeywell	
Diffracto	3M	
Automatix		
Eaton Corporation		
Vicom Systems, Inc.		
Cyberanimation, Inc.		
Reticon		

[a] Some systems are for in-house use only.

Typically, a machine vision system is trained to distinguish among objects (see Fig. 3-11) by showing it sample objects. It will find outlines of each object and, using various techniques, develop a classification so it can distinguish the different types.

More sophisticated processing techniques for identifying and locating objects are being developed and tested. For example, instead of requiring that the entire outline of an object be visible, some knowledge about the shape of the objects is used to "fill in" any edges that may be obscured by objects, shadows, or perhaps poor lighting. Other techniques include:

- Use of gray-scale information
- Use of three-dimensional information
- Use of color, texture, and other attributes

In general, machine vision systems will become more flexible in the images that can be processed, including the following capabilities:

- Identifying objects that overlap
- Accommodating for a change in perspective
- Fewer lighting requirement conditions

In addition to industrial devices, systems for interpreting images for other purposes are in the development stage. These systems can be viewed as a movement from sensing to interpreting, as more knowledge about the objects in the images and procedures for using it become incorporated.

Of the many types of industrial robot sensors, machine vision sensors are considered to be the most important. In fact, it has been said that in five years if

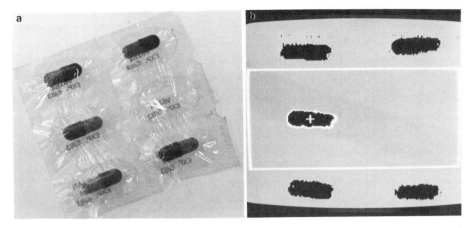

Figure 3-11 General Electric Optimation detecting a missing item. (a) Presence/absence application, (b) Optimation II determines pill is missing.

it does not have integral machine vision sensors you won't call it a robot. Machine vision sensors are by far the most developed of the sophisticated sensors in the robotics industry today. Machine vision is now a reality in the industrial world and can be a substitute for human vision in some industrial applications. The repeatability and accuracy of a machine vision system, and the ability to produce approximately the same results when given the same inputs, are its greatest virtues. Although machine vision does not yet have the extraordinary range of capabilities that human observers have, it can perform simple tasks such as monitoring and inspection much faster and more reliably.

Basic Elements of Machine Vision

A machine vision system (Fig. 3-12) consists of a light source, image sensors, an image digitizer, a system control computer, and some form of output. The image sensor of a machine vision system is defined as an electro-optical device that converts an optical image to a video signal. The image sensor is usually either a vacuum-tube TV camera or a charge-coupled solid-state sensing device.

Vidicons are the most common tube-type cameras. In these the image is focused on a photosensitive surface, where a corresponding electrical signal is produced by an electron beam scanning the surface. The electron beam passes easily through the photosensor at a highly conductive point caused by very intense light; fewer electrons pass through the photosensor where lower light levels have made it less conductive. Scanning the electron beam carefully across the entire surface produces electrical information about the entire image. Vidicon cameras offer the possibility of high resolution and high sensitivity at a comparable lower cost than solid-state cameras. However, there are several drawbacks to these types of cameras. They can suffer form image lag because of slow response speed, suffer form image burn or permanent retention of the image, or exhibit some form of geometric distortion and drift. In addition, the vidicon cameras are not sufficiently reliable when accuracy is critical because the electron beam that creates the TV signal can easily be deflected by external

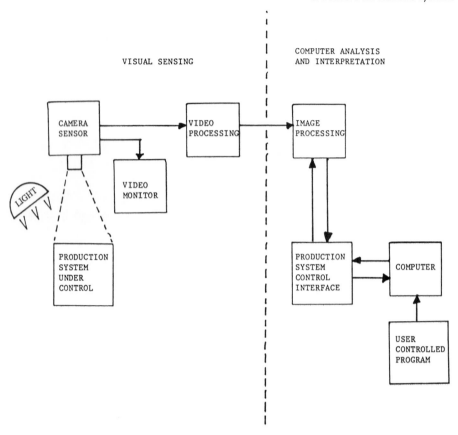

Figure 3-12 Machine vision system block diagram.

forces and magnetic fields. Therefore, except in special cases where resolution or lower cost dictates, a charge-coupled device (CCD) camera should be used as the image sensor of a machine vision system for an industrial robot.

Charge-coupled devices have been the major solid-state cameras used in industry. They were invented at Bell Laboratories in the 1960s, and although several companies are currently manufacturing different types of CCD cameras for machine vision systems, they function in a similar manner. An example of a vision system with a CCD camera is shown in Fig. 3-13. A CCD is a solid-state matrix sensor (Fig. 3-14) composed of multiple rows and columns of picture elements, also referred to as pixels. Light energy strikes the pixels, discharging a capacitance proportional to the light intensity and time exposure. A two-dimensional image can be produced based on the electrical information provided at each pixel. Standard commercial CCD cameras are available with pixel resolution of 128 × 128, 256 × 256, 320 × 240, and 380 × 488. The size of the image produced by a CCD camera is directly proportional to the amount of time required to process the information.

CCD cameras possess other disadvantages besides the limitation on the size of the image. Under highly intense light, there is an overflow of charge, or "blooming characteristics," to neighboring pixels. Blooming is not confined to CCDs, but it is less severe in the vidicon. The cameras can also have malfunc-

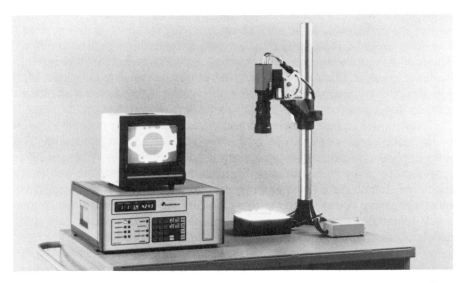

Figure 3-13 A vision sensing system with a charge-coupled device (CCD) camera. (Courtesy of Ham Industries, Inc.)

tioning pixels, sometimes an entire row of them. These "bad" pixels can often be concealed by pixel-averaging techniques during image processing. CCD solid-state cameras are usually better when compared to the tube-type cameras. Solid-state cameras offer no geometric distortion, no image drift, and virtually no image lag and do not suffer from image burn.

Either a vidicon or a CCD camera produces an image by generating an analog value to each pixel based on light intensity. Each of these signals must be digitized and stored in the random-access memory (RAM) of the system control computer before any computations can begin. There are two basic ways to process these analog signals into an image. The simplest and most widely used is a binary analog-to-digital (A/D) converter. The binary 1-bit A/D converter can only assign one of two acceptable values, light or dark, to each pixel. The

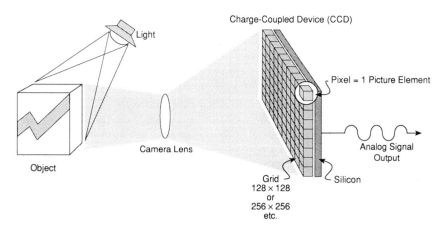

Figure 3-14 CCD sensor block diagram.

required processing speeds are much slower and the computations are much simpler to calculate than the second imaging process, gray-scale imaging. In gray-scale imaging, the analog values are digitized and then related to different shades of gray. By using an 8-bit microprocessor, the image can have up to 256 shades of gray. This imaging process requires unique software for each application. With a two-dimensional matrix of pixels, each possessing a certain shade of gray, an image can then be produced and shown on a video monitor.

Even though gray-scale imaging has a higher repeatability ratio for measurements, some experts believe that binary vision, which is fast and readily available, is good enough for most applications. For both gray-scale and binary images, there are two basic approaches to recognition: template and feature matching. Template matching may be understood by imagining a clear plastic sheet that has an object printed on it. To identify the object, the plastic template is moved until the printed image is aligned with the actual object. Using several templates, many objects can be identified and located. In a digital system, the template is stored in memory as a two-dimensional matrix. This system looks at an object and compares it with the closest digitized representation contained in its data base. If an exact match is not found, the system informs the operator of the imaging inconsistencies. With a feature-matching approach, the system uses transition in shape characteristics, such as dimensions, dimension ratios, area, brightness level, contrast, and orientation, to identify an object or find mistakes in it.

For a robot to be truly adaptive, it must have three-dimensional vision. The current three-dimensional systems use the technique of light striping and triangulation to create a topological representation of an object. When an object reflects projected beams of light, the light is deformed and shifted in position from a reference point, and this deformation can be measured. By using triangulation equations, measurements from any point on the object to the reference point can be determined and a three-dimensional image can be produced. Machine vision systems will continue to develop to meet the demand for adaptive automated applications.

Theory of Machine Vision

Machine vision is associated with the merger of one or more sensing techniques and computer technologies. Fundamentally, a sensor (typically a television-type camera) acquires electromagnetic energy (most frequently in the visible spectrum, i.e., light) from a scene and converts the energy into an alternate form of energy (voltage) that the computer can use. The computer then extracts information from the data (often first enhancing or otherwise processing the data), compares the information with previously developed standards, and outputs the results usually in the form of a response.

The Machine Vision Association of the Society of Manufacturing Engineers (SME) and the Automated Vision Association give the following definition of machine vision: "The use of devices for optical, noncontact sensing to automatically receive and interpret an image of a real scene, to obtain information and/or control machines or processes." The significant aspects of this definition are that machine vision involves automatic image interpretation for the purpose of control: process control, quality control, robot control, or machine control. The requirements addressed by machine vision technology are varied. Although the front end always consists in some form of image acquisition to be further processed and analyzed, the intended outcome of the analysis can be the analysis of one or several quite different attributes or parameters of the object based on the requirements of the application:

1. The simple presence or absence of an object, or a part of an assembly.
2. The general shape or profile of an object or one of its parts, and its distribution in groups.
3. The particular location or orientation of a part in an assembly.
4. The determination of the color of an object or some of its parts.
5. The determination of surface conditions of an object, such as finish, polish, texture, or dust. These are usually unwanted attributes in unpredictable and random locations.
6. The optical density at specified colors, or integrated color bands.
7. The determination of a dimensional property, such as length, thickness, depth, azimuth, angle, or depth of thread, and their distribution in groups.
8. Combinations of 1 to 7 above.
9. The use of motion analysis to obtain three-dimensional shape information as well as direction information.
10. Object recognition as distinct from checking the simple presence or absence of an object.

Some of these parameters relate to the cosmetic appearance of a product. The need for machine vision inspection arises in those cases from the psychological expectation that the good appearance of a product will result in its better acceptance in the marketplace.

Other parameters relate to the integrity of a product. An engine block, for example, should have its crankcase fully bolted before being placed in the chassis. A pharmaceutical blister package must contain a specified number of tablets, and they should be completely formed and of the right color. Still other parameters relate to the reproducibility or constancy of tolerances. The human eye, though sensitive and discriminating, cannot make quantitative judgments that are reproducible from event to event, even less from individual to individual observer. The color of a fabric, for example, could slowly change from hour to hour in one direction without a human inspector perceiving it. Another example is a closure that must fit the mating part of a container within specified tolerances. Still other conditions may prevail when, because of their small size, color, physical inaccessibility, or other limitation, some of the "visual" parameters cannot be seen by the unaided human eye but only by an appropriate sensor.

Whether it involves human vision or machine hardware, visual data acquisition proceeds essentially in three steps. In human vision, for example, the object should be properly lighted to make it "visible" to the human eye; second, the human eye itself, a lensing system, is needed to image the object on the sensor or the retina; finally, the retina should be somehow "read" and a signal conveyed to the brain by the optic nerve for further processing.

Similarly in machine vision (Fig. 3-15), the first step is to properly light the object to render it detectable by the sensor. The second step consists of imaging the object on the sensor, which converts the light energy to a proportional analog electrical signal. An analog-to-digital converter formats the image into a digital signal that enters the computer. The computer then manipulates the

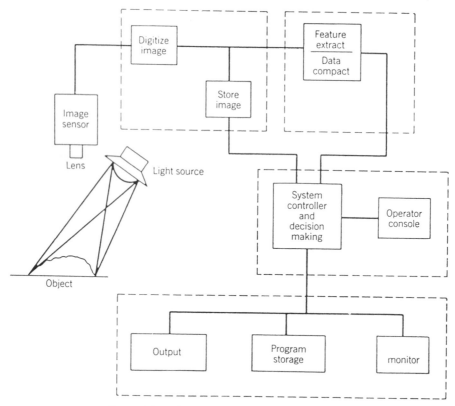

Figure 3-15 Theory of machine vision system diagram.

image data in ways to permit the extraction of the desired information about the objects, interprets this information, and decides and executes a course of action.

Contrast and Resolution

Image capturing typically involves acquiring the two-dimensional projections of a three-dimensional object. The two most important qualities of the image are contrast and resolution, that is, the attribute(s) of the image that will become the basis of an action or decision must be distinguishable and measurable.

Contrast is the range of differences between the light and dark portions of an image. Normally, contrast is measured between the feature containing the needed information and the background. The ideal image has ultimate contrast, with the desired information having intensity values of absolute white and background (everything else) intensity values of absolute black.

Resolution (or the ability to see two closely spaced objects) is a distance measurement associated with the smallest detectable object. The resolution required depends on the task of the machine vision system. If a system is needed to locate a part in X and Y to within 1 in., the system resolution needs to be less than 1 in. Unlike contrast, infinite resolution is not always desired.

Lighting and optics can have an effect on both contrast and resolution in many applications. Lighting and optics can be optimized to enhance the detectability associated with the variables for which a system is purchased or, conversely, can assist to diminish the influence of the variable on the data required to make a reliable "vision decision."

Lighting

In a given machine vision installation, dedicated lighting is strongly recommended because secondary sources of illumination may come from ambient lighting and the reflection of the primary source of light off other equipment, objects, or the floor and windows. The net result is a complex pattern of light in which uniformity is a compromise. This can affect the nature of shadows and shading on the surface, which can affect the recognition of the object. The objectives of lighting are:

- Optimize the contrast (gray-scale difference) associated with the condition one seeks to detect versus the normal state.
- Normalize any variances due to ambient conditions.
- Simplify image processing and, therefore, computing power required.

Lighting in a machine vision application can make the difference between a successful and an unsuccessful application. Illumination can either enhance features to be detected or obscure them. Poorly designed lighting can produce glare that may saturate the camera, create shadow that can include the data to be detected or obscure them, and generate low contrast or nonuniformity, thus making the inspection difficult. Sufficient illumination is also required because sensors have designated minimum levels—the minimum amount of light required to produce a video signal. Lighting considerations in a given application include:

- The type of light. Incandescent, fluorescent, quartz halogen, lasers, etc., all emit different wavelengths (colors) of light. The type used should illuminate the part's surface and also be measurable by the sensor type used.
- The lighting technique is the geometric setup between the part, any lights, and the sensor. This depends on what information is desired; maybe a silhouette is needed, or the bottom of a deep bore needs to be illuminated. Different lighting techniques would be used for each case.
- The control of the illumination may include the passive blocking of light with covers or shades.
- Geometry of propagation. There are three types of light sources: point, diffuse, and collimated. A single point of light will create shadows that accent edges. If shadows will block areas where information is needed, a diffuse light source will eliminate shadows.
- At times the shape of the light "beam" can be used as a method to gain information from the scene. Shapes can include points, lines, crosses, gratings, etc. These are called "structured lighting techniques," as shown in Figure 3-16.

The specific lighting technique used for a given application depends on:

- The object's geometric properties (specularity, texture, etc.)
- The object's color
- The background
- The data to be extracted from the object (based on the application requirement)

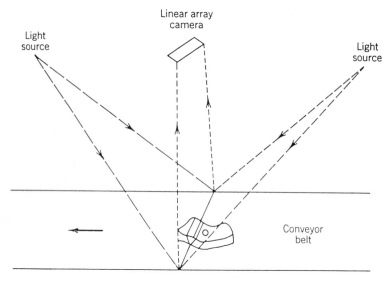

Figure 3-16   Consight system of structured lighting.

Optics

The optics create an image such that there is a correspondence between object points and image points for sensing. Except for the scaling or magnification factor, in an ideal optical system the image should be as close as possible to a faithful reproduction of the two-dimensional projection of the object. Consequently, attention must be paid to distortions and aberrations that could be introduced by the optics.

Many separate devices fall under the term "optics." All of them take incoming light and bend or alter it. A partial list would include lenses, mirrors, beam splitters, prisms, polarizers, color filters, and grating. Optics have three functions in a machine vision system:

- Produce a two-dimensional image of the scene at the sensor. The optics must place this entire image area, called the field of view (FOV), in focus on the sensor's light-sensitive area.
- Eliminate some of the undesired information from the scene image before it arrives at the sensor. Optics can perform some image processing by the addition of various filters. Examples include using a neutral density filter to eliminate 80 percent of the light in an arc welding application to prevent sensor burnout, using a filter in front of the sensor that allows only light of a specific color to pass, and using polarizer filters to eliminate image glare (direct reflections from the lights).
- Optics can be used in lighting to transfer or modify the light before it arrives at the scene in the same manner as optics are used between the scene and sensor described above.

Sensors

The sensor is a transducer that converts one form of incoming energy (light or acoustic) to an output of electrical energy. The conversion is linear, so the more intense the light impinging on the sensor, the greater the electrical energy generated. There are many types of sensors but they all belong to one of two groups: vacuum-tube sensors or solid-state devices, as mentioned in the introduction to this chapter.

Sensor Shapes

Sensors can vary according to the shape of the light-sensitive area: point, line, rectangle, or other. Each type has advantages for different image-capturing setups. The simplest type of sensor is a single-point photodiode. The output from this sensor would be one electrical signal with voltage proportional to the light intensity collected by the diode.

A line array sensor is no more than a fixed number of these single-point photodiode elements in a line or circle. An area array sensor is no more than a two-dimensional grid of these photodiode elements. The output of a line or area array sensor is a number of electrical voltages equal to the number of elements. The sensor adds special signals to tell which electrical voltage corresponds to which photodiode element (see Fig. 3-17).

A significant process occurs between the input and output of the sensor. The input was a continuous image projected from the optics onto the light-sensitive surface. The output is a number of individual electrical voltages. If these electrical voltages could be run backward through the sensor, the results would not be the original image. Figure 3-18 shows a comparison between the input and reconstituted output images. Note the patchwork or grid appearance. This grid effect occurs because of the finite number of sensor elements. For any one element, whatever portion of the image falls on it, only one value is generated. The value is proportioned to the average intensity of all the light falling on the element from all sources.

A/D Convertor

The output signal from the sensor consists of individual voltage samples from each photo element and the special signals to tell which voltage sample corresponds to which element. This information is placed end-to-end to create the analog electrical signal (Fig. 3-19). A digital computer does not process analog electrical signals. It needs a separate number (electrically coded) for each intensity value of each element, along with a method of knowing which intensity

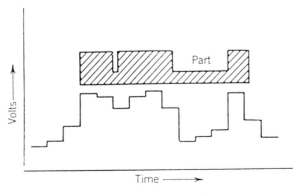

Figure 3-17 Output signal from a machine vision sensor.

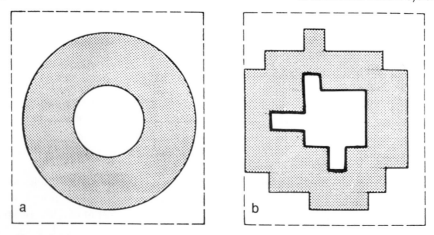

Figure 3-18 Input image and image reconstituted from sensor output.(a) Before, (b) after.

value corresponds to which sensor element. This transformation from an analog signal to an ordered set of discrete intensity values is the job of the A/D convertor.

The process of converting analog signals to digital values is called digitization. The number of possible digital values is important. The digital signal could have more information about the analog signal that represents the original image. As these intensity values range from black, the lowest value, to white, the highest value, they are called gray-level values. The actual gray level value is a function of the integration of four variables: illumination, viewpoint, surface reflectance, and surface orientation. The surface reflectance of an object is determined by surface characteristics such as texture and color material. The resulting distribution of light intensities forms an image.

Image Processing

Image processing is typically considered to consist of four parts.

1. Enhancement—the operations using the original image to create other images, finally resulting in an image(s) that contains only the desired information.
2. Segmentation—the process of separating objects of interest (each with uniform attributes) from the rest of the scene or background, thus partitioning an image into various clusters.

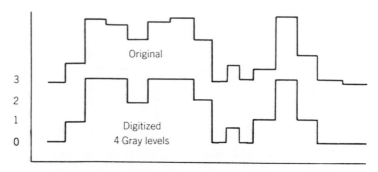

Figure 3-19 Digitization of an analog signal (2-bit values).

3. Feature extraction—the operations that extract feature information from the enhanced and/or segmented image(s). At this point, the images are not longer used and may be deleted.
4. Classification/interpretation—the operations that use the extracted feature information and compare the results with known standards. This setup answers the question of what the system was purchased for and outputs the results to the appropriate device.

Image Enhancement

Enhancement techniques transform an image into a "better" image or one more suitable for subsequent processing to assure repeatable and reliable decisions. There are three fundamental enhancement procedures: pixel or point transformations, image or global transformations, and neighborhood transformations.

Segmentation A scene can be segmented by windows, regions, or boundaries.

Windows Windows are established to isolate only those areas in a scene with the attributes of interest, for example, a hole. Only those pixels in the windows are processed, thus reducing the total number of pixels processed in a frame to a more manageable number and making it possible to handle more vision/decisions per unit time. The pixels in the windows can be processed in the same way the entire scene might have been processed: representations can be established or features extracted.

Region Segmentation The process of region segmentation involves partitioning an image into elementary regions with a common property (such as specific gray level or gray-level range), and then successively merging adjacent regions having sufficiently small differences in the selected property until only regions with large differences between them remain. A popular execution of this segmentation is based on using thresholding techniques to establish a binary image.

Thresholding The process of assigning "white" (maximum intensity) to each pixel in the image with gray scale above a particular value, with all pixels below this value becoming "black." That particular value is the threshold and is a gray-scale value. The resulting image, consisting of only black and white, is called a binary image. Thresholding was the first segmentation technique used, and almost all systems use it to some extent.

Edge Segmentation

Features can also be extracted based on edges, and edges can be obtained from a binary image based on transition locations in a gray-scale image. In the case of the latter, an edge is characterized by points of rapid change in the gray level of intensity. While edge detection is sensitive to changes in the intensity of a single pixel, it is not related to the individual intensities within patterns. Analysis of the edge intensity within a single pixel results in subpixel calculations of the location of an edge.

Many edge segmenting systems are based on detecting patterns of increasing and decreasing intensities or gradients generally found at the edges of objects. Since they are based on gradients they are less sensitive to illumination variations and can handle lower-contrast scenes.

Decision Making

Decision making, in conjunction with classification and interpretation, is characterized as heuristic, decision, or syntactic analysis.

Heuristic Analysis   In the heuristic case, the basis of the machine vision decision emulates how humans might characterize the image:

- Intensity histogram
- Black–white/black–white transition count
- Pixel counts
- Background/foreground pixel maps
- Background/foreground pixel counts
- Average intensity value
- Delta or normalized image intensity pixel maps
- X number of data points, each representing the integration of intensity over some area in the picture
- Row/column totals

Often companies that offer these products refer to the representation as a "fingerprint" or template. Some companies have executed these programs in hardware and consequently can handle some decision making at throughputs as high as 3000 per minute. These systems typically operate in a "train by showing" technique. During training (sometimes called learning), a range of acceptable representative products is shown to the system, and the representation that is to serve as the standard is established. The representation may be based on a single object or on the average of the images from many objects, or may include a family of known good samples, each creating a representation standard to reflect the acceptable variables.

In the operating mode, decision making is based on how close the representation from the present object being examined compares to the original or standard representation(s). A "goodness-of-fit" criteria is established during training to reflect the range of acceptable appearances the system should be tolerant of. If the difference between the representation established from the object under test and the standard exceeds the goodness-of-fit criteria, it is considered a reject. Significantly, the decision may be based on a combination of criteria (e.g., pixel counts and transition counts). The goodness of fit criteria then become based on statistical analysis of the combination of each of the "fit" criteria.

Decision making, in conjunction with these approaches, can be either deterministic or probabilistic. Deterministic means that given some state or set of conditions, the outcome of a function or process is fully determined with 100 percent probability of the same outcome given the same set of conditions. Probabilistic means that a particular outcome has some probability of occurrence (100 percent) given some initial set.

Decision Analysis   Decision theory analysis is frequently associated with the Stanford Research Institute (SRI) set of techniques. Decisions are made based on comparisons of the feature vector created from the specific geometric features that were selected for the decision training, such as area, perimeter, etc. In these types of "decision" approaches, objects are represented by "N" features, or an N-dimensional feature vector, and the decision is based on a distance measure in vector space. These techniques are especially well suited to recognition, verification, and location analysis.

Syntactic Analysis   The ability to make decisions based on pieces of an object usually relies on "syntactic" analysis, unlike the decision theory approach. In this case, the object is represented as a string, a tree, or a graph of pattern primitives and their relationships. Decision making is based on a parsing procedure. Another way to view this is as local features analysis, using a collection of local features with specified spatial relationships between various combinations. These primitives can be derived from binary or gray-scale images thresholded or edge processed. For example, three types of shape primitives are curve, angle, and line, which together can be used to describe a region. Image analysis involves decomposing the object into its primitives, and the relationships of primitives results in recognition. The primitive decision making can be performed using decision theoretic or statistical techniques.

Three-Dimensional Vision

Stereo vision is the process of combining features from two images of the same scene, taken from different viewing angles, to find the x, y, z position of some feature in the part. The diagram in Fig. 3-20 shows a typical stereo vision setup. By combining $(z1, y1)$, $(x2, y2)$, and some calibration data on the entire setup, one can find x, y, z, and the three-dimensional location of the object. It is necessary not only to know camera 1 and camera 2 calibration factors, but also the geometry of their setup. In reality, this is often done by calibrating with the object at several known x, y, z positions in the field of view.

Stereo vision is based on the assumption that the same point can be located accurately by both cameras. This leads to two cautions. The center of the surface of a round object, as shown in Fig. 3-20, is a poor choice because the point on the surface that appears to be the center differs for the two cameras. If the center of the object itself can be derived and used, it is a much better choice. A second caution concerns what is called the "correspondence problem." This applies when there are several identical objects in the field of view and it is

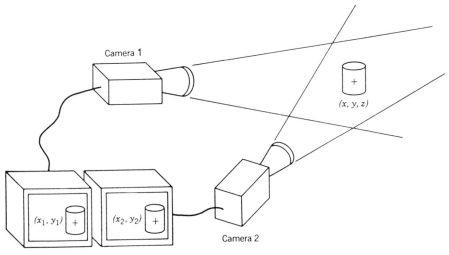

Figure 3-20   Stereo vision setup.

difficult to tell which feature seen by camera 1 corresponds to which feature seen by camera 2. Imagine an endless row of dots viewed by a stereo system. Information cannot be obtained from this image since it is not known which dots ''correspond'' unless the spacing between dots is used. This would prove difficult and does not always work. To prevent this, features must be selected that are unique either by themselves or in relation to their surroundings.

SUMMARY

The sensor industry's sales have doubled every year since 1980 and should continue to grow at least 20 to 30 percent annually for the foreseeable future. However, even with projected growth, the machine vision system industry has a difficult time getting its systems out of the lab and into the industrial world. The fundamental problem is the expectations gap between the factory users and the lab developers of the systems. Many factory users are waiting for machine vision systems to develop so that the chance of failure will be greatly reduced. They want to be sure that their machine vision system is economically justified, and they often complain that machine vision companies promise too much and do not design their equipment to perform well in tough industrial environments. On the other hand, machine vision companies say factory users expect too much of their systems. Until this gap is made smaller, progress will be restrained.

Another problem is that much of what machine vision companies make is custom-tailored. Customized machine vision systems increase buyer costs because the vendor is not able to sell the solution over and over again. Most vendors of machine vision systems are becoming more conservative in concentrating on fewer vertical applications and attempting to standardize their products in these areas. A machine vision company will find a problem in the real world to which it can apply a standardized solution. For example, it might have a standard software package that reads numbers and letters. A special version could be used by a pharmaceutical manufacturer to check the seal on bottles and read the lot numbers. The software would require instructions to adapt easily to the particular packaging machinery, lighting levels, vibrations, and other such conditions present in the customer's plant.

Many industrial manufacturers are beginning to realize that machine vision provides a very effective tool in reducing the high cost of rework and rejects and in significantly improving product quality. If manufacturers are going to compete internationally, they must employ machine vision to enhance their robots' flexibility and productivity.

4

APPLICATION OF ROBOTICS

EVOLUTION OF ROBOTIC APPLICATION

For the past 20 years, robots have been applied to manufacturing tasks in industries from automobiles to consumer electronics. The process of implementing robotic technology can be better understood if several applications are reviewed. The following sections discuss robot use in six different industries.

The capabilities of robots are limited, and the proper selection of the robot is only one of the important application ingredients. To ensure a successful, application, a total "system engineering" approach should be used. This chapter also addresses information that will be useful in designing and implementing a robot system.

The early robots were typically capable of moving an end-effector to specific, repeatable locations, and with the advent of continuous path control they could perform the intervening motion over a smooth, controlled path. Unloading die casting machines, spot welding, and paint spraying were all tasks within these capabilities and set the pattern for the first wave of industrial robots. With an early start and a history of successful implementations, these applications showed a rapid growth of robotic penetration through the end of the 1970s. Today, these are the most heavily penetrated applications, but the growth in these applications will eventually level off. The percentage of robots in these initial applications versus all categories of robots in use will decline as more demanding applications such as arc welding and assembly become robotized.

The beginning of the next wave of robot penetration can be seen today, with arc welding being the prime example. This generation of robots is characterized by systems with greatly enhanced sensory capabilities, as compared with the minimal sensing typical of the initial robot applications. This increased level of sensing is required by many of today's applications, and arc welding applications in particular are increasing due to new sensing and control technology. The quality of sensing available today is sufficient for initial implementations of robotic assembly, but developments that are now making their way from the laboratory to the shop floor will dramatically enlarge the potential market for robots in these applications. As a result, robot penetration will continue in the near future and these robots, especially in assembly applications, will eclipse the initial robot applications. Along with improved sensory capability and control, robots will be better integrated with surrounding equipment, including other robots. The logical extension of this integration is computer-integrated manufacturing (CIM) in which an entire production line of robots and automated machine tools is integrated and coordinated by a supervisory computer system. Such systems have been assembled; the major change expected in the near future is greater ease of integration as a result of robots being designed with integration capabilities from the start.

How the next generation of robotic penetration will occur is not entirely clear, but areas in which long-term research is now being performed give some indications. The key will be the incorporation of artificial intelligence and advanced sensors into robotic system operation and maintenance. The new robot applications will also stress systems integration for growth applications such as electronic component assembly and enhanced inspection systems based on machine vision integration with simple pick-and-place robots.

ROBOTIC USAGE BY INDUSTRY

Of all the components of the American manufacturing industry, only a few are making full use of industrial robots today. This section will briefly describe robot usage in different industries. Two points should be kept in mind: First, some of these industries are more clearly focused on automation than others. The aerospace industry is focused on several specific applications whereas light manufacturing is more of an organizational category than a coherent industry. Second, there is a significant amount of overlap between these industries. General Motors is clearly part of the automotive industry but is also heavily involved in foundry activities. This type of cross-industry linkage can affect the level of technology implemented by a company as strongly as competition from other members of its own industry.

The industry descriptions that follow will present information on how long the industry has been involved with robots and factors that have encouraged and discouraged robotic implementation. The current situation for each industry will be described and illustrated by examples of typical or innovative implementations. Finally, a qualitative assessment of each industry's responsiveness to robotic development will be provided.

Automotive

The involvement of the American automotive industry with robots dates back to 1961, when General Motors installed a robot die casting unloader. Even though early industrial robots were limited in their capabilities, these capabilities were well matched to the demands of many tasks in automotive manufacturing. When the automotive industry began installing robotic spot welders (Fig. 4-1), a pattern of robotic usage was established for the industry.

Figure 4-1   GMF robot spot welding on automobile production line.

Many factors have encouraged the automotive industry to implement robots. The environment in which many assembly operations are performed is noisy and hazardous, and the jobs are monotonous and fatiguing. Escalating hourly costs for personnel and increasingly stringent OSHA requirements for the work environment have steadily raised the total cost of labor. Robots are seen as a method of holding costs down with the added benefit of improved quality, a matter of increasing concern among U.S. automobile manufacturers in the face of foreign competition.

A major barrier to robotic implementation in most industries is the high initial robot system cost. This factor was less of a concern to automobile manufacturers because of the high volume of production; costs could be distributed over many production units. Furthermore, since the middle 1950s, the automotive industry has accepted yearly retooling as a fact of life; thus their reluctance to invest in capital equipment has been lower than in industries that retool on 10- to 15-year cycles.

Today, the automotive industry is the largest user of industrial robots in the United States, with approximately 50% of America's installed robots. Spot welding is the most robotized application; at the end of 1987, almost 80% of General Motor's robots were spot welders. Machine loading is also heavily robotized and spray painting robots are becoming common. The early pattern of simple robots performing simple tasks still holds true for the American automotive industry today.

However, this pattern in no way implies that this industry is complacent with respect to robots. In-house R&D efforts have kept the manufacturers abreast of new developments, and through-the-arc sensing robots for brazing body panels as well as machine vision-equipped robots for assembly are being actively pursued. While the robots in American automotive factories may reflect a certain conservatism, this industry has demonstrated a willingness to implement new technology as soon as it considers the technology to be sufficiently mature.

Foundry Industry

The foundry industry has been implementing robots since the early 1960s. Early material-handling robots were suitable for tasks like die unloading, which was the first foundry application for robots. The major motivation for robotizing foundry work has been the high risk to human workers. Virtually every foundry process from pouring molten metal to the final cleaning of a casting exposes workers to heat, noise, fumes, and dust (Fig. 4-2). Robots have been used to reduce this exposure and also to relieve humans of the fatiguing tasks of manipulating hot, heavy, metal parts.

The major barriers to increased robot utilization in foundry work have been limits of industrial robot flexibility and sensing. This is most clearly shown by the cleaning operations that until recently have remained a manual operation. The two major difficulties in automating the cleaning process have been the variability from casting to casting and the force or torque sensing required to control abrasive cutoff and grinding wheels.

Figure 4-2 Robots perform well in hazardous environments.

The foundry industry today is one of the leading users of industrial robots in the United States. Most of the robots in foundries are still performing material handling, for example, the robotic unloading of cast aluminum transmission housings at Doehler–Jarvis. Robots are also becoming common in investment casting, where the quality of the cast part is largely determined by the consistency of the mold. Robots have demonstrated their ability to achieve greater consistency than humans, in addition to being able to handle much heavier mold trees.

The demanding task of finishing castings is being performed by the Swedish firm of Kohlswa Jernverk using an ASEA robot. The installation uses torque and force sensing to control the metal removal rate and has demonstrated significant improvements in productivity over human performance as a result of the robot's ability to safely use higher powered grinding tools and to perform more consistently.

While the foundry industry may not be generally thought of as technologically innovative with respect to robotics, they have established themselves as a major user of robots. Robot implementations in this industry have overcome the problems associated with one of the harshest of the industrial environments and, through sophisticated techniques like force-controlled grinding, have demonstrated a willingness and ability to keep pace with emerging technology.

Light Manufacturing

Light manufacturing shows its most conspicuous use of robots in the fabrication of plastic parts. The environment surrounding injection molding equipment is hot and fume-laden and operator fatigue substantially reduces productivity. As with other industries, removal of personnel from a dangerous environment is a major incentive to introduce robots. Robotic implementation cost is the primary barrier in this industry; the small shops that comprise a significant fraction of this industry often can not afford to buy a simple material-handling robot. Therefore, it is not surprising that most of the robots in this industry are found in larger companies such as Motorola and General Electric.

Light manufacturing utilized about one-eighth of American robots by the end of 1987 and the bulk of them are used by larger companies in the injection molding process. A typical implementation is that used by Hoover in which a Prab robot unloads vacuum cleaner parts from the molding machine and presents them to a broaching machine for sprue removal. A more ambitious and fully integrated project by General Electric involves automating their Louisville, Kentucky dishwasher plant. In this plant, fully automatic injection molding machines are serviced by a computer-controlled conveyor system that is loaded and unloaded by robots (Fig. 4-3) produced by Cincinnati Milacron.

Electronics

The electronics industry has long been taking advantage of automation in certain areas. Hard automation is firmly established for insertion of components into printed circuit boards in large-batch electronics, and many of the processes involved in fabricating circuit boards (such as resist coating and etching) are also handled by automatic equipment. These repetitive, labor-intensive tasks are considered solved. In addition, the large-volume board component insertion is

Figure 4-3 Cincinnati Milacron robot used in General Electric plant. NOTE: Safety equipment may have been removed or opened to clearly illustrate the product and must be in place prior to operation. (Courtesy of Cincinnati Milacron, Industrial Robot Division.)

being done with hard automation at a speed that robots cannot hope to match, whereas small-batch board component insertion is commonly performed outside the United States, in countries with low labor costs.

Nevertheless, robots have penetrated this industry and robots involved in the electrical/electronics industry represented about one-eighth of the American industrial robots at the end of 1987. This application has been based on either using simple robots to replace humans in low demand but particularly unpleasant jobs at a lower cost or having the robots combine tasks normally performed by several people. A typical example of the first approach is used by Northern Telcom Canada Ltd. to assemble terminal blocks. This low-technology component is made by loading binding posts and a support block into a hot press, with the press applying heat and pressure to seal the posts into the support block. A robot is used and, while not significantly faster than a human operator, the robot can perform the task more economically by being able to operate continuously and by not requiring the special protective equipment needed by humans when handling hot (500° F) parts.

An example of a sophisticated application in which several tasks are combined is a process used by the Digital Equipment Corporation. A robotic cell is used to insert keycaps into keyboard assemblies and the first task performed by the cell is inspection of the keycaps prior to assembly. Using an Autovision machine vision system, the robot examines all incoming keycaps, rejects any with incorrect legends or flaws, and loads acceptable keycaps into magazines for use by the second robot that performs the actual insertion. This combination of consistent inspection with actual assembly results in better quality control and is likely to set a pattern for assembly applications in this industry.

The electronics industry has been slow in implementing robots because, in part, many potential high-volume applications are already being performed by hard automation, and the recognition of flexible manufacturing processers has not been adopted in the United States. However, the level of interest in sophisticated robots, such as machine vision-equipped assemblers, is very high. As robots with enhanced capabilities become available, this industry appears ready and willing to use them.

Heavy Equipment Manufacturing

The heavy equipment manufacturing industry began their major involvement with robotics for arc welding in the late 1970s. Their interest in robotic welding has been motivated by the same reasons as other industries: the cost and limited supply of skilled welders and the long-term health risks associated with the welding environment. This industry, more than most industries that use arc welding, has frequent need to weld thick workpieces that are difficult to weld and generally require flux-cored welding wire, which is particularly unpleasant to work with. However, the heavy equipment industry operates in relatively small batches, which tends to make cost justification of robots more difficult because of fewer production units over which to distribute costs. For this industry, robots must show major productivity gains to be cost-effective.

Nevertheless, robots have made significant penetration into heavy equipment manufacturing, with this industry having approximately 14% of American industrial robots at the end of 1987. Welding is the most common application, as typified by the use of Cincinnati Milacron robots by the Locomotive Products Division of General Electric to weld large structural elements for diesel–electric locomotives. While the volume of production of these units may not be large, these robots have justified their installation by performing all the needed welds in as little as half the time required by humans. NAVISTAR has invested heavily in robots for production of their series 50 tractors. Nine machining cells, each equipped with two CNC turning centers that are loaded and unloaded by Cincinnati Milacron robots, are used to turn gear blanks for the transmissions. A material-handling robot produced by Prab is then used to transport ring gears through heat-treating operations and a DeVilbiss three-robot system then spray paints (Fig. 4-4) much of the tractor chassis.

The preceding examples, coupled with the maintenance of in-house robotics R&D groups by other companies in this industry (such as John Deere and Co.), indicate that heavy equipment manufacturers are interested in and willing to make use of robots as the technology becomes available.

Aerospace

The involvement of the aerospace industry with industrial robots is relatively recent compared to the automotive and foundry industries. In 1975, General Dynamics demonstrated the feasibility of a robotic workstation for drilling aircraft wings (Fig. 4-5). However, it was not until four years later that their first production robotic workstation, funded by the Air Force MANTECH

P-100 DIMENSIONS

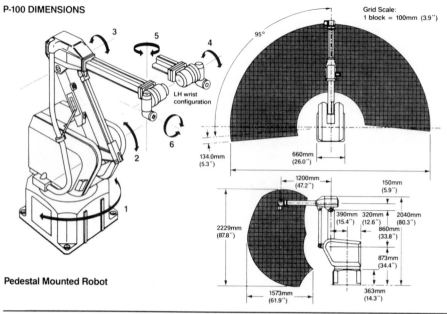

Pedestal Mounted Robot

SPECIFICATIONS	Axis Identification	Motion Range	MAXIMUM Travel Speed
Repeatability: Static: 0.5 mm			
Dynamic: 2.0 mm			
(At max. speed + load)	(1)	190°	103°/sec
Drive Type: Brushless AC Servomotor	(2)	110°	143°/sec
Temperature Range: 0 - 45°C	(3)	115°	143°/sec
Max. Painting Speed: 1200 mm/sec	(4)	540°	252°/sec
Weights (approx.) Manipulator: 460 kg	(5)	540°	338°/sec
Controller: 400 kg	(6)	540°	573°/sec

Figure 4-4 Work envelope for DeVilbiss painting robot. (Courtesy of The DeVilbiss Company.)

program, went into operation drilling pilot holes in composite materials. Early robots had little impact on the aerospace industry, largely because of the need for a higher level of precision than early robots offered.

Many factors have encouraged the introduction of robots into aerospace manufacturing. The Air Force, through the MANTECH and TECHMOD programs, has made plain its interest that its contractors implement robotics. The competitiveness of the U.S. industrial base requires the use of the most cost-effective manufacturing techniques available. Beyond cost-effectiveness, sheer precision of fabrication is critical; each new generation of aircraft is more demanding to manufacture than the prior one. Human techniques, using specially designed tools and carefully worked out methodologies, have kept up with demands for increasing precision but may have reached the limits of development. On the other hand, robotic techniques are still in the early stages of development and show room for improvement. Health hazards represent an area of major concern in the aerospace industry, especially with respect to many of the spray-deposited coatings and composite materials. Robots offer an obvious way to remove humans from these hazards.

The major impediments to aerospace use of robots have been the need for

Figure 4-5 Cincinnati Milacron T² robot drilling holes in F16 aircraft fuselage. NOTE: Safety equipment may have been removed or opened to clearly illustrate the product and must be in place prior to operation. (Courtesy of Cincinnati Milacron, Industrial Robot Division.)

high precision and the small batch sizes typical of the industry. Drilling and routing to the required precision require the use of templates, and fabrication and maintenance of templates for each part is an expensive proposition. Although the aerospace industry has been prominent in robotic R&D, it has been slow to implement robots in production. The reluctance to purchase expensive hardware for small-batch production and limited lifetime contracts will probably continue to act as a deterrent to use of robots in aerospace manufacturing.

An overview of current robotics technology can be given by studying the level of penetration of various robot applications in different industries. Since reliable numbers of robots actually being used in each industry are not very accurate, it is more appropriate to describe the robot penetration in a rather qualitative manner. Table 4-1 shows a plot of industries versus basic applications for robot technology. If an application has been well established in a significant number of industrial installations, it is indicated by a solid circle. If an application is not reported in use anywhere and is unlikely to be adapted by that industry in the near future, it is characterized by a hollow circle. Note that applications not relevant to a particular industry are indicated by a dash. Those applications that are marked by a half-filled circle belong to a group of applications that has been practiced in isolated cases or are being demonstrated with prototype units.

Table 4-1
Penetration of Current Robotic Applications in Various Industries

	Application[a]											
Industry	Spot welding	Arc welding	Material handling	Inspection	Assembly	Painting/ coating	Sealing/ coating	Finishing	Investment casting	Die casting	Forging	Plastic molding
Automotive	●	◑	●	◑	◑	●	◑	○	○	●	○	○
Foundry	—	—	●	○	—	—	—	◑	●	●	●	—
Nonmetal Light Manufacturing	—	—	●	○	◑	—	●	—	—	○	—	●
Electrical/ Electronics	○	◑	●	●	●	○	◑	—	—	○	—	○
Heavy Equipment Manufacturing	○	●	●	○	○	◑	○	◑	○	○	○	○
Aerospace	—	◑	◑	◑	○	●	◑	◑	◑	○	○	○

[a] ●, significant penetration; ◑, moderate penetration or being introduced; ○, no penetration; —, not relevant.

ROBOT APPLICATIONS

This section describes the basic robot applications, including material handling, welding, inspection, assembly, painting/coating, sealing/bonding, finishing, investment casting, die casting, forging, and plastic molding.

Material Handling

The technological issues involved in current material-handling applications range from the more routine to the very complex. In the simplest cases, the "pick-and-place" process, the robot (see Fig. 4-6) needs only to move to a

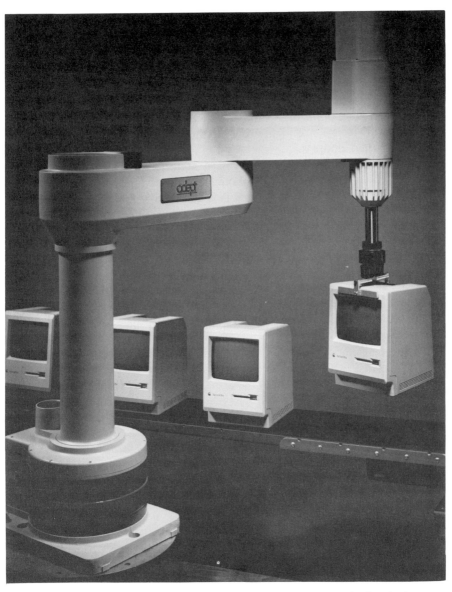

Figure 4-6   Adept Three ™ SCARA robot. (Courtesy of Adept Technology Inc.)

prescribed location, grasp an object, move to a second prescribed location, and release the object. In the more advanced implementations, the robot may use any combination of specially engineered grippers such as magnetic or vacuum grippers, some method of smooth path control, or various sensors to locate and verify acquisition of the workpiece. The level of sophistication, then, generally depends on the specific needs of each individual application.

While the percentage of material-handling processes performed by robots is still not very high, the number of robots involved in these processes is very large and is steadily rising. This is due largely to the vast number of basic material-handling applications performed in industry. While not all material-handling applications are suitable for robotization, there is still significant room for robot penetration into many material-handling operations, especially tool load/unload type operations.

The driving factor for robotization of material-handling applications depends heavily on the work volume. If the batch size is very large, then hard automation is generally more economical than robots. Similarly, if the batch size is very small, then human labor is usually more economical than robots. However, there may be overriding reasons for using robots in applications where they would be less economical than other methods. These reasons may include work in an unpleasant or hazardous environment such as the foundry environment (Fig. 4-7), or highly repetitive or difficult work that would cause fatigue in human laborers.

With the exception of high-precision material handling, most material-handling processes can now be robotized without further technological advances, albeit at some cost. There is a key trade-off in material-handling operations, namely, precise fixturing versus the ability to locate an object accurately and to grasp it easily. For those applications where positioning must be very precise, it is necessary to know exactly where the workpiece is and where is the most efficient place to grasp it. This can currently be done by utilizing standard fixturing techniques. However, fixturing reduces the flexibility of the robot and increases the system cost. As sensing technologies and gripper designs improve and become cost-effective, applications requiring great precision will use sensing devices and multipurpose grippers rather than fixturing systems.

Figure 4-7 Prab Robots' heavy-duty robot inserts and removes billit into a 2300° F furnace.

Figure 4-8 Material-handling robot stacking plates.

Material handling, in one form or another, is the basis for virtually all robotic applications. The primary function of a robot is to move an object, be it a tool, inspection device, or workpiece, from one point in space to another. In a stricter sense, however, material handling refers simply to moving workpieces. This could include reorienting, palletizing (Fig. 4-8), or simple pick-and-place operations. The basic material-handling process elements are broken down as follows:

- locating the object to be moved
- grasping the object
- moving the object through a prescribed path
- orienting the object
- depositing the object in a prescribed location

Material handling, though composed of a series of simple tasks, involves some subtle considerations. Locating the workpiece, for example, is not a trivial task. Depending on what manufacturing process preceded the handling step, the workpiece may or may not be presented with a known location and orientation. Considerations involved in actually moving the object include the weight, momentum, and inertia of the object, the desired path, and acceleration and deceleration speeds. A third process consideration in material handling is the geometry of the object to be manipulated. Small delicate objects (eggs) cannot be handled with the same methodology as large solid objects (engines). How and where objects are grasped can be critically important. A final consideration in material handling is the terminal position of the object. Workpieces that are palletized must be manipulated with much higher precision than those being placed randomly on a conveyor.

The basic hardware and software elements present in robotic material handling have evolved directly from the process under consideration, for example, the question of locating the object to be moved. Classically, this has been done with the use of elaborate fixturing techniques. If the workpiece is always "fed" to the robot in a very precise location, the robot need only to go to that location and grasp the object, unaffected by variations in part location. Fixturing, however, must be specially designed for each application and is therefore expensive. With the advances in sensing techniques such as machine vision pattern recognition, prices for sensing systems have become competitive with prices for some fixturing systems. Because sensing systems are inherently more flexible than fixturing systems, there has been an increase in the percentage of sensing systems associated with material-handling processes, from simple binary verification of part acquisition to complex determination of actual part location and orientation.

The question of part orientation also influences the elements involved in robotic material handling. Robot manipulator arms are available with different numbers of axes or degrees of freedom. The more axes a robot has, the more dextrous it is, but also the more expensive it is. For orientation applications, a robot with many degrees of freedom is required. Conversely, simple pick-and-place operations require robot arms with few degrees of freedom.

End-effectors have also evolved under the influence of process considerations. Gripper geometries (Fig. 4-9) are largely determined by the workpiece or pieces involved and are generally custom engineered for each application. Current designs include vacuum, two-finger, and jaw grippers, magnetic pick-ups, and combinations of these.

The robot controllers used in material-handling applications have varying degrees of complexity depending on the other elements involved. The advances in controller capability have been driven by the increasing demands of the specialized robotic hardware developed for individual applications. Robots with six degrees of freedom require a more complex controller than robots with only three degrees of freedom. Current controller technology available for material-handling applications include fine path control, algorithms to calculate kinematic and dynamic properties needed for varying arm speeds and payload weights, obstacle avoidance, complex grasping algorithms, and sensory integration capabilities.

The highly repetitive nature of most material-handling applications makes it an ideal candidate for robotic automation. Any operation as monotonous or tedious as a pick-and-place type of movement, especially with heavy loads, produces worker fatigue. Robot automation removes this from the process. The accuracy of robots is another advantage of robotic automation, especially in a palletizing or depalletizing operation.

Even though sensing is becoming more widely used in robotic material handling, some advances in sensing technology would allow robotic automation to penetrate a wider variety of applications. For example, more accurate slip sensing would enable real-time recovery techniques to be more effective, and

Figure 4-9   End-effector gripper on Prab robot. (Courtesy of Prab Robots.)

faster pattern recognition algorithms would allow more effective real-time location, as in bin-picking applications (Fig. 4-10).

A typical application is a large manufacturer's use of a robot to palletize and
depalletize different types of blocks. The robot uses a gripper specially engineered to handle the sometimes brittle blocks with a minimum of breakage. The
following benefits were realized with the robotic system:

- Labor savings—With the addition of the robot, one less worker per shift
  was necessary.
- Increase of productivity—Even with one less worker per shift, productivity doubled.
- Quality improvement—With the specially engineered hand and accuracy
  of the robot, the defective part rate dropped significantly.
- Safety/environment—The heavy loads, dust, high temperature, and
  safety hazards of working with the heavy load previously caused a high
  labor turnover rate. With the implementation of the robot, the manufacturer eliminated its dependence on an unreliable work force.

It should be noted that many of the application examples in subsequent sections
are, in fact, expanded specialized versions of material handling techniques.

Figure 4-10   Machine vision bin-picking robot system. (Courtesy of ORS.)

Welding

The technological sophistication of different robotic welding implementations varies from application to application. For example, most spot welding robot tasks require repeatability. Smooth path control and external sensing are generally not necessary, but the robot needs to repeatedly move to a given point, independent of the path it takes. Complicated arc welding, on the other hand, may require a much higher degree of sophistication. In general, the robot needs not only to go to a specific point or set of points, but to traverse a given path with controlled speed and acceleration. In addition, it is desirable to have the capability of altering the preset path to respond to changing welding conditions. This requires not only a high sophistication level of individual components, such as sensor systems, but also a complex integrated method of control.

Because the level of advanced technology necessary for spot welding is relatively low, robots penetrated spot welding applications early. Currently, automobile spot welding uses the largest number of robots of any heavy manufacturing process in the United States. In contrast, robots have not been as successful in penetrating arc welding applications. As the technology necessary for complex arc welding procedures has become available, however, the number of arc welding robots has risen significantly.

The driving forces for robotic implementation have been improved quality

Figure 4-11   ABB IRB-90 (left) spot welding and IRB-60 (right) arc welding of cabinets. [Courtesy of ASEA Brown Boveri (ABB).]

and reduced costs. While the robot is not necessarily always fast enough to justify its cost through increased throughput, the consistent quality of robotic welding is usually better than human welding. This is true both for spot welding (Fig. 4-11), where fatigue due to heavy equipment and long shifts is sometimes a problem, and for arc welding, where consistency over a long weld path may lead to difficulties. Continued and increased use of robots for spot welding is not dependent on further advances in new technology.

Increased use of robotic arc welding is heavily dependent on advances in sensing and control technology. As sensing techniques improve, robotic arc welders will be able to autonomously adapt the weld path and parameters to meet varying weld conditions. This ability will reduce or eliminate the current need for expensive, precise fixturing mechanisms. The emphasis in this section is on arc welding because it is more demanding and has shown less penetration by robots than spot welding. However, both spot welding and arc welding are discussed. The basic process elements are:

Arc Welding

- align parts to be welded
- heat parts at seam by generating an arc between welding electrode and workpieces
- apply filler material as needed
- monitor weld for bead width, penetration depth, seam filling

Spot Welding

- align pieces to be joined
- clamp pieces between welding electrodes
- heat pieces at weldpoint by passing a high current between welding electrodes

Parts alignment is vital to satisfactory performance in both types of welding. The two aspects of parts alignment can be characterized as setup (how the parts to be joined are positioned to each other) and seal alignment (how well the surfaces or edges to be joined are aligned with each other). Both of these characteristics are established by the fixturing used to hold the parts and the dimensional correctness of these parts. Setup determines if the unit as a whole will be acceptable and is not affected by the actual welding operation. Seam alignment affects the welding operation by dictating the amount of filler material required. If the seam alignment is very poor, an acceptable weld may be impossible. Figure 4-12a illustrates the two aspects of parts alignment. Figure 4-12b illustrates poor setup due to improper fixturing; although the seam could be welded, the finished unit would be unacceptable. Figure 4-12c shows good setup but poor seam alignment as a result of a bad edge on the horizontal piece. Poor seam alignment is common when welding heat-treated parts because of the resultant dimensional changes and warpage.

In addition to positioning the workpieces correctly with respect to each other, positioning of the welding tool with respect to the workpieces is also critical for successful welding. For spot welding, the electrodes must be brought together from each side of the workpieces, aligned with each other and perpendicular to the surfaces of the workpieces. If the workpieces are deeply contoured, access to the inner side of the weld can be difficult; large workpieces require a long, precise reach to bring the welding electrodes together at a point far from the outside edge of the workpieces.

Arc welding as a line (and in some cases volume) process involves additional geometric and kinematic complexities. Motion of the welding torch along the seam must follow a smoothly controlled path to maintain a uniform weld seam. Since the arc is affected by the geometric relation of the electrode to the workpieces, motion control must not only move the torch along the proper path, but also control the torch orientation with respect to the workpieces. To maintain the proper heating rate of the workpieces, the speed that must be controlled is that of the electrode tip with respect to the workpieces, taking into account any rotation of the torch to track a contour.

Another critical factor is temperature control of the parts at the point of welding. This control is exerted through control of the electrical parameters of the welding operation for spot welding: for specific thicknesses of specific materials, a controlled amount of current is passed through the workpieces at the weld point for a sufficient length of time to melt the workpiece surfaces together. For arc welding, an additional parameter that affects heating is speed along the seam. Inadequate control of temperature of the seam boundaries produces bad welds: if the temperature is not raised sufficiently high, the weld penetration will be inadequate, whereas temperatures that are too high can produce burnthrough and seam gaps (see Fig. 4-13).

The arc welding robot includes a manipulator arm(s), controller, and sensing subsystems described below. The mechanical robot manipulator arms used

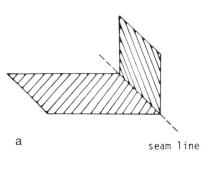

a   seam line

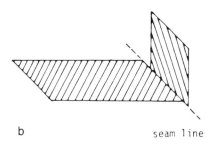

b   seam line

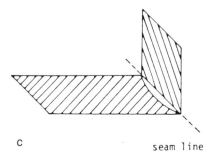

c   seam line

Figure 4-12 Parts alignment for welding (a) Ideal alignment, (b) poor set up, good seam alignment, (c) good set up, poor seam alignment. (Courtesy of U.S. Air Force.)

for welding require a great deal of dexterity to properly locate and orient the welding tool. For arc welding, six degrees of freedom are usually required, three to smoothly control torch location as the seam path is followed and three to maintain the correct orientation of the electrode with respect to the workpieces. Load capacity is another important aspect of mechanical performance for welding because the welding tools can be heavy and the power leads are thick and rather stiff. Additionally, inert gas arc welding requires a gas supply hose that adds to the mechanical load. These supply lines add a component of resistance to flexing at each joint and require additional force to overcome.

Spot welding, because of its relative simplicity, can be performed by simple controllers operating in an open-loop mode; arc welding requires more sophistication from the controller. In the latter, sophisticated path control algorithms

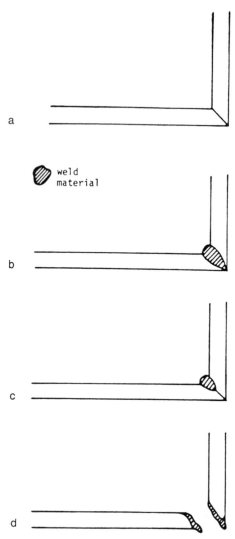

Figure 4-13   Effect of applied heat on weld penetration. (a) Prior to welding, (b) ideal penetration, (c) inadequate heating: insufficient penetration, (d) excessive heating: burnthrough. (Courtesy of U.S. Air Force.)

are required to move the electrode tip along a smooth path while controlling the orientation and speed of the electrode tip. Seam tracking for adaptive path control to accommodate discrepancies between actual and expected seam location requires a controller that can integrate sensory information. Interfacing with the environment for purposes of controlling welding parameters, such as arc current or rate of feed of welding wire, can be used to enhance the adaptive capability of a welding robot but adds to the required sophistication of the controller.

The first sensors used for robotic welding were simple tactile probes that rode along the weld seam to guide the welding torch. More recent applications have used through-the-arc sensing. The principle behind this method is that the position of the welding tip, with respect to the surface of the workpieces,

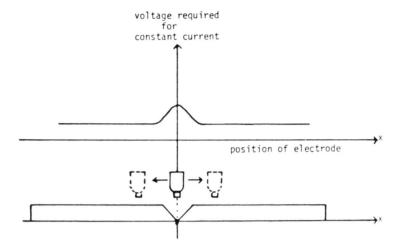

Figure 4-14 Through-the-arc sensing. (Courtesy of U.S. Air Force.)

determines the effective length of the arc, which in turn affects the voltage required to maintain a constant current (see Fig. 4-14). Using an explicitly programmed back-and-forth motion perpendicular to the seam, a robot can constantly verify the location of the center of the joint, and this information can be fed back to keep the weld centered on the seam. This same technique has also been used for applications requiring large amounts of filler material to be deposited to reinforce the seam.

Machine vision sensing is used for some welding applications and reflects improvements in flexibility, reliability, and cost of machine vision systems attained in the last several years. Two major problems are addressed by machine vision systems: seam tracking and weld characteristic monitoring. Visual seam tracking detects the center of the seam by recognizing the discontinuity in reflected light from the two workpieces or by interpreting the image of a strip of light projected onto the seam at an angle (see Fig. 4-15). For weld monitoring, visual systems have been developed that examine the shape and size of the weld puddle. This information can be used to indicate the penetration depth of the weld, whether the weld seam is forming symmetrically, and whether the welding speed is appropriate.

The consistency of robots in welding is a major advantage over human welders. In spot welding, if an assembly requires 20 spot welds, the robot will always make 20 spot welds (something that apparently cannot be assumed for human welders). If the robot system is properly set up, each weld will be executed properly, even those that are difficult to reach. Consistency with robots is also a major advantage in arc welding: when properly set up and supplied, a robotic arc welder will produce a weld each time that is as good as that of an expert welder.

Environmental factors in welding have an adverse effect on the productivity of human welders. The heat in the vicinity of welding operations can become oppressive, and the fumes, especially when using flux-cored welding wire, are unpleasant and can be hazardous. Protective gear, including gloves and especially a welding mask, are heavy and uncomfortable and cause fatigue. Since the

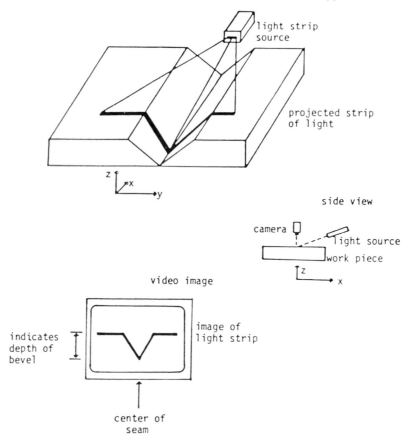

Figure 4-15   Structured light. (Courtesy of U.S. Air Force.)

arc produces significant amounts of ultraviolet light, exposed areas of skin rapidly develop sunburn; this exposure is uncomfortable in the short term and potentially hazardous in the long term.

Another major advantage of robots in arc welding is the limited pool of available skilled human welders. To become an expert welder requires extensive training and years of experience. This, coupled with the unpleasant aspects of the work, limits the number of people entering the field, while the negative aspects of the work encourage personnel to leave the field. As a result, the supply of expert welders is limited and the cost of using expert welders has risen steadily.

Current implementations of robotic welding require elaborate and costly fixturing to keep deviations in the parts alignment within the relatively narrow tolerance range. Improvements in sensing systems are steadily expanding this tolerance range but a human expert welder can still successfully weld a seam whose misalignment is beyond the capability of the most sophisticated welding robot.

Selection of a sensing system for robot welders requires significant trade-offs between flexibility and speed. While machine vision-based systems provide very good adaptive control, they tend to be relatively slow because of the processing requirements of the image interpretation. Visual sensing is further complicated by the variable light level at the workpiece. Two-pass machine vision systems first scan along the seam to be welded without striking the arc in order to memorize the exact path needed for the weld. This minimizes the machine vision difficulties but increases the time required for the process and does not allow the machine vision system to monitor the weld parameters during welding.

A typical welding application is one used by the Locomotive Products Division of General Electric, which has been using robots since the end of 1981 to weld bolsters, the structural elements of a locomotive frame on which the power trucks are mounted. Robots are used in conjunction with 6000-pound-capacity positioners to weld these assemblies, which consist of steel plates up to 1 1/4 in. thick. The introduction of the robots has reduced the time required to perform all the needed welds to one-half of that previously required.

Robots are also used by the Aircraft Engine Business Group of GE to weld stainless-steel components of fan frame hubs for jet engines. Cycle time, including part loading and unloading, has been reduced from the four hours required for manual welding to one hour. The actual arc time of the robot has been reduced to 24 minutes, thus reducing the heat build-up in the assembly, and the greater precision in control of arc current, torch speed, and orientation has improved the quality of the final assembly.

Inspection

Robotic inspection generally uses the most technologically advanced robot systems available. As sensor technology improves, inspection applications will become more varied. Sensing systems currently used for robotic inspection include two-dimensional and lightstripe machine vision systems, as well as force sensing and binary tactile sensing. However, other types of sensing are also being implemented as advances in infrared, ultrasonic, and eddy-current sensing technologies have brought the price of these sensors down to a cost-effective level. In addition, control technology is a key element of robotic inspection processes. To perform an inspection task, the robot needs an internal model of the ideal workpiece from which to make comparisons. In theory, this model could be as simple as a linear measurement, such as the part must be 8 in. long, or as complex as a detailed three-dimensional model of the part. Robot controllers are becoming sufficiently sophisticated to hold and even automatically generate a complex internal model of the workpiece. As machine vision technologies improve and the prices drop, robotic inspection is becoming more common. Because inspection processes are increasingly coupled to assembly tasks, the use of robotic inspection will increase with the rise of robotic assembly.

The primary reason for using robots in inspection tasks is quality control. The consistency and repeatability of the robot and the control algorithms that compare the workpiece to a model allow for not only greater but more predictable levels of quality. Once a tolerance has been preset, the robot (Fig. 4-16) will reject any inferior part and accept any part that meets the tolerances, thus eliminating any subjectivity from the process. This consistency and predictability aid in manufacture and process planning. A secondary reason for using robots for inspection is the capability of in-process inspection, which allows for inspection of workpieces in hazardous environments.

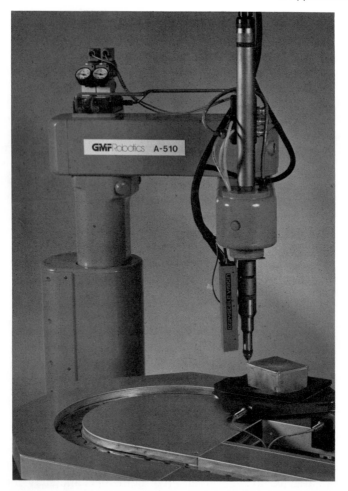

Figure 4-16   GMF robot with machine vision sensor inspects component.

Even though the use of robots for inspection is increasing, further techno-logical advances will speed the penetration of robotic technology into inspection processes. One of the most important factors that hold back the use of robotic inspection is not availability of new technologies but rather the need for decreas-ing the cost and increasing the speed of current technologies. The research areas of color, three-dimensional real-time vision, and precision tactile sensing arrays are very active and when developed they will expand the scope of robotic inspection.

Inspection, as it is performed in the industrial environment, usually consists of examining a workpiece either during or just after the manufacturing process. This complicates the inspection process by requiring the robot to determine the location and the orientation of the workpiece. For manufacturing applications, a general inspection scheme consists of:

- getting the part from its previous position
- establishing a known orientation for the part

- matching the object with an appropriate reference model or models
- determining if the workpiece is within acceptable tolerances of the reference model
- sorting the object by part type or quality control

Selection of the inspection points is the first process consideration encountered in industrial robotic-aided inspection. Ideally, it would be desirable to inspect a workpiece throughout the entire manufacturing process, thereby helping assure that total quality is measured. However, this is not usually economically practical. It is necessary, then, to choose the most logistically beneficial inspection point or points in the production process to inspect the workpiece.

A second consideration in industrial inspection is that of comparison method and thresholding. In general, a workpiece can be inspected for many different qualities; it is important for both quality and economic factors to inspect only those properties of a workpiece that can distinguish between desirable and undesirable pieces. In addition, it is necessary to determine exactly how close a measured property must be to the reference model to be considered acceptable.

An increasingly important consideration in industrial inspection is that of flexibility. It is often desirable to have the capability of inspecting several different types of parts, either simultaneously or in different batch runs. This requires the ability to accurately choose from among several reference models depending on which part is to be inspected.

Robotic inspection is usually performed in one of two modes: either by having the robot move the workpiece in front of a fixed sensor, such as a camera, or by having the robot move the sensor around the workpiece. In general, it is more efficient to have the robot carry the lighter of the two objects. In either case, it may be necessary for the manipulator to have a high degree of dexterity and accuracy, depending on the geometry of the object to be inspected.

There are currently three main types of sensing hardware available: tactile sensors, machine vision, and custom-designed complex sensors. Tactile sensors used for inspection can be either point sensing (including simple touch probes or contact switches) or tactile arrays (Fig. 4-17). Although current tactile arrays used in manufacturing consist of binary elements, tactile arrays with force sensing are also now being used. Machine vision sensing is also incorporated in one of the two modes: imaging, in which an object is noted as either being there or not, with possibly some image enhancement techniques, or pattern recognition, which can include scene interpretation. In addition, there are many

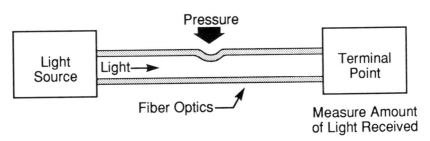

Figure 4-17   Configuration of fiber-optic tactile sensor.

custom-designed sensors, such as infrared sensors to detect heat given off by a workpiece and magnetically induced eddy-current sensors used in metal-crack detection, or combinations of these sensors for special applications.

There are many justifications for using a robot in an industrial inspection scheme. The robot's immunity to fatigue and use of high-precision criteria allow for more consistent quality control and sorting results. Using a robot for inspection may allow in-process inspection to be performed in a hazardous environment, and robots can use sensory properties not available to humans, such as infrared and eddy currents. In addition, the use of robots for inspection allows for the electronic integration of inspection into the manufacturing process, thus providing an enhanced degree of flexibility and consistent high-quality inspections.

The current constraints in robotic inspection concern both software and hardware issues. Pattern recognition algorithms, both for tactile contour maps and for visual scene understanding, are still too slow to allow extensive real-time processing of the sensory information. Tactile sensing arrays are not sensitive enough to give real-time texture information and the size and cost of most sensing hardware make it inappropriate or infeasible in a number of applications.

A typical application is a very sophisticated inspection process used by a major computer manufacturer to orient and inspect keycaps prior to loading them into magazines for use in an automated assembly system. Keycaps are shipped in bulk by the supplier and then separated by keycap shape, color, and legend. Keycaps are dumped into a bowl feeder that orients the caps and feeds them into a track leading to a visual inspection station. This inspection system rejects keycaps with defects, incorrect legends, flawed legends, or surface defects and then loads acceptable keycaps into magazines that are used subsequently by the keyboard assembly system.

For the machine vision system to ''learn'' the characteristics of a specific keycap, the operator steps through a menu-driven procedure that inputs characteristics of the key (such as light text legend on dark background), establishes the inspection window (i.e., what part of the visual field to process), and specifies the legend expected for the key. The system then prompts the user to feed a small number of keycaps known to be good through the inspection system to fine-tune the inspection criteria. The results of this learning process are saved on a data base and used to provide specifications anytime a batch of that specific keycap needs to be inspected. The entire inspection requires about two seconds per key.

Assembly

Robotic assembly operations may be performed at a variety of sophistication levels. For easy-mating assemblies, low levels of sensor and path control sophistication are used, while for the more critical assemblies, complex force sensing and machine vision (Fig. 4-18) may be necessary. In addition to advanced sensing requirements, critical path control may also be required. The geometry of assembling two closely fitted workpieces is not trivial; although a human can easily compensate for slight misalignment, a robot cannot always make the minute corrections in position and angle of attack to properly assemble

Figure 4-18   GMF robot with advanced sensing system for assembly operations.

two workpieces. Although completely accurate and efficient assembly control methods are not yet available, partial solutions to this problem are being used in production.

The major factor in robotic assembly, as is the case for robotic material handling, is the throughput volume. For very large volumes, hard automation with fixturing systems is more economical than robotics, while for very small batches, human labor can be more economical than robots. For those volumes of work where robots have the potential for being economical, robotic assembly has the advantage of increased consistency over human labor. As for inspection, the high repeatability of the robot affords a higher and more predictable level of quality control than do human systems. A secondary incentive for using robots for assembly involves clean room and hazardous or unpleasant environments. Using a robot for an operation that must be performed in a clean room eliminates the complications of human preparation for the clean room.

The three most important technical barriers to extended use of robotics in assembly tasks are sensor technology for easier part acquisition, force feedback control, and advanced control technology for accurate assembly algorithms. Additionally, error recovery algorithms are currently not sufficiently sophisticated to do much more than simply abort an operation. Ideally, these algorithms should be able to isolate the problem and, if the problem is not critical, continue the assembly task.

There are two major categories of assembly applications: closely fitted and easy-mating. The first of these deals with tight-tolerance components that are generally fragile and require precise assembly motions. Easy-mating applications generally deal with larger components that are somewhat compliant. The basic process elements are:

- Acquire parts
- Orient and set up parts
- Perform assembly—slide, insert, snap, press, stake
- Inspect
- Deposit finished assembly—palletize

The range in weight and size of parts to be handled can vary widely from a small spring up to a cast assembly housing. Furthermore, press fitting or staking as part of the assembly operation may require load capacity (i.e., strength) well beyond the weight of the parts involved. Any tooling that grips the parts must be able to accommodate the variety of shapes and sizes of parts involved in the operation and handle them gently enough to avoid marring or deformation of delicate components.

Closely fitted components require precise assembly motions because of their tight tolerances and may not incorporate any aids in positioning, such as beveling or chamfering. Attempting to assemble close-tolerance parts that are not properly positioned is likely to damage the parts and ruin the entire assembly. While press fitting is intended to require force for insertion, misalignment of the parts can raise the force required and ruin the parts.

Detection of errors during assembly operations is critical for the unit being worked on and in the assembly process itself. A flawed assembly is not only defective itself but, if not detected, can be incorporated into a larger system that will then also be defective. If a particular step in the assembly sequence begins producing a high error rate, it may indicate a problem with the assembly technique or with a batch of components. Quality control can be implemented as a part of the assembly process and may include inspection of incoming components, inspection during assembly, and inspection of the finished assembly.

The basic elements of an assembly robot are the manipulators, controller, and sensing units. Manipulators are used in closely fitted assembly and are generally small and precise to match the requirements of a specific assembly task. The required load capacity need not be great but should be adequate for press fitting, staking, or application to assembly of units other than that originally implemented. End-effectors used in assembly operations are usually specially designed for the specific parts to be handled.

Robot controllers for assembly applications can be set up for varying levels of sophistication. If parts are presented in an unstructured way, the controller must have the ability to search for and recognize the parts needed. Low-clearance mating operations, since they frequently require positioning accuracy that is better than the manipulator accuracy, require that the controller be able to use some type of adaptive part mating algorithm for final alignment. Sensing elements include:

- Tactile sensors—Binary sensing is useful as a simple test of whether or not a part is in place, that is, to sense that a part has been dropped. Force sensing allows monitoring of parts alignment during insertion since misalignment causes excessive resistance. The abrupt change in applied force, when mounting snap-on parts, can be used to determine that the part is completely seated.

- Machine vision sensors—Machine vision is becoming popular in assembly applications because of its flexibility. It is used to locate parts for grasping, to check orientation, and to inspect parts prior to assembly.
- Proximity sensors—Light-emitting diodes (LEDs) and phototransistor detectors have been placed in the end-effectors in some applications as an alternative to binary tactile sensing to verify that a part is in the gripper.
- Sound sensors—Sound detectors have been used in assembly operations both to verify that a snap-on part has seated and to detect the sound of a dropped part so that corrective action can be taken.

Consistency is a major advantage of robots in assembly work. If the parts supplied to the robot are within specifications and the robot programming is set up properly, the robot will assemble each unit in precisely the same way. In contrast, human performance on monotonous tasks varies and makes quality control difficult. Furthermore, human assemblers sometimes apply excessive force to poorly fitted parts to finish a unit. This is a source of marginal or defective assemblies that can be eliminated by programming an assembly robot to limit insertion force.

In a clean room environment, a great deal of personnel time is spent preparing to enter, leave, and reenter the clean room between shifts. Once a robot is set up to operate in the clean room, it loses no production time in leaving and reentering the clean room.

Parts acquisition is a major technological constraint in robotic assembly at this time. Structured parts presentation (e.g., palletized supply, indexed presenter, etc.) solves some of the problems but can be prohibitively expensive, especially for small batches. Using the robot's sensing capability to locate and orient parts requires sophisticated (by today's standards) and costly sensing and control components. Furthermore, today's technology has not yet completely solved the "bin-picking" problem (acquisition of parts from a jumbled and overlapping pile), although there is a great deal of promising research addressing this problem and a cost-effective solution is near.

The fundamental problem of placing one part inside of another part, especially for close-fitted parts, has long been taken for granted because of the ease with which a human can solve the problem. However, when using robots in closely fitted assembly operations, jamming is a common problem and many current algorithms to improve parts alignment reduce the speed of the operation noticeably. While currently available remote compliance centers (RCCs) are helpful, their range of accommodation is not large, they are not programmable, and they are not totally successful in preventing jamming due to misalignment. Current work on the generic "peg-in-a-hole" problem and the explicit geometry of jamming are likely to result in more effective and efficient methods of assembling tight-tolerance parts.

At this time, error-handling methodologies for assembly sequences still require improvement. Not only should an error during assembly be detected but recovery from the error should be attempted. Whether recovery consists of discarding the entire assembly and starting over or discarding a single part and trying again, it should be determined by the type of error and the part of the assembly sequence involved. When an error is detected in present systems, most assembly robots simply stop and wait for human assistance to fix the problem.

An interesting example of robotic assembly has been demonstrated by Stanford Research Institute (SRI) in using two coordinated robot arms, one with a force sensing wrist and the other with a hand-mounted camera, to assemble a part of a printer carriage. Four types of parts are involved in this assembly: a square shaft with four plastic rocker arms already attached, four plastic rockers that snap into the rocker arms, and two sizes of roller shafts that snap into the rockers. The sequence begins with robot arm number 1, the one with the camera attached, picking up the shaft/rocker arm assembly and placing it in a specially designed support fixture. Robot arm 1 then acquires rockers and places them in the correct location with respect to the rocker arms. Robot arm number 2 is used for assembly because of its force sensing capability. The force exerted by robot arm 2 is monitored as it presses on the rocker, with seating indicated by a rise in force followed by an abrupt drop as the rocker snaps into place. While this is being done for all four rockers, robot arm 1 has placed the roller shafts in an aligning fixture. In the next step, robot arm 1 lifts the shaft/rocker arm/rocker assembly and turns it over, placing it on top of the fixtured roller shafts. Robot arm 2 then pushes down on each rocker until it snaps onto the roller shafts. Force sensing is again used to sense completion of the snap fit.

Painting/Coating

In general, robotic painting and coating operations (Fig. 4-19) require a very low level of technological sophistication; for example, sensors are not widely used. The most critical aspect of the robot technology necessary for painting tasks is smooth path control. In some of the more recent painting applications, however, the robot controller is called on not only to direct the path of the robot and control the painting apparatus, but also to coordinate the painting with the movement of an assembly line and with other concurrent operations such as automobile door opening.

Because robotic painting and coating operations require a minimum level of technology, in combination with the fact that this technology has been available for some time, robots have shown a heavy penetration into the painting industry, especially automobile paint-spraying applications. In fact, several different robot manufacturers have built reputations solely on their paint-spraying robots.

The majority of painting robots, as mentioned, are used by the automobile industry, and because they deal with fairly high volumes of throughput, the robots are more cost-effective than human workers. In addition, there are several other important considerations for using robots in painting operations. One consideration is quality. If a satisfactory painting path is programmed into the robot, it will follow that path exactly, cycle after cycle, day after day. This will result in very consistent high-quality painting. In addition, the spray painting environment is potentially very hazardous to humans, and by replacing a human with a robot, the manufacturer not only removes a human from a hazardous environment but also eliminates the need for expensive ventilation systems

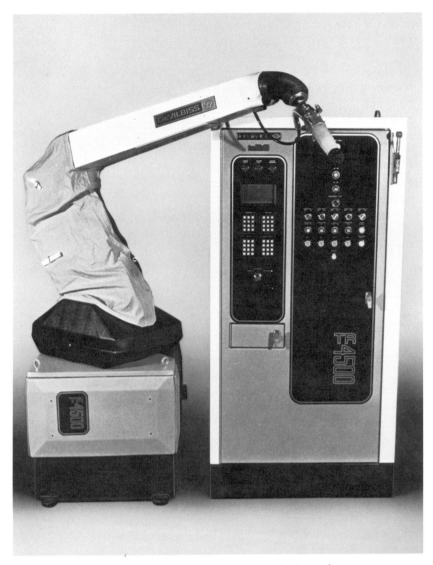

Figure 4-19   The DeVilbiss TR-4500 spray finishing robot.

and protective masks that are necessary when a human is performing the painting.

Workpieces or assemblies to be painted by robots still require accurate fixturing, which is expensive and not readily modified. The use of machine vision sensing would considerably enlarge the field of application for painting robots. What is required is the further development of lower-cost three-dimensional vision technology.

There are a variety of ways to apply coating materials to objects that are included in this application. Painting can be performed by techniques ranging from dipping to electrostatic spraying. Although it does not deal with paint, thermally sprayed coating to produce a metallic surface is included because the method of deposition is very similar to spray painting. Of these methods, spray painting is the most common in manufacturing and is the primary focus of this section. The basic process elements are:

Dip Coating
- lower workpiece into coating material reservoir
- lift out
- allow to drain; spinning can be used to remove excess

Flow Coating
- pour paint over workpiece
- allow to drain

Paint Spraying
- atomize paint
    - air spraying uses the mixing of paint with high-pressure air
    - airless spraying applies pressure directly to force paint through nozzle
- direct paint to target
    - air and airless spraying use residual momentum from the atomizing process
    - electrostatic spraying uses electrical attraction between the charged paint droplets and the oppositely charged target

Thermally Sprayed Coating
- metal coating material
    - flame spraying feeds coating into gas (e.g., propane) flame
    - arc spraying feeds coating material through an electrical arc
- atomize molten coating material with compressed air jet
- direct spray to target

The goal of painting/coating applications is generally to achieve an even, controlled thickness coating on the target. Too thick a coating is wasteful and may cause problems from excessive drying time, while too thin a coating may defeat the purpose of the process. In dip and pour coating, control of the viscosity of the coating material and manipulation of the object during the draining (e.g., tilting or spinning) are used to control the coating process. In spraying operations, coating thickness and evenness are determined largely by the path and speed of the spray gun with respect to the target. A successful coating requires that the spray gun be moved smoothly along its path, maintaining a constant distance and speed while following the contour of the surface to be painted. This path control problem becomes much more complex when the object to be painted is moving along an assembly line or requires manipulation, such as door opening (Fig. 4-20) in automotive applications.

The painting of large assemblies requires mobility from the painter and increases the difficulty of producing an even coating because of the distance over which the paint evenness must be maintained. Convoluted and partially enclosed structures are especially difficult to paint and require that the spray gun be moved into confined spaces and carefully manipulated to provide even coverage of interior surfaces.

The environment in which spray painting is performed is harsh since the process itself generates solvent vapors and a paint mist that envelop the work area. Personnel working in the vicinity of painting operations wear protective clothing and breathing gear to reduce exposure to these hazards, but the price of

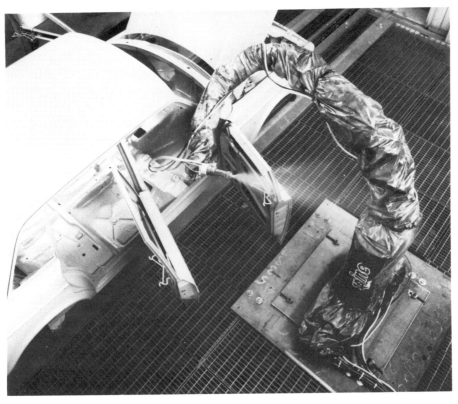

Figure 4-20   Spine spray painting robot for complex automobile locations.

protection is worker discomfort and fatigue. Not only is the environment unhealthy but the risk of fire or explosion is severe. The accumulation of paint mist
in confined spaces can become severe enough to reduce visibility and paint
buildup on surfaces and equipment requires frequent removal for cleaning.

The basic requirement for painting and for coating is mechanical dexterity.
Dexterity is needed by the robot manipulator arm; in most cases robot arms with
five degrees of freedom will allow painting of three-dimensional surfaces, although one or more additional degrees of freedom or mobility enhance the
ability of the robot to reach interior spaces. Actuators must be explosion proof
because of the flammable atmosphere, and therefore hydraulic actuators are
generally used.

Large assemblies require robot manipulators with large work volumes or
some form of mobility such as a rail transport system. End-effectors usually
consist of permanently mounted spray guns, although some models allow a
walk-through teaching handle to be attached.

The primary task of robotic controllers in spray painting applications is to
provide smooth, continuous path control along the surface being painted. Virtually all the current robotic painters are programmed by the walk-through method
in which a skilled painter physically moves the robot arm along the desired path
while the robot records the required motions. The moving target situation can be
programmed in this way with the constant speed of the target added to the
learned path by the controller. Editing capability is highly desirable to allow

corrections or adjustments of the program, since changes to walk-through-taught programs generally require that the entire program be retaught from the beginning.

Very little sensing is incorporated in painting robots; satisfactory results are achieved with good path control, carefully taught programming, and reliable painting equipment. The improvement in consistency is a major basis for cost justification for all the painting/coating applications. Once successfully programmed, a robot will turn out properly painted or coated pieces unaffected by fatigue, paint fumes, or boredom. Not only does this consistency raise the quality of the process, it also reduces the waste of deposited paint material as a result of the precision of its path and spray stop and starts. Overspray can be minimized when programming and the robot will repeat this saving every duty cycle.

Removing personnel from the spray painting environment not only protects their comfort and health but also reduces the ventilation requirements for the spraying area, which are based on hazard to humans. The energy required to heat or air-condition the fresh air brought in for the painter is substantial, and increasingly stringent environmental standards on venting of contaminated air require more and more sophisticated and expensive cleaning of paint-laden air before it can be released into the environment.

As in arc welding, the skill required of a human painter to produce high-quality paint finishes quickly is the result of substantial training and experience. Reducing the standards required for a painter expands the pool of available personnel but may require slowing down the assembly line, thereby increasing the number of units requiring correction or allowing quality control standards to slip. Robots offer a solution to the problem of conflicting demands for higher productivity and quality versus human aversion to working in unpleasant and unhealthy environments.

Current industrial painting robots incorporate little or no sensing. As a result, there is virtually no fault detection capability incorporated in the robot. Inspection of surfaces prior to coating for dents, gouges, or contamination, if performed at all, is done by human inspection. Process monitoring is largely restricted to detection of gross failure of the painting equipment, such as a clogged paint nozzle. Current technology could be applied to provide constant monitoring of the spraying process, including average droplet size and velocity and paint spray density. This type of monitoring would allow adaptive reaction to fluctuations in the paint supply, thus improving quality control and reducing the incidence of parts that require repainting.

The walk-through programming method most commonly used for painting robots is cumbersome. Although current users, whose painting is predominantly large batch, consider this time-consuming setup process acceptable, users who operate on smaller batches would find it uneconomical. The higher cost of painting robots is also a major barrier to the use of robots for small batches.

A manufacturer of molded plastic parts for the audio industry has installed a robot to do the final painting. The robot uses a five degrees of freedom articulated arm with 32K words of available memory, programmable with either continuous path or point-to-point motions. Parts handling is accomplished by means of a double conveyor system arranged in a "V" pattern on either side of the robot. This arrangement increases the throughput of the system. In addition to the advantages of removing workers from a dangerous environment and reducing the company's dependence on skilled labor, the manufacturer has seen a 140 percent increase in daily productivity as well as an eightfold reduction in defective parts.

General Motors has installed what they believe to be the most advanced painting system in use at their Doraville, Georgia assembly plant. The painting system consists of one painting robot and one door-opening robot mounted on tracks on each side of an assembly line. All four machines operate under computer control. The path tracking is accomplished by operating a single robot in the teach mode and then mirror-imaging the taught path into the robot on the opposite side of the line. With this system General Motors claims to be able to paint all external surfaces plus interior surfaces such as station wagon tailgates, deck lids, pickup truck beds, door hinges, and door openings.

Sealing/Bonding

Although each bonding application will have its own specific considerations, there are several generic steps that are performed in a bonding application:

- securing the workpiece to a fixed, known position
- applying the bonding material
- aligning the workpieces
- fixing the workpieces together

Sealing applications may involve two workpieces or may involve simply covering a hole in one workpiece.

In sealing and bonding, one of the major application considerations is the speed at which the material sets up. Because of the short working time of most commercial bonding materials, successful applications require a well-controlled and coordinated process scheme. The applicator speed must be adjusted to give a minimum application time, as well as be coordinated with the material pumping and flow rates to ensure that a consistent bead of material is maintained. The path must be well planned to cover an appropriate area with economy of both time and material. In addition, the applicator must be accurately controlled through this path in each repetition to maintain economy.

The basic robot requirements for sealing and bonding are similar to those necessary for paint spraying and arc welding. These include five or six degrees of freedom in the robot manipulator for dexterity and continuous path control capabilities in the controller. End-effectors for sealing consist of specialized sealant applicators mounted directly on the end of the robot arm. Controllers for bonding robots usually have the ability to directly control the flow rate of the sealant through the nozzle. Machine vision systems and specialized air jet sensors have recently been used to detect breaks in the material bead and the weight of the material container is monitored to prevent the supply pump from running dry.

The high repeatability of a robot can significantly reduce wastage in this application since the robot, once programmed with an economical path, will follow this path more closely than a human worker can. Robots can increase productivity by applying sealing or bonding material faster than a human and by eliminating the fatigue that results from manipulating the heavy adhesive gun. A final incentive for the use of robots is the removal of human workers from an environment of very high temperatures and noxious fumes.

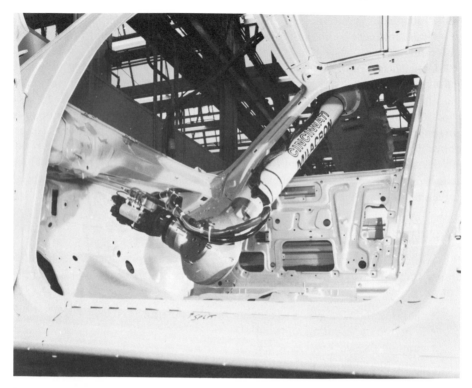

Figure 4-21   Cincinnati Milacron T^3 646 robot applying sealant to automobile floor pan. NOTE: Safety equipment may have been removed or opened to clearly illustrate the product and must be in place prior to operation. (Courtesy of Cincinnati Milacron, Industrial Robot Division.)

Because sealing applications (Fig. 4-21) are fairly straightforward, most problems encountered can be solved with proper planning techniques. One problem that has not been solved, however, is that of error handling. Although sensors can detect a missed section of bead, appropriate methods are not yet widely used for returning to repair the gap.

At a General Electric plant in Kentucky, a robot is being used to apply a foamed hot metal adhesive to seal perforations in refrigerator cases. Refrigerator cases are transported horizontally along a conveyor to the sealing station, where they are automatically tipped so that the holes to be covered are on an angle. The robot applies a metered amount of sealant above the hole and gravity pulls the sealant over the hole to seal the hole. In less than 14 months the investment in the robot application paid for itself.

Finishing

Finishing refers to painting or coating operations that are performed as the last step in the manufacturing process. In the strict manufacturing sense, however, finishing refers to a category of cleaning processes, such as:

- trimming flash by:
  - saw trimming
  - spark cutting

      – laser cutting
  • grinding flash
  • sanding
  • deburring
  • polishing

The first consideration in the finishing process is the shape of the part to be processed. This part, usually a casting, will be "raw" in the sense of having unpredictable burrs and pieces of flashing in unknown positions. The scattered flashing and heavy weight of the workpiece make manual handling potentially dangerous and automated handling difficult. Depending on the condition of the workpiece, it may be necessary to perform a combination of finishing operations with or without inspection between the process steps. The cleaning processes themselves must be considered both to prevent deformation of the workpiece and to minimize the production of irritants such as dust and grit.

There are two generic modes in which finishing operations are performed. In one mode, the finishing tool (grinding wheel) is fixed in a permanent position. The robot picks up the workpiece, orients it, and passes it over the tool in a prescribed path. In the other mode, the workpiece is positioned in a jig and the robot moves the finishing tool. Payload weight can determine the mode selected: it is usually desirable to have the robot hold the lighter of the two objects. If the robot holds the tool, it may either hold the finishing tool in a standard gripper or have the tool mounted permanently on the robot arm. Automatic tool changing also is used for finishing operations to enhance production flexibility.

Specialized controllers and sensors are important for finishing operations. The relative needs for each of these are interdependent. If there is no sensing involved, the robot needs to have a very accurate model of the finished part stored in a data base, to which it can refer during the finishing operation. On the other hand, an integrated system, using machine vision to detect flaws and force sensing to guide the finishing tool, would not need such a detailed model. The current state of practice is to use a simple internal model of the part combined with low-level sensing, such as force sensing. Although force sensing provides an adequate means of controlling an operation such as grinding, the robot must still be programmed to traverse the entire workpiece. Additional sensing, such as machine vision, could be used to guide the finishing tool to only those areas of the workpiece that require cleaning.

A Swedish foundry has installed a two-robot system for grinding operations. The first robot carries a permanently mounted grinding wheel and is used to cut ingots. The robot is equipped with both force and torque sensing, the latter used to detect wheel wear. Workpieces are fixtured on a rotating two-position worktable. The second robot handles the igots directly, passing them by several finishing machines that compose a work cell.

A truck manufacturer is using a robotic system that finishes cast iron gear housings. In the first step of the process, the robot arm picks up an abrasive cutoff wheel driven by a hydraulic motor that is used to remove risers and external flash from the raw casting. In the second stage, the robot replaces the cutoff tool with a gripper that picks up the casting and moves it to a floor-mounted grinder. Before grinding, a sensor on the robot arm locates the surface of the grinding wheel to set a reference that compensates for wear of the wheel. The casting is then moved against the wheel to remove the parting line along the outside diameter of the casting. Flash is removed from the inside of the casting by positioning the casting over a floor-mounted impact tool fitted with a chisel. The final finishing step, deburring inside surfaces, is performed by moving the casting to a floor-mounted abrasive deburring machine. This deburring machine includes automatic wear compensation and programming to shut down the system in the event of tool failure. The robot operates unattended during the night shift, with tool replacement and maintenance being performed during the day shift.

Human workers in the finishing environment are exposed to a variety of hazards, including high noise levels, airborne dust and grit, and disintegrating grinding wheels. Robots can remove humans from these dangers and so enhance plant safety.

Investment Casting

Investment casting is based on single-use molds; a new mold must be formed for each casting. The molds are formed in the following way. First, a wax model of the part is formed. The model is then coated with a lubricating and releasing agent. The mold is then dipped into a ceramic slurry and coated with sand. The slurry/sand mixture is allowed to dry and the dipping is then repeated. After five or six coats, the mold is placed in a heating unit, usually a steam autoclave, to melt out the wax model. The hollow mold is then fired in a kiln and used for the metal casting.

The most critical consideration for a successful investment casting is quality control of the ceramic shell. Consistent thickness of the individual coats of ceramic slurry will result in a more uniform and higher-quality finished shell. The dipping, rotating, and swirling motions, while the mold is in the slurry, are all important factors in the final coat thickness and must be carefully controlled. Other considerations in investment casting are the wide range of weights to be lifted from the beginning to the end of the coating cycles and the time and temperature control necessary during the drying cycle.

The basic robot elements necessary for investment casting operations are similar to those required for dip painting. In addition, it may be necessary to have a particularly robust robot manipulator to handle the weights involved; in some applications payloads can weigh hundreds of pounds by the end of the dipping process. A desirable, though not essential, robot element used in investment casting is a flexible and easily reprogrammable controller. Easy reprogramming allows for economical small-batch jobs.

A robot is well suited to performing the dipping operations for investment casting because the key to a quality shell is the consistency of the slurry coats. Once a successful pattern of dipping, rotating, and swirling the mold in the slurry is programmed into the controller, the robot will repeat those motions exactly. Another factor favoring a robot to perform the dipping operations is fatigue. The heavy weights involved often cause fatigue in human workers who dip the mold, which reduces consistency and productivity. The cost of current robotic systems is not always justified for these applications. Chapter 5 provides the criteria for investment justification.

A manufacturer of marine outboard engines has been using robots in their investment casting applications since 1974. The implementation was straightforward and required a minimum of plant reorganization. At full manufacturing output, this company produces many different types of castings ranging in weight from 1/4 to 8 1/2 pounds. Each type of casting requires six individual coating cycles with specific dipping and swirling motions. The robot controller is responsible for cycling the slurry bath motors as well as the fluidizing bed air supply. This robot implementation has increased both output and casting quality.

Die Casting

The die casting process, unlike the investment casting process, reuses the mold in which the product is cast. This necessitates additional steps to maintain the quality of the mold. The process consists of:

- preparing the die
  - clearing the mold of any obstructions
  - lubricating the mold
- pouring the liquid
  - checking the temperature of the liquid metal
  - controlling the pour rate of the liquid
- controlling the time and temperature of the cooling cycle
- extracting the workpiece from the die
- checking the mold for parts remaining in the die

There are several variable process considerations that must be carefully controlled for a successful die casting. These include temperature, which must be controlled for molds to be predictable, and cooling time. There is a delicate balance between the metallurgical requirement for adequate cooling time and the economic need for short cycle times. Die cleaning and lubrication between cycles must be thorough and consistent to prolong die life and give higher-quality castings. A final consideration in die casting is safety when handling molten metal.

The basic robot requirement for die casting is similar to that involved in general material handling, that is, an average manipulator dexterity. In addition, there are several robot elements that are especially useful in the die casting environment. These include temperature-protected end-effectors, which are necessary when working at high temperatures involved in die casting, and smooth path control. Although not necessary for simple workpiece handling, smooth path control becomes useful in the delicate mold-cleaning process.

An important justification for choosing a robot to work in a die casting environment is the consistency of the robot. The high repeatability of the robot can reduce scrap by as much as 20 percent, thus increasing productivity and decreasing remelt costs. Furthermore, consistent and accurate die cleaning can significantly increase the useful lifetime of the die. Removing humans from a hazardous environment and having the capability of integrating the casting and finishing operations are additional reasons to use robots.

Although robotic die casting is fairly straightforward, there are several sensing capabilities that would enhance the current state of practice. These include better detection of incomplete part removal from the die and better real-time temperature sensing and control during the cooling process.

De-Wel's casting plant, in Dowagiac, Michigan, casts parts for a variety of users, including automotive and appliance manufacturers. One of their most successful robot applications consists of servicing two die casting machines. The robot loads one machine, turns 180 degrees, unloads the other machine, sprays the die with lubricant, deposits the piece into a quench tank, reloads the machine, then turns back to the first machine.

Forging

Forging is an important process in many manufacturing processes and is a very simple operation. At its greatest level of complexity, forging consists of:

- acquiring the workpiece
- placing the workpiece in a furnace
- transferring the heated part from the furnace to a forging press
- cycling the press
- removing and quenching the workpiece
- inspecting the workpiece
- depositing the workpiece

Although forging is a simple process, it does require careful control of several variables, namely, timing and temperature. The preforge temperature of the workpiece must be precisely controlled for consistently successful forging. This can be accomplished by altering the time that the workpiece spends in the furnace, by altering the furnace temperature directly, or by a combination of both. After forging, the workpiece may need to be quenched. Improper quenching times or temperatures could result in undesirable crystallization of the metal. The environment of dirt, smoke, noise, and high temperatures typical in a foundry is an additional consideration that affects productivity.

The basic robot elements necessary for forging applications are similar to those required for general material handling, that is, average dexterity in the robot manipulator movements to acquire, orient, present, and remove the workpiece from the furnace and press. Variations of robot elements that are used in forging applications include specialized end-effectors, sensors, and controllers (Fig. 4-22). The end-effectors used in forging must be heat resistant. The high temperatures involved in forging can easily damage the hydraulic or electrical systems of an unprotected end-effector. Sensors that are used in forging have been developed to take advantage of the forging conditions, for example, infrared sensors are used to detect the positions and status of a workpiece based on its heat output. Robot controllers used in forging applications are usually modified so that they can communicate with their environment; for example, the controller may be equipped to sense and/or control the furnace temperature or to cycle the presses.

The harsh environment of the workplace is probably the most important justification for using a robot in forging applications. Because of the heat, dirt, noise, and smoke, a human may need to take as much as three to four hours of work breaks during one production shift. A robot can usually run continuously, unhampered by the environment. In addition, the precise nature of the robot controller allows very accurate and repeatable timing and motion control. This increases the consistency and quality of the forged parts. While current robot controllers are capable of real-time temperature sensing, they still need more sophisticated adaptive control of timing and temperature.

An aircraft engine manufacturer has successfully incorporated a robot into the forging process in the manufacture of jet engine airfoil blades. This applica-

Figure 4-22 Sterling–Detroit forge robot arm.

tion begins with the robot acquiring the raw part from a vibrating parts feeder/ orienter. An infrared sensor is used to check that the feeder is in fact loaded. The robot loads the part into a standard rotating hearth furnace that is coupled to the robot controller. The temperature of the furnace is sensed by thermocouple sensors, which detect simple over or under threshold conditions, while the position of the table is controlled by a stepper motor. After the hot workpiece is removed, the robot controller causes the furnace door to close, checks to see if the part is in fact in the gripper (by means of another infrared sensor), instructs the manipulator to load the part into the press, and then cycles the press. After cycling the press, the controller signals the press to eject the part, checks to verify that there is no part in the press, and then repeats the entire process.

Plastic Molding

As with die casting, the individual processes associated with plastic molding are simple (Fig. 4-23). The plastic molding cycle consists of:

- loading the plastic charge into the die mold
- loading the die mold in the molding machine
- cycling the molding machine
- extracting the molded part
- inspecting and finishing if necessary

Plastic molding is similar to die casting in that it involves most of the same process considerations as die casting. Among the more important are: time and temperature control, consistent and accurate die cleaning and lubrication, balancing the need for adequate cooling time against the need for fast cycle times, and the harsh environment of the molding workstation. Specific to plastic molding, however, are the noxious fumes given off by the molten plastic and the delicate handling requirements of the pliant plastic.

The basic robot requirements for plastic molding applications are also similar to those of general materials handling. Useful robot element variations for plastic molding include specialized end-effectors and controllers. To speed cycle times, the robot must handle the molded parts while they are still warm. The end-effectors used for this handling must be able to manipulate the hot, compliant parts without deforming them. As in die casting, the robot controller must be interfaced with the peripherals that it will be controlling, such as the molding machine. The justifications for using robots in plastic molding are similar to those in die casting. These include increased quality due to the control, consistency, and repeatability of the robot and the removal of workers from the hazardous environment.

The major technological barriers to the increased use of robots in plastic molding involve sensing and control. Current sensing systems cannot detect rapidly enough very small parts of the molded piece that adhere to the die to avoid interfering with the cycle time. As a result, robotic systems either leave occasional remnants in the die, which ruins the next molded part, or clean the entire die each cycle, which reduces the lifetime of the die.

An appliance manufacturer is using robots in the molding of vacuum cleaner parts. A pick-and-place robot removes two molded parts at a time from a dual-cavity injection molder, using a specially designed twin gripper. The robot presents each part to a broach machine for sprue removal and then deposits the

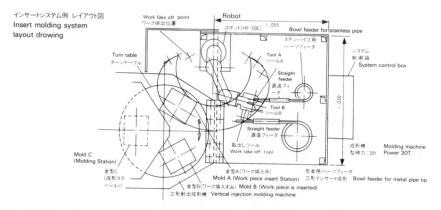

Figure 4-23   Floor layout of Pentel plastic molding system. (Courtesy of Pentel of America, Ltd.)

parts on a cooling conveyor. The elimination of an unpleasant and hazardous job was the primary motivation for installing the robot, but the increased productivity allowed an investment payback of less than two years.

IMPLEMENTATION FACTORS

The question of whether or not to implement robotics technology usually arises from the realization of a problem in the flow of production for which robotics offers a possible solution. Other solutions to the situation may be available and a justification analysis (see Chapter 5) should be performed to determine which approach is most desirable after all factors are considered. If the analysis indicates a robotics solution, everyone who is to play a major role in the implementation process must be familiarized with the technical approach chosen and should be encouraged to participate in the installation.

Upper management needs to know what the system can do for the company. These people will decide the basic policy toward robotic technology and will take most of the risks. Therefore, all data, the advantages, and the disadvantages must be presented accurately.

Middle management needs the same information as upper management but they need more technical detail. Middle management will be responsible for setting up the implementation mechanism once the go-ahead is given and they must realize the need for training the engineering staff in this new technology. Clear, deliberate, long-term planning is essential to successful robotics implementation.

Other personnel to include in preliminary planning are the plant and assistant plant managers and operation and engineering managers. They must be fully informed of how the implementation will affect them and must take an active part in the implementation or serious problems or more probably failure will occur. Signing an appropriations request prepared by lower management is not necessarily an active interest. At this level of presentation, the abilities and limitations of robotics must be explicit. Special emphasis should be given to the importance of related equipment, because whether the robot or its support malfunctions, the robot is usually blamed. Two areas that are often neglected in order to cut costs are training of support personnel and the procurement of sufficient ancillary equipment to support the maintenance of the robot. Neglect in these areas could easily mean failure. One should also be careful about overzealousness and the rush to "get that thing into production." Full and complete production planning is absolutely essential and cannot be overemphasized.

Production supervision should be included in all planning and engineering aspects. Few people have more intuitive feel for the actual process in question than those who watch and participate in it every day. Effective production supervision knowledge can save considerable time.

The engineering staff should be fully trained at the manufacturer's facilities. Hands-on experience for this group is essential for the engineers must know the robot thoroughly to design an efficient system around it. Considerable time and money can be wasted in false starts and changeovers when details concerning capabilities and limitations are overlooked because of a hasty, uninformed approach. The training is well worth the time and effort and should not be neglected. A successful education phase will create an environment that is favorable to the smooth implementation of this new technology. The strongest assurance for success is a group of knowledgeable engineers and technicians backed by enlightened management.

The next step begins the real work. A thorough analysis of the area of application should be performed to determine the functional requirements and technical specifications that will determine the form of the robotic system. Some items that should be considered before choosing a robot for the application are tolerances, work volume, layout, data storage, tooling, environment, and testing.

Tolerances

For the intended application, a careful and thorough study should be made to determine whether the positioning ability of the robot is within the required tolerance. Repeatability is a critical parameter for programs that, once taught, will be run continuously for an extended period of time. The maximum allowable error must be determined. The long-term repeatability error of the robot must be less than this value for successful results. If the tolerances cannot be held with currently available robots, the difference may be compensated for by compliant tooling or active sensory feedback control schemes. These alternatives may be developed by the manufacturer or by the user. In either case, reducing positioning errors of a robot below its off-the-shelf capabilities costs money. For quick, economical implementation, applications that do not require the robot system to operate at the limits of its optimum capabilities are best.

When positional accuracy is a critical factor, a well-defined and precise reference index is essential. This is especially true when the limits of the manipulator's working range are approached or when off-line programming is used. Robots generally are aligned to a reference plane and most of them require fastening to a secure base that can be used as the reference. Using a plane or axis on the robot manipulator itself as a reference may be advantageous for a more accurate reference index, not only for the robot but also for the equipment associated with it. This method will eliminate possible alignment errors in the robot mounting and will assist in better defining the workspace of the robot.

An accurate automatic indexing procedure may reduce the requirement for a precise alignment of the components in the workstation. The accuracy with which the position of all components is known, however, will be essential in the planning of those tasks that approach the limits of the working range of the robot.

Work Volume Selection

The size and shape of the work volume (Fig. 4-24) for a particular application are selected through an analysis process in which the application and certain constraints are considered. The application, whether pick-and-place, a manufacturing process, assembly, or inspection, will establish basic criteria and a minimum working range. For example, selecting a work volume that will accommodate working in a horizontal plane or orienting the wrist in a unique

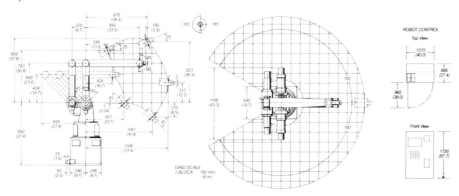

Figure 4-24   Illustration of work volume for Cincinnati Milacron T³ 735 robot.

position would be an application criterion. Assembling small components is a light manufacturing assembly application that would require only a small work volume; it also may require a robot with a high degree of articulation.

Constraints on work volume selection may be found in two areas: installation environment and in-house design capability. The first constraint, the area available for robot installation, may restrict work volume selection because of the nature of the existing production facility or because of management-directed limitations. The available area must be able to accommodate the work volume, associated equipment, parts flow, and maintenance and operator activities. As the work volume of a manipulator increases, the number of things it can collide with also increases. For example, the floor and ceiling of a normal room are within the reach of a large robot when it holds an 18-in.-long tool. Arrangement of the work area so that the required work volume is minimized is advantageous, provided crowding does not interfere with production or safety. The second constraint, management limitations, could indicate a less-than-favorable attitude toward robotics that should be dealt with early to ensure project success.

The extent or desired depth of tool design for a particular application can be an important factor in selecting work volume. Under certain conditions, fixtures, part positioners, or end-effectors may have to be designed quite differently because of the work volume. As previously mentioned, an assembly robot may require only a small work volume, however, this may necessitate extensive tooling designed to supply and transfer parts to and from and within the work area. Use of a robot with a larger work volume could possibly reduce the tool design task.

Simple quantification does not supply adequate information for work volume selection. The application and design constraints discussed here must be correlated with the production facility layout in making the final decision on a robotic system design.

Production Facility Layout

The selection of an appropriate production facility layout requires consideration of the preceding information concerning applications, manipulators, control systems, tooling, and control architecture. Generally there are two opposed schools of thought related to facility layout: the "in-line" school and the "centralized" school. A third approach, the "cellular" school, combines the best features of the other two.

- In-Line—Proponents of the in-line school maintain that it is most cost-effective to arrange several relatively simple robots along a more-or-less conventional transfer line (Fig. 4-25) and make each robot do a few simple operations on a part as it passes by. This approach effectively replaces people on an assembly line with robots on a one-for-one basis. An advantage of this arrangement is that it can be relatively easy to pull out a malfunctioning robot and replace it temporarily with a person.
- Centralized—The centralized school of thought recommends a few complex high-performance robots that perform many complex or precise operations on the same workpiece. One advantage of this arrangement is that some duplication of equipment can be avoided; a disadvantage is the inevitable crowding and inaccessibility that result from the number of part feeders and transfer lines surrounding the robot.
- Cellular—A cellular approach is to use the in-line approach to put together kits of parts, jigs, and perhaps some specialized tools on general-purpose pallets. A single transfer line would then carry a stream of these kits in and out of a work cell station where a high-performance robot would quickly put the various parts together and create a subassembly. This would allow the robot arm(s) to operate without the obstruction of part feeders and tool holders and any machine vision systems used would have a clearer view of the work area.

Figure 4-25 In-line installation of GMF robots.

Data Storage

The amount of data storage required for the application should be considered when choosing a robotic system. The size and number of programs to be run determine the storage requirements. In some installations, the capacity of the internal system storage is insufficient for complete operation. If it is not feasible to remedy this with the addition of more storage capacity, then the next option is generally the increased use of data transfers. With this technique, the operation is divided into parts and transferred sequentially after each part is accomplished.

Tooling

The tooling requirements are at least partially determined by the intent of the application and the performance capabilities of the robot, for example, tolerances or load capability. Some tools can be purchased from the robot manufacturers, whereas other unique tools will have to be developed by the user. Since the tooling can drastically affect the costs, choosing a robot that will allow for a minimization of tooling costs would be advantageous.

Environment

The robot system must be able to withstand the extremes of the environment in which it will operate. Temperature, vapors, dust, vibration, and electro-magnetics all must be taken into account and compared to the limitations of the robotic system. This requirement also applies to any peripheral system the user intends to install with the robot system. Generally, the reliability of the entire system will depend on the reliability of each individual critical component. Failure will occur if this aspect is overlooked.

In general, the requirements of the application should be analyzed very thoroughly and compared to available features offered by the various manufacturers. If the available systems cannot meet these requirements, a system to meet some of the requirements should be chosen and the remaining requirements should be compensated for by manufacturer/user development. Care should be taken to ensure that those specifications left unsatisfied can be compensated for in an economical manner. The goals are minimum total cost and reliable system performance under the existing conditions. A good analysis at this stage will determine the future of the project more than any other single factor.

Testing

When the robot arrives at the plant, it is useful and convenient to establish a test and acceptance shop. The robot should not affect the production operations until it has been developed completely and shown to be reliable. This is best accomplished in a test setup situation. A plan should be prepared for the installation and checkout of the robot, performance studies, development of compensation schemes, fabrication of peripheral compensation systems, tooling studies and fabrication, system integration, testing and debugging, trials, reports, and demonstrations. A realistic plan will help to maintain schedules.

One must allow sufficient time to do the work as well as to report and demonstrate its success. At this stage one has the opportunity to ask for extra time. Asking for and receiving a loose schedule at the beginning of a project and finishing early is far better than overcommitting the project and having to slip the schedule repeatedly. If the robot is not production ready as initially projected, few people will be sympathetic. A pressure situation will develop and may result in hasty and sometimes disastrous decisions that become irreversible.

A production-ready system that was perfected in the test setup and thoroughly tested is now ready for integration into the factory operations. Fundamental changes in the system should not be attempted from this point forward. Under close supervision, the robotic system should be dismantled and carefully relocated in the factory production area. This relocation is another critical milestone in the implementation process; the robotic system must not be damaged or altered during the move. After installation on the factory floor, the system must again be checked out and debugged thoroughly to confirm that the system functions exactly as it did before the move. The operating personnel should be checked out on the system and trained further if necessary. If all checks out well, the system is ready for production.

SYSTEMATIC APPROACH
TO ROBOT APPLICATION

The following steps provide a systematic approach (Fig. 4-26) to robot application. These major action steps will help organize your approach for using robots.

    I. Applications Development
       A. Become familiar with basic capabilities and limitations of available robots.
       B. Make initial survey of potential applications. Look for tasks that meet certain criteria:
          1. Operation within robot's capabilities.
          2. Operation does not require judgment by robot.
          3. Operation justifies use of robot.
       C. Initial survey yields list of potential applications: make more detailed study.
       D. Choose first application.
          1. Suggestion: for first application, pick simplest job on list.
          2. Study the job; make sure you know everything that must be done.
          3. Consider any alternatives other than robot.
          4. Look at possible advantages of mounting robot in other than usual feet-on-the-floor attitude.
          5. Consider reversing the usual bring-the-tool-to-the-work approach by having the robot carry the work to the tool.
          6. Try to anticipate all the things that could go wrong with anything associated with the job.
          7. Consider backups for the robot.
          8. Consider the environment.

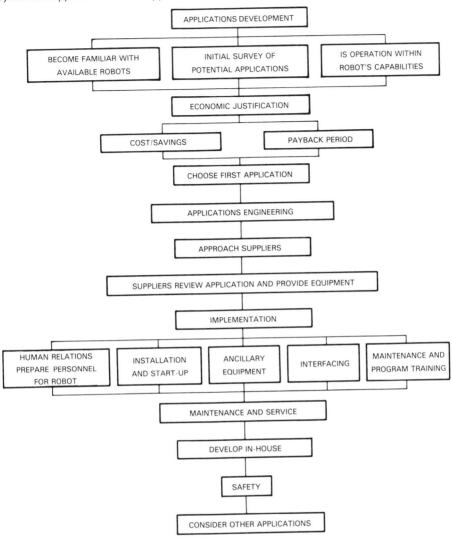

Figure 4-26 Approach for the consideration of robots implementation. (Courtesy of Unimation/ Westinghouse)

9. Consider equipment relocation and revisions.
10. Consider space requirements.
11. Consider future requirements.

II. Applications Engineering

A. Select robot with sufficient reach, speed, memory, program capacity, and load capacity to do the job. Provide some extra capacity if possible.

B. Consider protection of robot from contamination from environment (dust, paint, overspray, metal particles, excessive heat, etc.). Intrinsic safety or explosion proofing may be required.

C. Make layout of installation: determine location, possible interferences, and facilities changes required.

    D. Determine interfaces required between robot and other equipment. Perform computer simulation of system integration.

    E. Determine changes required to other equipment.

    F. IMPORTANT: Provide adequate safety interlocks and guards to protect personnel in the area (also, protect robot from material-handling equipment or other possible damage).

    G. Provide end-of-arm tooling: look at various alternative ways of picking up part.

    H. If line tracking is required, provide for installation and interconnection of suitable feedback device.

    I. Provide for backup equipment or plan to protect production when robot is down.

    J. Provide for spare parts and test equipment for maintenance.

III. Implementation Procedures

    A. Do as much preparatory work for installation as possible ahead of time.

      1. Service drops.

      2. Floor preparations.

      3. Interfacing.

      4. Equipment relocation.

      5. Equipment revisions.

      6. Development of end-of-arm tooling.

      7. Development of safety system.

      8. Maintenance of programming training.

      9. Human relations: prepare personnel for robot.

    B. Installation and start-up.

      1. Generally, robot manufacturer will provide some assistance.

      2. Anticipate some start-up problems (programs may have to be refined, tooling adjusted, timing and interlocks tuned in, etc.).

    C. Monitor the operation.

      1. Keep track of downtime to identify recurring problems, not only with robot but also with external equipment.

      2. Make comparison between estimated and actual costs, savings, and performance for future reference.

      3. Continued surveillance of operation may suggest ways to incrementally improve it.

    D. Maintenance and service.

      1. Develop in-house programming and maintenance capabilities.

        a. Make sure you cover all shifts.

        b. Make sure shifts have adequate tools, test equipment, and spare parts to do their job.

        c. Provide for regular retraining.

      2. If possible and practical, provide a spare machine.

      3. Give maintenance people total responsibility for robot's performance.

IV. Safety

    A. Think safety.

      1. Keep people away from robot and vice versa. Install guard rails around area outside the robot's range (removable section or access to remove robot if required).

2. Emergency stop outside robot's range.
3. Comply with OSHA, local regulations, SME, and company standards.
4. Train maintenance people thoroughly. If possible, use two people for maintenance and programming—the "Buddy System."
5. Develop detailed safety plan.

These four major action steps will assure that you have considered the fundamental concerns in systematically applying robotics to your applications.

5

JUSTIFICATION OF ROBOTICS

BACKGROUND

Peter Drucker, noted professor, author, and management expert, stated in *The New Realities* that:

> We have known for a long time that there is no one right way to analyze a proposed capital investment. To understand it, we need at least six pieces of information: the expected rate of return; the payout and the investment's expected productive life; the discounted present value of all returns through the productive lifetime of the investment; the risk in not making the investment or deferring it; the cost and risk in case of failure; and finally the opportunity cost that is the return from alternative investments. Every accounting student is taught these concepts. But before the advent of data-processing capacity, the actual analyses would have taken man-years of clerical toil to complete. Now anyone with a spreadsheet should be able to do them in a few hours. The availability of information thus transforms the capital investment analysis from opinion into diagnosis, that is, into the rational weighing of alternative assumptions. Information transforms the capital-investment decision from an opportunistic, financial decision, governed by the numbers, into a business decision based on the probability of alternative strategic assumptions. As a result, the decision both presupposes a business strategy and challenges that strategy and its assumptions. What was once a budget exercise becomes an analysis of policy.

As Drucker noted, in most cases the major factors justifying the use of robots for manufacturing are economic factors. A robot manufacturing system represents a sizable capital investment and hopefully an even more sizable return on investment.

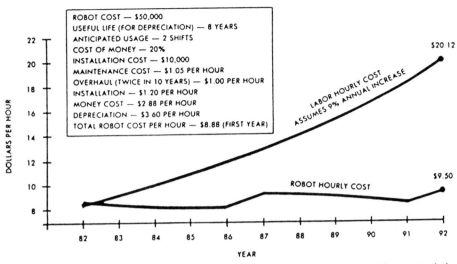

ROBOT COST — $50,000
USEFUL LIFE (FOR DEPRECIATION) — 8 YEARS
ANTICIPATED USAGE — 2 SHIFTS
COST OF MONEY — 20%
INSTALLATION COST — $10,000
MAINTENANCE COST — $1.05 PER HOUR
OVERHAUL (TWICE IN 10 YEARS) — $1.00 PER HOUR
INSTALLATION — $1.20 PER HOUR
MONEY COST — $2.88 PER HOUR
DEPRECIATION — $3.60 PER HOUR
TOTAL ROBOT COST PER HOUR — $8.88 (FIRST YEAR)

Figure 5-1 History of labor cost and robot cost in the automotive industry. Direct labor cost includes fringe benefits; robot cost includes support.

Robots provide labor cost reductions, as shown in Fig. 5-1 and intangible benefits that may on their own justify using an industrial robot. Some of these factors are:

- Increased productivity
- Improved quality
- Better utilization of materials
- Safer performance of hazardous operations and undesirable tasks
- Advancement of manufacturing technology
- Adaptability
- Enhanced competitive advantage

The economic justification of industrial robots may be ideally viewed as a part of the overall process of long-range planning for flexible automated manufacturing. Economic analyses of robotic technology applications serve two purposes. They predict the potential economic feasibility of the project and also provide a comparison between implementation alternatives. The comparison is useful in the iterative design and optimization of an industrial robotic system. Particularly when an emerging technology such as robotics is being evaluated, the management decision process requires accepted methods of economic rationalization.

ECONOMIC FACTORS

Increased productivity results from the industrial robot's ability to maintain a constant pace throughout the entire work shift, rather than the robot's ability to

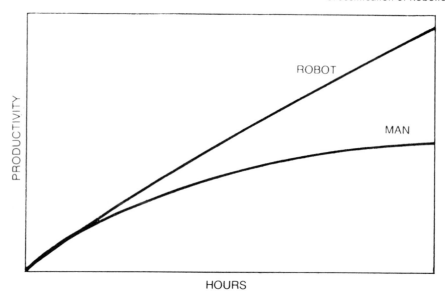

Figure 5-2 Robot productivity through constant pace operation.

perform tasks faster than a person, as shown in Fig. 5-2. In some cases, a person can outperform a robot in terms of speed with which a task is completed, especially in some complex manipulative tasks. However, a person usually cannot maintain this performance level for an entire shift because of fatigue. Generally, robot technology provides a tireless worker and increases productivity by maintaining a constant rate of production for extended periods of time. The average cycle time for parts tends to be lower for robots, with the result that more parts are produced per shift, and this increased productivity represents an economic gain.

These advantages are realized through the consistent operation of the robot. Once an optimum procedure is defined and programmed into the robot for a particular task, that task will be consistently performed in the optimum manner every time. The result is fewer bad parts that have to be scrapped and less material waste, which results in measurable economic gains. By operating the robot for more than one shift, a plant can, within a couple of years, realize significant additional production cost savings over normal operation, which pay for the investment in robots.

Robots can also be used to perform undesirable or hazardous tasks, and the result is additional cost savings. If ignored, employee complaints about poor working conditions (i.e., excessive noise, dust, fumes, heat, dirt, heavy loads, fast pace, or monotony) can lead to poor product quality, work stoppages or slowdowns, uncompleted operations, poor attitude with regard to workmanship, high labor turnover, absenteeism, grievances, or sabotage, and can result in higher-than-normal operating and insurance costs. Compensation may require overtime to make up production losses, rework and repair, and expenses for processing grievances, hiring replacement personnel, and training new workers. In many cases, use of robots is a cost-effective solution.

In some applications, one or a limited number of robots may be installed for developmental purposes. The intent here is to gain the knowledge and expertise that are required to implement similar robot applications in an actual production setting where economic benefits are more direct. Economic returns are usually realized in the follow-on production applications. In fact, the costs of developmental implementation research are often factored into the cost of the follow-on production application.

Whether programmable or not, most robots have a degree of adaptability that allows them to be moved around or used in different types of tasks, thereby increasing their usefulness and potential return on investment. However, few managers will accept the adaptability of a robot as a justification for installing one without a plan of how it can and will be used in different applications. Adaptability may be a possibility but often is not accepted as a justification factor unless a serious implementation plan is established. Usually the feasibility of adapting to other applications will diminish as development progresses and the enhancements specifically designed for the primary application are added (e.g., tooling and facilities layout). Adaptability is an intangible asset that may become useful in a contingency situation.

Enhancement of a company's competitive position has both direct and indirect economic implications. The direct benefits are obvious. Lower production costs resulting from the use of robots give a manufacturer a pricing advantage over competitors. The inherent flexibility of robot manufacturing systems indirectly affects the economics. Shifting market demands are easily met by increasing or decreasing production rates on various products without changing the size of the work force. New products also can be introduced quickly and easily, often with little change to production facilities.

Robots are frequently used to perform operations that are potentially hazardous to human workers. These hazardous operations include press loading and unloading or working in toxic atmospheres or extremes of ambient temperatures. Improved safety can result in reduced sick leave, hospitalization costs, and plant operating costs, thereby providing economic justification. However, a robotic solution to safety problems may not always be economical and improved safety procedures may also be investigated.

Although the previously discussed factors should play a key role in the evaluation of the robot installation, the weight of the final decision should rest on an economic analysis. Economic analysis considerations fall into two major categories: cost avoidance and cost savings. These economic factors are described next.

There are numerous methods of economic analysis for any capital investment. The selection of a method depends on the size of the investment, the amount of risk involved, the projected life of the investment, company financial condition, whether the investment is for new or replacement equipment, management policy, and many other criteria determined by a particular situation. An economic analysis is a systematic examination of a complex business activity that will aid in making a decision about a capital investment by providing a basis upon which to make the decision. If the analysis is undertaken to justify a decision already made, the true purpose of the analysis is misguided.

In general, there are two situations for which an economic analysis is used. The first situation involves investment in equipment to replace an existing production method. In the first case, the purpose of the analysis is to identify the least expensive method to accomplish the production task. The second case is a comparison of the present production method and one or more new production

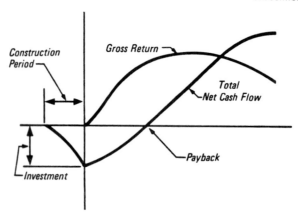

Figure 5-3   Life cycle of a capital investment.

methods. The task of justification in the second case becomes difficult because it is based on investment cost compared to savings over the cost of an existing production method. Since the savings are determined relative to the present method, there is no absolute measure of profitability because the savings depend as much on how poor the present method is as on how good the proposed method is.

The life cycle of a capital investment will typically follow a pattern, as shown in Fig. 5-3. Initially, money flows out until the project comes on line. From then on, savings first recover the investment and then produce net earnings. The project first breaks even and later recovers all the earlier negative cash flows to produce net earnings.

ECONOMIC ANALYSIS METHODS

There are three basic methods for performing a cost/benefit analysis that appear to be the most popular. The first is relatively straightforward and simple and is called the *Payback Method*. The second is the *Return on Investment* or *ROI* analysis. Both of these are restrictive in that the analysis is like a snapshot of the situation and does not consider changes in investments, on-going costs, or benefits (savings) over a period of time, essentially the life of the investment; these methods are losing favor to a more complicated, but reasonable, approach that considers the investment, savings or benefits, and the value of money over the life period of the investment. This third method is known as *ROI with Discounted Cash Flow*.

Detailed descriptions of the three methods are outlined in the following pages. The accuracy of the estimates for the future on-going costs and benefits will depend on the available data and the effort expended. It should be kept in mind, however, that any analysis involves a look into the future and the further one has to look the cloudier the picture becomes. Therefore it may be fruitless to attempt a close analysis that, in any event, is based on a number of long-range predictions.

Payback Method

Probably the most direct cost/benefit justification analysis formula involves a payback analysis. This is simply the total investment divided by the yearly savings that result in the number of years to pay back the investment. Although this may be considered an oversimplification by some, it has two distinct advantages, namely:

- It is simple and readily understood,
- It is easy to calculate.

The payback formula is:

$$\text{Payback period in years} = \text{Total yearly investment savings}$$

The payback formula can be strengthened by considering taxes, tax credits, and depreciation. In this case the formula would appear as follows:

$$\text{Payback period} = \frac{\text{Total investment} - \text{tax credit}}{\text{Sav} - (\text{Sav} \times \text{TR}) + (\text{Dep} \times \text{TR})}$$

where Sav = yearly savings, TR = tax rate, and Dep = yearly depreciation. It should be noted that the tax credit was withdrawn in 1987, however, discussions are under way in Congress to return it and therefore it is shown here for possible future use.

It should be noted that the initial investment plus all the on-going costs and benefits (savings) must still be investigated and itemized. This need be done only for the first year, however. It is assumed that these factors will remain constant for the life of the robot.

Return on Investment Method

Another measure to consider in a justification analysis is the percentage return on investment (ROI). In its simpler form, this is merely the reciprocal of the payback period:

$$\text{ROI} = \frac{\text{Savings} - (\text{savings} \times \text{tax rate}) + (\text{depreciation} \times \text{tax rate})}{\text{Total investment} - \text{tax credit}}$$

Return on Investment Considering Discounted Cash Flow Method

ROI after considering discounted cash flow and expressed as a percentage is one of the approaches that is gaining popularity. This method considers the value of money and the fact that a dollar now will be worth more at some time in the future, based on the interest it would earn. Conversely, a future dollar is worth less when considered in the present, also based on an interest rate. This is referred to as present worth.

Example of Present Worth

If a savings of $1000 were expected three years hence as the result of an equipment investment and the interest rate that would be expected if the money were invested in a bank is 10%, then the value of the $1000 savings in present terms, also referred to as present worth, is only $750. If the expected interest rate were 15%, then the present worth of the $1000 would be less, close to $650. These future present-worth savings are compared to the present, or initial, investment. The present-worth formula is

$$P = F \times \frac{1}{(1 + i)}\, n$$

where P = the present worth of the future money, F = the value of the future money, n = the period (year) under consideration, and i = interest rate for the period.

This can be refined further by considering inflation, which has the opposite effect of interest earnings. Whereas future money is worth more because of interest earned, it is worth less as a result of inflation. The present worth of future money would therefore be worth less because of the interest it would have earned and more because of inflation:

$$P = F \times \frac{(1 + \text{inf})^n}{(1 + i)^n}$$

where inf = percentage rate of inflation for the period n. Some analysts prefer not to use the inflation factor.

Consider again the $1000 savings that would result three years hence, an interest rate of 10%, and an inflation rate of 5%; the present worth of the $1000 savings would be

$$P = \frac{\$1000 \times (1 + .05)}{(1 + .10)} = \frac{\$1000 \times (1.158)}{(1.331)} = \$870$$

Further, if $1000 were to be saved in each of three successive years, considering a 10% interest rate and a 5% inflation rate, the total savings would be $3000, whereas the present worth of the savings would be something less, for example,

$$P = \frac{\$1000 \times (1 + .05)^1 + \$1000 \times (1 + .05)^2 + \$1000 \times (1 + .05)^3}{(1 + .10)^1 \qquad\qquad (1 + .10)^2 \qquad\qquad (1 + .10)^3}$$

$$P = \qquad \$954 \qquad + \qquad \$911 \qquad + \qquad \$870 \qquad = \$2735$$

The return on investment (ROI) is the percentage interest rate that would be earned based on the accumulated savings for n years considering present worth, when compared to the investment. This can be expressed by the following formula in which i is the ROI.

$$\text{Robot investment} = \frac{(\text{Sav} - [\text{Sav} \times \text{TR}] + [\text{Dep} \times \text{TR}]) \times (1 + \text{inf})^1}{(1 + i)^1}$$

$$\text{for year 1}$$

$$= \frac{(\text{Sav} - [\text{Sav} \times \text{TR}] + [\text{Dep} \times \text{TR}]) \times (1 + \text{inf})^2}{(1 + i)^2}$$

$$\text{for year 2}$$

$$= \frac{(\text{Sav} - [\text{Sav} \times \text{TR}] + [\text{Dep} \times \text{TR}]) \times (1 + \text{inf})^n}{(1 + i)^n}$$

for year n

where Sav = savings for the year, TR = tax rate for the year, Dep = depreciation for the year, i = interest rate or ROI, inf = inflation rate, and n = the year under consideration.

Calculating the ROI

The i noted in the preceding formula represents the return on investment that can be expected over the number of periods (years) being considered. The ROI would therefore depend on the amount of the total savings, considering present worth, as weighed against the investment over the operating lifetime of the investment. Calculating this ROI would be a very time-consuming and complex task if it were not for the computer. The RobotJustification Program provided at the end of this chapter can be used to calculate ROI.

Many corporate capital equipment policies draw a strict line on acceptable levels of ROI, specifying that only returns of 30% or over are acceptable, or at least open to further consideration. This can be a very narrow and harmful viewpoint when considering investment in advanced manufacturing technology such as robots. The ROI figure should not be considered alone when analyzing a robot but rather in conjunction with the intangible noneconomic benefits.

ROBOTJUSTIFICATION ANALYSIS

Technology Research Corporation has developed the RobotJustification software program. At the conclusion of this chapter, the program is provided in the BASIC language. The RobotJustification Program is designed for IBM PC and compatible computers and is unique in having been tailored specifically for analyzing industrial robot applications, including an evaluation of applicable tax and depreciation benefits and the calculation of the return on investment over the standard eight-year life of a robot.

With the RobotJustification computerized worksheets, analysis is straightforward, as cost justification has been divided into three separate categories. The first is a determination of the total investment. The second measures the effect of the investment on operations, expenses, and profitability. The third is an analysis of the return in relation to the required investment. This program devotes a single worksheet to each category. As with most programs, the user supplies data for some cells while the rest is calculated automatically by the program. A sample of the worksheets with an analysis of a particular robot has been provided for reference.

Investment Worksheet

The worksheet shown in Fig. 5-4 itemizes the costs, tax credits, and depreciation total associated with the initial robot installation investment. Most line

Description	Cost	Status	10% Tax Credit	5-Year Depreciable Amount	Expensed Amount
I. Robot Cost					
Robot	50000	C	5000	50000	0
Modifications	15000	C	1500	15000	0
Option 1 Heavy-Duty Drive	5600	C	560	5600	0
Option 2 Computer Upgrade	3400	C	340	3400	0
Option 3 System Cover	400	C	40	400	0
Option 4 Mounting Option	90	C	9	90	0
Option 5	0	C	0	0	0
Option 6	0	C	0	0	0
Training Costs	2000	C	200	2000	0
Maintenance Supplies	2000	C	200	2000	0
Test Equipment	400	E	0	0	400
Total Robot Cost	78890				
II. Tooling Costs					
Hand or Gripper	4000	C	400	4000	0
Fixtures	0	C	0	0	0
Materials Handling Costs	2700	C	270	2700	0
Total Tooling Costs	6700				
III. Installation Costs					
Mechanical Installation	17000	C	1700	17000	0
Electrical Installation	2800	C	280	2800	0
Vendor Assistance	0	C	0	0	0
Total Installation Costs	19800				
IV. Engineering Costs					
In-House Design (Specific)	30000	C	3000	30000	0
In-House Design (Research)	10000	N	0	0	0
Outside Engineering	10000	C	1000	10000	0
Programming	2000	C	200	2000	0
Total Engineering Costs	52000				
Totals	157390		14699	146990	400

Total Investment	157390	
Investment Tax Credit	14699	C = Capital
Net Investment	142691	E = Expensed
		N = Neither
Total Depreciable 5 Years	146990	
Depreciable Fraction	.95	
Net Depreciable	139641	
Total Expensed	400	

Figure 5-4 Investment worksheet.

items on the Investment Worksheet are eligible to be "capitalized," provided the purchaser can document the costs that are attributable to the robot installation. Areas such as training costs, maintenance supplies, equipment, mechanical and electrical installation, and research may not be eligible if it cannot be clearly demonstrated that these costs are solely for this particular robot installation.

Companies have different approaches toward "capitalizing" these costs. Investment costs that are not "capitalized" are often eligible to be "expensed." These "expensed" items are not depreciable but can reduce taxable profit. Some companies have a policy of "expensing" costs that are less than $500.

The description of each cost on the Investment Worksheet is given. Determine the cost of each line item and determine if it can be "capitalized" or "expensed." If the cost can be "capitalized," enter 1 in the status column; if it can be "expensed," enter 2. If the cost can be neither "capitalized" nor "expensed," enter 3. The worksheet could then automatically calculate the amount of the tax credit, the total amount eligible for five-year depreciation, and the total "expensed" cost. The tax advantages from expensing will be seen in the first years of operation. The terminology used in the RobotJustification Investment Worksheet program is briefly described in the following section.

Robot Cost

Robot: This is the base cost or direct cost of the standard robot in question. It does not include options, modifications, or changes.

Modifications: This covers any special modifications to the machine performed by the robot vendor. The cost of special nonstandard changes to the machine, changes in machine specifications, or nonstandard additions such as special computer interfaces and software routines could be added here.

Options: Most robots and, in fact, most machine tools have a long list of necessary options. "Necessary options" are those features not included in the base price of a machine but are required for its operation. Consider that in many cases it is simpler to provide a base machine that is only 90 percent complete than to add the final 10 percent in the form of a variety of standard options that can be mixed or combined to provide the best possible machine for a particular need at the lowest possible cost. One must also be careful to determine the proper cost of an industrial robot. Do not assume that the base price quoted by the manufacturer covers the necessary configuration of the desired application. The various options required to perform the operations in question should be listed here with their associated costs.

Training Costs: If the cost of both program training and maintenance training is not included with the cost of the machinery, it should be added here. This training is a very necessary part of industrial robot installation. Training costs, not only the direct costs charged by the vendor but also the travel and lodging expenses for those involved, should be considered as part of the investment in the robot installation. Some vendors provide free training for several operators per robot but do not provide travel or wage expenses.

Maintenance Supplies: Another expense that must be considered part of the robot cost is the investment in various maintenance supplies and backup components. Unless downtime of a day or more on the industrial robot is acceptable, a stock of maintenance supplies and replacement parts will be necessary. Most robot manufacturers have a recommended spare parts list, and in general this should provide a good guideline of the necessary investment in maintenance supplies.

Test Equipment: Certain installations may require various pieces of test or diagnostic equipment. Items such as a digital voltmeter or continuity tester should be available to any robot installation. While the cost of most of these items is relatively small, it should be included as part of the cost of the industrial robot installation.

Total Robot Costs: The Investment Worksheet will calculate all the foregoing items and place the total in this column. This total is the full cost of the robot equipment minus any special tooling directly related to this particular installation. These costs represent the fixed costs of a robot system of this type.

Tooling Costs

Hand or Gripper: A hand, gripper, manipulator, tool, or torch holder will be necessary for the robot to perform its function. The cost of any of this special tooling actually attached to the robot should be included in the analysis.

Fixtures: In many applications, some type of special fixturing separate from the robot itself may be necessary. These can be special holding fixtures in a spray painting application or special clamp fixtures in a welding application. Whenever these fixtures are necessary for an installation, their costs must be considered. Summarize the cost of any special fixturing required and enter it into the analysis.

Materials-Handling Equipment: In many installations, parts must be delivered to a point within reach of the industrial robot for the installation to function properly. These expenditures include any conveyors, slides, part-feeding devices, and transfer devices. The cost of this related materials-handling equipment is shown on the worksheet.

Total Tooling Costs: The worksheet will add the last three lines to give a value for the total tooling expenditure associated with this particular installation. This expenditure can vary greatly from installation to installation and is generally dependent on the complexity of the job being performed.

Installation Costs

Installation costs are all the costs associated with the actual installation of the robot. They include the costs of site preparation, any special foundation work, utility drops and hookup, all the interface devices connecting the industrial robot to the various part feeders or conveyors, any rearrangement costs including relocation of various pieces of equipment and rerouting of stock, and all changes to standard pieces of production equipment. The costs of necessary safety devices, fences, and guardrails should also be included.

Mechanical Installation: All direct and indirect mechanical labor, mechanical components, and mechanical machine changes should be included. Also include costs for relocation of various machines, fabrication of the necessary guardrails, and safety fences.

Vendor Assistance: While some robot vendors include the cost of a technician during start-up as part of the initial machine costs, others do not. If there is a charge for having a vendor representative present during the installation start-up, that cost should be considered here.

Total Installation Costs: The Investment Worksheet adds mechanical, electrical, and vendor assistance costs to give the total installation cost. This total is the amount of effort and labor necessary to locate and hook up an industrial robot in a specific application.

Engineering Costs

Engineering efforts can be divided into two categories. The first of these is the design function. The design function determines precisely, detail by detail, how the robot will perform the necessary tasks. It includes deciding which wires will be connected together and which interconnects and safety interlocks are required. This design effort can be conducted either in-house or by an outside engineering contractor. The second form of engineering necessary for the implementation of an industrial robot system is the program development sequencing and machine start-up.

In-House Design (Specific): The anticipated number of hours of in-house engineering effort required to develop and implement the specific industrial robot application should be multiplied by the appropriate loaded engineering cost per hour. This cost (per hour) should take into account the secondary cost of employment, including fringe benefits, unemployment insurance taxes, and the appropriate indirect overhead expenses.

In-House Design (Research): The anticipated number of hours spent on research into the use of industrial robots, but that cannot necessarily be directly attributed to the present industrial robot, is entered here. This line cost is separated from in-house design (specific) to reflect different tax savings eligibility. Design "research" may not be deductible, whereas "specific" design may be eligible for investment tax credits and accelerated depreciation. This specific effort should be multiplied by the appropriate loaded engineering cost per hour. This cost (per hour) should take into account the secondary cost of employment, including fringe benefits, unemployment insurance taxes, and the appropriate indirect overhead expenses.

Outside Engineering Design: This area is reserved for those fees and associated expenses involved in hiring outside consultants or applications engineers to assist in the development and implementation of a robotics program.

Programming: The engineering or programming effort necessary to develop, debug, and back up the robot program properly should be indicated here. To develop programming costs, estimate the total number of engineering hours necessary and multiply that number by the programmer's loaded cost per hour.

Total Engineering Costs: The Investment Worksheet program calculates the total engineering cost by adding together the cost of in-house engineering design, outside engineering design, and programming.

The Investment Worksheet will automatically fill in the Credit, Depreciation, and Expenses columns and sum their totals. It then calculates the net investment by subtracting the tax credit from the total investment.

Annual Savings/Costs Worksheet

Figure 5-5 provides an example of the Annual Savings/Costs Worksheet. The terminology used in the Annual Savings/Costs Worksheet program is briefly described in the following sections.

Annual Operating Costs

Both the savings and costs from the industrial robot installation will be calculated on an annual basis. These costs and savings may be calculated on an hourly basis, daily basis, or on any other time frame. However, all the expenses and savings must be calculated on the same basis.

Indirect Labor: The total indirect labor necessary to support the daily and weekly operation of the industrial robot should be indicated here. This includes labor that is necessary to load and unload chutes, provide material-handling services to and from the industrial robot, provide cleanup of the area, and provide tooling changes and adjustments.

Description	Cost
I. Annual Operating Costs	
Indirect Labor	5000
Maintenance Labor	4700
Programming	800
Supplies	800
Depreciation (as a cost)	17836
Other 1	0
Other 2	0
Other 3	0
Other 4	0
Other 5	0
Other 6	0
Total Operating Costs	29136
II. Annual Savings	
Direct Labor	96000
Indirect Labor	1000
Materials	7500
Reduced Rejects	0
Reduced Rework	1000
Other 1 Reduced Ventilation	700
Other 2 Less Safety Equipment	300
Other 3	0
Other 4	0
Other 5	0
Other 6	0
Total Annual Savings	106500
III. Production Capacity Effect	
Sales Value	100
Direct Materials	30
Increased Capacity	500
Total Capacity Effect	35000
Total Annual Return	112364

Figure 5-5 Annual Savings/Costs Worksheet.

Maintenance Labor: The estimated annual cost of maintenance and repair of the installation should be indicated here. This cost should be the number of maintenance hours expected times the hourly costs of maintenance personnel, including all auxiliary expenses and fringe benefits.

Programming Labor: The estimated annual cost of developing and maintaining programs for the robot should be indicated here. This cost is the number of man-hours expected each year times the cost of a programmer (whether an engineer, production supervisor, or system analyst) times the hourly cost of the individual in question, including overhead expenses such as fringe benefits.

Supplies: Supplies include any support materials, utilities, or services required each year to operate the proposed system.

Depreciation (as a cost): The robot depreciates each year as it becomes older. The Annual Savings/Costs Worksheet assumes that the industrial robot's value goes down by one-eighth of the initial investment for each of the eight years of its life. This shows up as an annual cost on the worksheet and is calculated automatically. This depreciation schedule differs from the five-year accelerated depreciation tax schedule used for tax purposes only on the Return on Investment Worksheet, since this is the actual depreciation, but not the depreciation recognized by the U.S. Internal Revenue Service.

Other Costs: Include any additional or unique costs associated with the operation of the installation that have not been covered in any of the preceding categories.

Total Operating Costs: The Annual Savings/Costs Worksheet adds all the labor, supplies, depreciation, and other costs associated with the operation to yield the total operating costs. Keep in mind that these costs represent increases that would not be present if the robot installation were not made. In other words, one is not trying to take into account all of the operating and production expenses associated with the product, but only those expenses associated with the use of the industrial robot installation.

Annual Savings

Savings per year represent those savings or changes in the normal costs associated with production that are directly attributable to the installation of an industrial robot.

Direct Labor: The number of direct labor hours saved by the installation each year should be multiplied by the direct labor cost per hour, including overhead expenses and fringe benefits, to develop the direct labor savings per year. Figure 5-6 shows how the average hourly wage of production workers will more than double in a decade. It should be pointed out that these average earning figures do not include employee benefits and overtime, which could run from 50 to 130 percent more per employee. Once management becomes convinced of productivity gains and quality improvements that can be achieved through the positive contribution of robots, it becomes easier to adequately cost justify a robot system after considering the rate of increase in hourly production wage rates.

Indirect Labor: This area is reserved for any savings realized in indirect labor because of the robot installation. Such savings might include reduced cleanup requirements in spray painting applications and reduced tooling or die maintenance in some plastics operations. The estimated number of hours saved

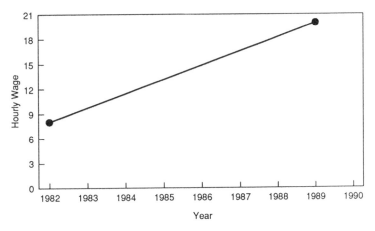

Figure 5-6   Direct labor hourly wages of production workers.

each year should be multiplied by the indirect labor costs, including overhead expenses such as fringe benefits per hour, to obtain the indirect labor savings.

Materials: Any annual savings in direct production materials should be calculated and recorded here. Material savings might include reduced paint usage in a spray painting application, reduced die lubricant usage in a die casting operation, or reductions in the amount of adhesive applied in an automatic gluing operation. For example, significant material savings can be obtained by using spray painting robots as shown in Fig. 5-7.

Reduced Rejects: The increase in the number of parts that will not be rejected for quality reasons has a value that should be indicated here. The value of these parts is the sales value of the product minus the direct material times the number of parts saved from rejection. The rationale behind this formula is explained in further detail in the Production Capacity Effects section.

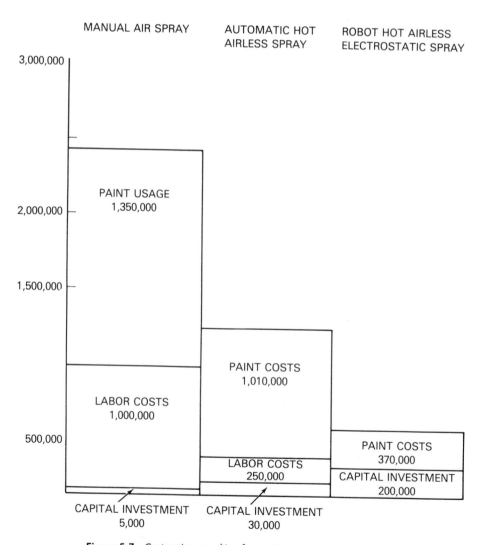

Figure 5-7   Cost savings resulting from using spray painting robots.

Reduced Rework: The reduced number of rejects resulting from industrial robot production methods can reduce the need for materials and labor normally associated with rework. This material and labor savings should be calculated on the estimated reduction in rejects each year. Indicate the amount saved here.

Other Savings: This area is for any additional savings not covered earlier that will result from the installation. This includes areas such as investment tax credits; higher sales because of higher quality; reduced requirements for air makeup; exhaust or emission controls in painting operations; and reduced requirements for supplies such as gloves, safety shoes, and safety glasses.

Total Annual Savings: The Annual Savings/Costs Worksheet calculates the total savings from the installation on an annual basis by adding the direct labor savings, indirect labor savings, materials, quality effects, and other miscellaneous savings.

Production Capacity Effects

Assume that a certain amount of direct labor and overhead is expended each day. By dividing the total cost (labor and overhead) by the number of parts produced, one can determine the labor and overhead cost per part. If the number of parts produced increased while the labor and overhead stay the same, the labor and overhead associated with each part go down. However, calculating the difference for each part produced when the installation of an industrial robot increases capacity can be a complicated and confusing affair. To simplify this, consider the situation from a different angle. Assume that a certain level of labor and overhead is associated with the production of 100 parts. If 120 parts are produced now with the same labor and overhead, the only additional cost for the production of the additional 20 parts is the raw material used. Since the labor and overhead of a single part times 100 parts pays for the entire labor and overhead expense, then it is reasonable to assume that the additional 20 parts resulting from increased efficiencies do not have labor and overhead costs associated with them. The profit made on those additional 20 parts is the sales price of the part minus the cost. The cost, in this case, is only the raw materials involved.

To calculate the value of increased production capacity resulting from the installation of an industrial robot, take the sales value of a single part, subtract from that the direct materials associated with the part, and multiply the remainder by the number of additional parts that can be produced in a one-year period as a result of the robot installation. The result of that multiplication is the production capacity effect.

Return on Investment Worksheet

Both the investment required and the increased profits derived from the robot installation have now been determined, and it is time to analyze these figures. One simple and straightforward method is shown in the example provided in Fig. 5-8, which calculates the return on investment (ROI) using data from the previous two RobotJustification worksheets (Figs. 5-4 and 5-5). The base year contains the investment totals. Years 1 through 8 cover the eight years of the industrial robot's planned life. The Return on Investment Worksheet

Description	Year 1	Year 2	Year 3	Year 4	Year 5	Year 6	Year 7	Year 8
Annual Return	112364	112364	112364	112364	112364	112364	112364	112364
− Expensed	400	0	0	0	0	0	0	0
+ Deprec. (Cost)	17836	17836	17836	17836	17836	17836	17836	17836
− Deprec. (Tax)	20946	30721	29325	29325	29325	0	0	0
= Taxed Income	108854	99479	100876	100876	100876	130200	130200	130200
xTax Rate	0.46	0.46	0.46	0.46	0.46	0.46	0.46	0.46
= Annual Taxes	50073	45760	46403	46403	46403	59892	59892	59892
Net After Tax	62291	66603	65961	65961	65961	52472	52472	52472
xDiscount Rate	0.807	0.526	0.343	0.224	0.146	0.095	0.062	0.040
= Discount Net	50292	35052	22628	14750	9615	4986	3250	2118
Payback	$ − 80,400	$ − 13,797	$ + 52,164	$ + 118,125	$ + 184,086	$ + 236,557	$ − 289,029	$ − 341,501

Net Investment	142691
Total Return After Taxes	484192
Return on Investment	53.41%
Payback in Years	2.2

Figure 5-8   Return on Investment Worksheet.

assumes the costs and savings will be the same for Years 1 through 8. The single exception is that "expense" items from the Investment Worksheet (Fig. 5-4) show up as expenses in Year 1 only, providing a tax benefit for that year.

Total Investment, 10 Percent Tax Credit, and Net Investment come directly from the Investment Worksheet and are calculated by the Return on Investment Worksheet. The worksheet assumes that all investment is in the base year.

The next portion of the worksheet calculates annual taxes. Total Return per Year for Years 1 through 8 is taken from the Annual Savings/Costs Worksheet. Expensed Investment is taken from the Investment Worksheet and subtracted in Year 1 only. Depreciation (as a cost), from the Annual Savings/Costs Worksheet, is added in since this value is not used for tax purposes. Depreciation (for taxes) is the depreciable amount for each year using five-year accelerated depreciation. This amount is the Net Depreciable Amount from the Investment Worksheet times the factor (.15 in Year 1, .22 in Year 2, .21 in Year 3, .21 in Year 4, and .21 in Year 5) for each year as allowed by the tax law. Taxable income therefore becomes Total Return/Year minus Expensed Investment (Year 1 only) plus Depreciation (as a cost) minus Depreciation (for taxes). This value is then multiplied by the corporate tax rate (i.e., 46 percent) to arrive at Taxes. A different tax rate may be entered, if applicable. All calculations are performed automatically in the RobotJustification program.

The next section calculates Net After Tax and is simply the Net Investment (base year only) plus the Total Return per Year (Years 1 through 8) minus taxes. The worksheet performs the calculation automatically.

The Return on Investment (ROI) is calculated by the RobotJustification program. The worksheet will calculate the reduced value of future dollars and show this for each year in the Discount Rate row. Multiplying the Net After Tax times this Discount Rate, the worksheet calculates the Discounted Net After Tax for each year. The Return on Investment Worksheet shows the calculated result of the total net investment, the total return after taxes, the return on investment, and the payback in years.

Using the analysis shown in Fig. 5-8, a comparison of one versus two shift operations was performed. For the single-shift application, the RobotJustification analysis indicates a return on investment of 23 percent and a payback period of 4.0 years. A similar analysis using the same investment data with the

Table 5-1
One-Shift Versus Two-Shift Operation

Application	Net investment	Net return year after tax	ROI	Payback
One shift	$142,621	$35,000	23%	4.0 years
Two shifts	$142,621	$60,000	53%	2.4 years

robot on two shifts provided a 53 percent ROI and a payback period of 2.4 years, as shown in Table 5-1.

As expected, two-shift utilization yields a greater return and provides earlier investment payback. During the economic analysis process, the adjustment of various factors (such as the number of shifts of operation) and the comparison of each option is beneficial not only in justifying the investment but also in planning for an optimum return.

It can be noted here that the analyses may or may not include some factors that could affect the feasibility of the investment. For example, increasing labor costs or declining productivity rates, which may influence the investment decision, may not be projected in the analysis.

Although the use of robots may be justified for a variety of reasons, most motivation will be supplied by the economics of the situation. A successful justification requires consideration and quantification of all potential costs and cost benefits other than direct labor replacement factors. Many of the cost factors can only be estimated during the justification preparation. It is important, therefore, that the original estimates be as accurate as possible.

ROBOTJUSTIFICATION BASIC PROGRAM

All the BASIC program code needed to conduct an industrial robot justification analysis is now given. A short-form step-by-step procedure for loading the RobotJustification program on the IBM PC after the BASIC program is installed follows:

- Power off
- Insert DOS diskette
- Turn power on
- At date press enter
- At time press enter
- At prompt A > type BASIC
- Press Enter
- Remove DOS diskette
- Insert RobotJustification diskette
- Press F3 (Load)
- Type in ROBOT
- Press Enter
- Press F2 (Run)

The RobotJustification BASIC program follows.

```
10 REM RobotJustification Program
20 REM TITLED ROBOT.BAS
30 REM DIMENSION ARRAYS
40 DIM VALUE$(85),INVDESCRIP$(21),INVCOST(21),VALUE(64),STATUS$(21),TAXCREDIT(21
),DEPREC(21),EXPENSED(21),ANNUALDESCRIP$(25),ANNUALCOST(25),VALUEB$(85)
50 REM CLEAR SCREEN AND DISABLE FUNCTION KEYS
60 CLS
70 KEY OFF
80 FOR X=1 TO 10:KEY X,"":NEXT X
90 REM PRINT INTRODUCTORY TEXT
92 PRINT  TAB(24) "ROBOT COST JUSTIFICATION PROGRAM"
94 PRINT:PRINT TAB(15)"COPYRIGHT 1983, BY TECHNOLOGY RESEARCH CORPORATION"
96 PRINT:PRINT TAB(16) "PREPARED BY V. DANIEL HUNT AND JEFFREY A. WATIKER"
98 PRINT:PRINT "      THIS PROGRAM DETERMINES THE COST ECONOMICS OF AN INDUSTRIAL
 ROBOT PURCHASE":PRINT:PRINT "USING THREE WORKSHEETS: INVESTMENT WORKSHEET, ANNU
AL SAVINGS/COSTS WORKSHEET,"
99 PRINT:PRINT "AND RETURN ON INVESTMENT WORKSHEET.  AFTER EACH WORKSHEET IS COM
PLETE THE":PRINT:PRINT "PROGRAM WILL ASK THE USER IF THEY WISH A PRINTOUT OF THA
T SINGLE WORKSHEET."
100 PRINT:PRINT "HOWEVER, IT ALSO ALLOWS THE USER TO HAVE ALL THREE WORKSHEETS L
INE PRINTED":PRINT:PRINT "AT THE END."
110 LOCATE 24,1
120 PRINT "PRESS ANY KEY TO CONTINUE";
130 A$=INKEY$:IF A$="" THEN 130
140 REM HAVE USER CHOOSE DEFAULT DATA SET
150 CLS
152 PRINT "FIRST, SELECT THE SET OF DATA VALUES FOR THE DEFAULT DATA.":PRINT:PRI
NT "IF YOU SELECT 1=ALL ZEROS THEN YOU ENTER ALL NEW DATA.":PRINT:PRINT "IF YOU
SELECT 2=SAMPLE ROBOT YOU BEGIN WITH THE";
154 PRINT "SAMPLE SHOWN IN THE DOCUMENTATION.":PRINT:PRINT "IF YOU SELECT 3=YOUR
 LAST ROBOT YOU CAN USE DATA STORED FROM A PREVIOUS PROGRAM";:PRINT:PRINT;"RUN."

156 PRINT:PRINT "THE WORKSHEETS HAVE AN EDITOR SO YOU CAN CHANGE ANY DATA YOU LO
AD INTO THE":PRINT "DEFAULT LATER IN THE PROGRAM."
170 LOCATE 16,1
180 PRINT "1=ALL ZEROS
190 PRINT "2=SAMPLE ROBOT
200 PRINT "3=YOUR LAST ROBOT
210 PRINT:PRINT "WHICH DO YOU CHOOSE (1/2/3) ?"
220 DD$=INKEY$:IF DD$<>"1" AND DD$<>"2" AND DD$<>"3" THEN 220
230 REM ERASE OLD DATA VALUES
240 FOR X=1 TO 85: VALUE$(X)="":NEXT X
250 FOR X=19 TO 64: VALUE(X)=0: NEXT X
260 REM GET NEW VALUES
270 IF DD$="1" THEN GOSUB 2000
280 IF DD$="2" THEN GOSUB 3000
290 IF DD$="3" THEN GOSUB 4000
300 REM ASSIGN DESCRIPTION NAMES TO INVESTMENT WORKSHEET
310 INVDESCRIP$(1)="Robot"
320 INVDESCRIP$(2)="Modifications"
330 FOR X=3 TO 11
340 INVDESCRIP$(X)=VALUE$(X-2)
350 NEXT X
360 FOR X=9 TO 21
370 READ INVDESCRIP$(X)
380 DATA "Training Costs","Maintenance Supplies","Test Equipment","Hand or Gripp
er","Fixtures","Materials Handling Costs","Mechanical Installation","Electrical
Installation","Vendor Assistance"
390 DATA "In-house Design(Specific)","In-house Design(Research)","Outside Engine
ering","Programming"
400 NEXT X
410 REM ASSIGN COSTS TO INVESTMENT WORKSHEET BY MATCHING EACH DESCIPTION WITH TH
E APPROPRIATE DATA VALUE.
420 FOR X=1 TO 21
430 INVCOST(X)=VALUE(X+18)
440 NEXT X
450 REM ASSIGN STATUS CODES TO INVESTMENT WORKSHEET
460 FOR X=1 TO 21
470 STATUS$(X)=VALUE$(X+64)
480 NEXT X
490 REM PERFORM CALCULATIONS FOR INVESTMENT WORKSHEET
500 GOSUB 5000
510 REM PRINT INVESTMENT WORKSHEET
520 GOSUB 6000
530 REM IF USER INDICATED CHANGES IN INVESTMENT WORKSHEET MAKE CHANGES
540 IF INVESTMENTCHANGES$="Y" THEN GOSUB 7000
550 REM HAVING MADE CHANGES RECALCULATE AND PRINT INVESTMENT WORKSHEET
560 IF INVESTMENTCHANGES$="Y" GOTO 490
570 REM IF USER WANTS A PRINTOUT OF INVESTMENT THEN PRINTOUT WORKSHEET
580 IF PRINTINVESTMENT$="Y" THEN GOSUB 8000
590 REM ASK USER TO INDICATE WHEN READY TO ADVANCE TO ANNUAL SAVINGS/COSTS WORKS
```

```
HEET
600 LOCATE 24,1:LOCATE ,,1
610 PRINT "PRESS ANY KEY TO ADVANCE TO ANNUAL SAVINGS/COSTS WORKSHEET          ";
620 NP$=INKEY$:IF NP$="" THEN 620
630 REM ANNUAL SAVINGS/COSTS WORKSHEET SECTION
640 CLS:PRINT "PREPARING TO DISPLAY ANNUAL SAVINGS/COSTS WORKSHEET"
650 REM ASSIGN DESCRIPTION NAMES TO ANNUAL SAVINGS/COSTS WORKSHEET
660 FOR X=1 TO 4
670 READ ANNUALDESCRIP$(X)
680 DATA "Indirect Labor","Maintenance Labor","Programming","Supplies"
690 NEXT X
700 FOR X=5 TO 10
710 ANNUALDESCRIP$(X)=VALUE$(X+2)
720 NEXT X
730 FOR X=11 TO 15
740 READ ANNUALDESCRIP$(X)
750 DATA "Direct Labor","Indirect Labor","Materials","Reduced Rejects","Reduced
Rework"
760 NEXT X
770 FOR X=16 TO 21
780 ANNUALDESCRIP$(X)=VALUE$(X-3)
790 NEXT X
800 FOR X=22 TO 24
810 READ ANNUALDESCRIP$(X)
820 DATA "Sales Value","Direct Materials","Increased Capacity"
830 NEXT X
840 REM ASSIGN COSTS TO ANNUAL SAVINGS/COSTS WORKSHEET BY MATCHING EACH DESCRIPT
ION WITH THE APPROPRIATE DATA VALUE
850 FOR X=1 TO 24
860 ANNUALCOST(X)=VALUE(X+39)
870 NEXT X
880 REM PERFORM CALCULATIONS FOR ANNUAL SAVINGS/COSTS WORKSHEET
890 GOSUB 9000
900 REM PRINT ANNUAL SAVINGS/COSTS WORKSHEET
910 GOSUB 10000
920 REM IF USER INDICATED CHANGES IN ANNUAL SAVINGS/COSTS WORKSHEET MAKE CHANGES

930 IF ANNUALCHANGES$="Y" THEN GOSUB 11000
940 REM HAVING MADE CHANGES RECALCULATE AND REPRINT ANNUAL SAVINGS/COSTS WORKSHE
ET
950 IF ANNUALCHANGES$="Y" THEN GOTO 880
960 REM IF USER WANTS A PRINTOUT OF ANNUAL SAVINGS/COSTS WORKSHEET THEN PRINT WO
RKSHEET
970 IF PRINTANNUAL$="Y" THEN GOSUB 12000
980 REM ASK USER AT BOTTOM OF SCREEN TO INDICATE WHEN READY TO MOVE TO RETURN ON
 INVESTMENT (ROI) WORKSHEET
990 LOCATE 24,1:PRINT "PRESS ANY KEY TO ADVANCE TO RETURN-ON-INVESTMENT WORKSHEE
T                     ";
1000 PP$=INKEY$:IF PP$="" THEN 1000
1010 REM RETURN ON INVESTMENT WORKSHEET
1020 CLS:PRINT "PREPARING TO DISPLAY RETURN ON INVESTMENT WORKSHEET"
1030 PRINT "THIS WILL TAKE A FEW SECONDS. PLEASE WAIT."
1040 REM TURN OFF FLASHING CURSOR
1050 LOCATE ,,0
1060 REM ASSIGN TAX RATE VARIABLE THE PROPER VALUE FROM DEFAULT DATA SET
1070 TAXRATE=VALUE(64)
1080 REM PERFORM CALCULATIONS FOR RETURN ON INVESTMENT WORKSHEET
1090 GOSUB 13000
1100 REM PRINT RETURN ON INVESTMENT WORKSHEET ON THE SCREEN
1110 GOSUB 15000
1120 REM IF TAX RATE WAS CHANGED RECALCULATE AND REPRINT RETURN ON INVESTMENT WO
RKSHEET
1130 IF ROICHANGES$="Y" THEN GOTO 1080
1140 REM IF USER WANTS A PRINTOUT OF ANNUAL SAVINGS/COSTS WORKSHEET THEN PRINT W
ORKSHEET
1150 IF PRINTROI$="Y" THEN GOSUB 16000
1170 REM ASK USER IF A PRINTOUT OF ALL 3 WORKSHEETS IS DESIRED
1180 LOCATE 24,1:PRINT "WOULD YOU LIKE A PRINTOUT OF ALL THREE WORKSHEETS (Y/N)
?                     ";
1190 YY$=INKEY$:IF YY$<>"Y" AND YY$<>"y" AND YY$<>"N" AND YY$<>"n" THEN 1190
1210 IF YY$="Y" OR YY$="y" THEN PRINT3$="Y" ELSE PRINT3$="N"
1220 IF PRINT3$="Y" THEN GOSUB 8000
1230 IF PRINT3$="Y" THEN GOSUB 12000
1240 IF PRINT3$="Y" THEN GOSUB 16000
1250 REM SEE IF USER WISHES TO SAVE THIS DATA IN LAST ROBOT DEFAULT DATA SET CAL
LED LASTBOT.DTA
1260 LOCATE 24,1:PRINT "WOULD YOU LIKE THIS DATA TO REPLACE THE LAST ROBOT DATA
CURRENTLY ON DISK(Y/N)?";
1270 YY$=INKEY$:IF YY$<>"Y" AND YY$<>"y" AND YY$<>"N" AND YY$<>"n" THEN 1270
1280 IF YY$="Y" OR YY$="y" THEN REPLACE$="Y" ELSE REPLACE$="N"
1285 IF REPLACE$="Y" THEN LOCATE 24,1:PRINT "PLEASE WAIT: STORING THIS DATA IN L
```

```
AST ROBOT DEFAULT DATA FILE.                              ";
1290 IF REPLACE$="Y" THEN GOSUB 17000
1300 REM ASK USER IF HE WANTS TO MAKE ANOTHER RUN
1310 LOCATE 24,1:PRINT "THIS CONCLUDES THE PROGRAM DO YOU WISH TO MAKE A NEW RUN
 (Y/N) ?                  ";
1320 YY$=INKEY$:IF YY$<>"Y" AND YY$<>"y" AND YY$<>"N" AND YY$<>"n" THEN 1320
1330 IF YY$="Y" OR YY$="y" THEN NEWRUN$="Y" ELSE NEWRUN$="N"
1340 IF NEWRUN$="Y" THEN RUN
1900 END
1999 REM ***************************************************************************

2000 REM SUBROUTINE TO PREPARE TO USE ALL ZEROS DEFAULT DATA, REQUIRES DEFAULT S
TATUS CODES BE SET EQUAL TO "C"
2010 PRINT "PREPARING TO USE ALL ZEROS DATA SET"
2020 FOR RECORD=65 TO 85
2030 VALUE$(RECORD)="C"
2040 LOCATE 10,1
2050 NEXT RECORD
2060 REM SET TAX RATE DATA ITEM EQUAL TO .46
2070 VALUE(64)=.46
2080 RETURN
2999 REM ***************************************************************************
3000 REM SUBROUTINE TO GET VALUES FROM SAMPLE.DTA DATA FILE
3010 PRINT "LOADING SAMPLE DATA SET"
3020 OPEN "SAMPLE.DTA" AS #1
3030 FIELD #1, 25 AS DA$
3040 FOR RECORD=1 TO 85
3050 GET #1, RECORD
3060 VALUE$(RECORD)=DA$
3070 NEXT RECORD
3080 CLOSE
3090 FOR X=19 TO 64
3100 VALUE(X)=CVS(VALUE$(X))
3110 NEXT X
3120 RETURN
4000  REM SUBROUTINE TO GET VALUES FROM LASTBOT.DTA DATA FILE
4010 PRINT "LOADING LAST ROBOT DATA
4020 OPEN "LASTBOT.DTA" AS #2
4030 FIELD #2, 25 AS DA$
4040 FOR RECORD=1 TO 85
4050 GET #2, RECORD
4060 VALUE$(RECORD)=DA$
4070 NEXT RECORD
4080 CLOSE
4090 FOR X=19 TO 64
4100 VALUE(X)=CVS(VALUE$(X))
4110 NEXT X
4120 RETURN
4999 REM ***************************************************************************
5000 REM SUBROUTINE TO PERFORM CALCULATIONS FOR INVESTMENT WORKSHEET
5010 REM CALCULATE 10% TAX CREDIT, DEPRECIATION, EXPENSED AMOUNTS
5020 REM THE STRING COMPARISONS USE GREATER THAN/LESS THAN COMPARISONS TO AVOID
COMPARISON PROBLEMS BETWEEN UNEQUAL STRINGS SUCH AS "C" AND "C ".
5030 FOR X=1 TO 21
5040 IF STATUS$(X)>"BZ" AND STATUS$(X)<"CA" THEN TAXCREDIT(X)=INVCOST(X)*.1 ELSE
 TAXCREDIT(X)=0
5050 IF STATUS$(X)>"BZ" AND STATUS$(X)<"CA" THEN DEPREC(X)=INVCOST(X) ELSE DEPRE
C(X)=0
5060 IF STATUS$(X)>"DZ" AND STATUS$(X)<"EA" THEN EXPENSED(X)=INVCOST(X) ELSE EXP
ENSED(X)=0
5070 NEXT X
5080 REM CALCULATE TOTAL ROBOT COST
5090 ROBOTCOST=0
5100 FOR X=1 TO 11
5110 ROBOTCOST=ROBOTCOST+INVCOST(X)
5120 NEXT X
5130 REM CALCULATE TOTAL TOOLING COSTS
5140 TOOLINGCOST=INVCOST(12)+INVCOST(13)+INVCOST(14)
5150 REM CALCULATE TOTAL INSTALATION COSTS
5160 INSTALLATIONCOST=INVCOST(15)+INVCOST(16)+INVCOST(17)
5170 REM CALCULATE TOTAL ENGINEERING COSTS
5180 ENGINEERINGCOST=INVCOST(18)+INVCOST(19)+INVCOST(20)+INVCOST(21)
5190 REM CALCULATE TOTAL INVESTMENT=TOTAL COST
5200 TOTALINVESTMENT=ROBOTCOST+TOOLINGCOST+INSTALLATIONCOST+ENGINEERINGCOST
5210 REM CALCULATE TOTAL TAX CREDIT,TOTAL DEPRECIABLE, AND TOTAL EXPENSED
5220 TOTALTAXCREDIT=0:TOTALDEPREC=0:TOTALEXPENSED=0
5230 FOR X=1 TO 21
5240 TOTALTAXCREDIT=TOTALTAXCREDIT+TAXCREDIT(X)
5250 TOTALDEPREC=TOTALDEPREC+DEPREC(X)
5260 TOTALEXPENSED=TOTALEXPENSED+EXPENSED(X)
5270 NEXT X
```

```
5280 REM CALCULATE NET INVESTMENT
5290 NETINVESTMENT=TOTALINVESTMENT-TOTALTAXCREDIT
5300 REM CALCULATE NET DEPRECIABLE
5310 NETDEPREC=TOTALDEPREC*.95
5320 RETURN
5999 REM ***************************************************************

6000 REM SUBROUTINE TO PRINT INVESTMENT WORKSHEET
6010 REM CLS AND PRINT HEADINGS
6020 CLS:PRINT TAB(30) "INVESTMENT WORKSHEET"
6030 PRINT "DESCRIPTION" TAB(28)"COST" TAB(34) "STATUS" TAB(41) "DESCRIPTION" TA
B(68) "COST" TAB(74) "STATUS"
6040 REM PRINT STATUS CODE DESCRIPTIONS
6050 PRINT TAB(32) "C=CAPITAL" TAB(72) "C=CAPITAL";
6060 PRINT TAB(32) "E=EXPENSE" TAB(72) "E=EXPENSE";
6070 PRINT TAB(32) "N=NEITHER" TAB(72) "N=NEITHER";
6080 REM PRINT DESCRIPTION, COST, AND STATUS OF 21 COST ITEMS
6090 REM DETERMINE PRINTING LOCATION FOR EACH ITEM
6100 FOR X=1 TO 21
6110 IF X<3 THEN LOCATE (X+5),1:GOTO 6180
6120 IF X<9 THEN LOCATE (X+5),1:GOTO 6220
6130 IF X<12 THEN LOCATE (X+5),1:GOTO 6180
6140 IF X<15 THEN LOCATE (X+7),1:GOTO 6180
6150 IF X<18 THEN LOCATE (X-9),41:GOTO 6200
6160 LOCATE (X-7),41:GOTO 6200
6170 REM PRINT DESCRIPTION, COST, AND STATUS AT LOCATION SELECTED ABOVE
6180 PRINT INVDESCRIP$(X) TAB(27);:PRINT USING "######";INVCOST(X);:PRINT TAB(36
);:PRINT USING "\ \";STATUS$(X)
6190 GOTO 6230
6200 PRINT INVDESCRIP$(X) TAB(67);:PRINT USING "######";INVCOST(X);:PRINT TAB(76
);:PRINT USING "\ \";STATUS$(X)
6210 GOTO 6230
6220 PRINT "Option";X-2;:PRINT USING "\          \";INVDESCRIP$(X);:PRINT TA
B(27);:PRINT USING "######";INVCOST(X);:PRINT TAB(36);:PRINT USING "\ \";STATUS$
(X)
6230 NEXT X
6240 REM PRINT TOTAL ROBOT COST, TOTAL ENGINEERING, AND TOTAL INSTALLATION COST
AT THE APPROPRIATE SPOTS ON THE SHEET
6250 LOCATE 17,1:PRINT "TOTAL ROBOT COST";TAB(27);:PRINT USING "######";ROBOTCOS
T
6260 LOCATE 22,1:PRINT "TOTAL TOOLING COSTS";TAB(27);:PRINT USING "######";TOOLI
NGCOST
6270 LOCATE 9,41:PRINT "TOTAL INSTALLATION";TAB(67);:PRINT USING "######";INSTAL
LATIONCOST
6280 LOCATE 15,41:PRINT "TOTAL ENGINEERING";TAB(67);:PRINT USING "######";ENGINE
ERINGCOST
6290 LOCATE 17,41:PRINT "TOTAL INVESTMENT";TAB(67);:PRINT USING "######";TOTALIN
VESTMENT
6300 LOCATE 18,41:PRINT "TAX CREDIT";TAB(67);:PRINT USING "######";TOTALTAXCREDI
T
6310 LOCATE 19,41:PRINT "NET INVESTMENT";TAB(67);:PRINT USING "######";NETINVEST
MENT
6320 LOCATE 20,41:PRINT "TOTAL DEPRECIABLE 5YR.";TAB(67);:PRINT USING "######";T
OTALDEPREC
6330 LOCATE 21,41:PRINT "NET DEPRECIABLE (95%)";TAB(67);:PRINT USING "######";NE
TDEPREC
6340 LOCATE 22,41:PRINT "TOTAL EXPENSED";TAB(67);:PRINT USING "######";TOTALEXPE
NSED
6350 REM ASK AT THE BOTTOM OF THE WORKSHEET IF THE USER WISHES TO CHANGE ANY OPT
IONS, COSTS, OR STATUS CODES ON THE INVESTMENT WORKSHEET
6360 LOCATE 23,1:PRINT "THESE ARE THE CURRENT VALUES. DO YOU WISH TO CHANGE, ADD
, OR DELETE ANY OPTIONS OR CHANGE ANY COSTS OR STATUS CODES (Y/N) ?";
6370 REM MAKE CURSOR BLINK
6380 LOCATE ,,1
6390 YN$=INKEY$:IF YN$<>"Y" AND YN$<>"y" AND YN$<>"N" AND YN$<>"n" THEN 6390
6400 IF YN$="Y" OR YN$="y" THEN INVESTMENTCHANGES$="Y" ELSE INVESTMENTCHANGES$="
N"
6410 IF INVESTMENTCHANGES$="Y" THEN 6460
6420 REM NO CHANGES. ASK USER IF A PRINTOUT IS DESIRED.
6430 LOCATE 23,1:PRINT "                 ";"WOULD YOU LIKE A PRINTOUT OF THIS INVESTMENT WORKSHEET
 (Y/N) ?";
6440 YY$=INKEY$:IF YY$<>"Y" AND YY$<>"y" AND YY$<>"N" AND YY$<>"n" THEN 6440
6450 IF YY$="Y" OR YY$="y" THEN PRINTINVESTMENT$="Y" ELSE PRINTINVESTMENT$="N"
6460 RETURN
6999 REM ***************************************************************
7000 REM SUBROUTINE TO CHANGE INVESTMENT WORKSHEET
7010 REM ASK FOR CHANGES IN EACH DATA ITEM
7020 FOR X=1 TO 21
7030 CLS
7040 LOCATE 10,1
```

```
7050 REM ONLY OPTIONS HAVE CHANGING DESCRIPTIONS
7060 IF X<3 OR X>8 GOTO 7270
7070 REM CHANGE OPTION NAMES
7080 PRINT "Option ";X-2;" IS CURRENTLY NAMED:";INVDESCRIP$(X)
7090 PRINT "DO YOU WISH TO CHANGE THIS NAME (Y/N) ? ";
7100 CN$=INKEY$:IF CN$<>"Y" AND CN$<>"y" AND CN$<>"N" AND CN$<>"n" THEN 7100
7110 IF CN$="N" OR CN$="n" GOTO 7130
7120 INPUT " CHANGE TO";INVDESCRIP$(X)
7130 REM CHANGE OPTION COSTS
7140 PRINT:PRINT:PRINT "Option ";X-2;" CURRENTLY COSTS:";INVCOST(X)
7150 PRINT "DO YOU WISH TO CHANGE THIS COST (Y/N) ? ";
7160 CC$=INKEY$:IF CC$<>"Y" AND CC$<>"y" AND CC$<>"N" AND CC$<>"n" THEN 7160
7170 IF CC$="N" OR CC$="n" GOTO 7190
7180 INPUT "CHANGE TO";INVCOST(X)
7190 REM CHANGE OPTION STATUS CODES
7200 PRINT:PRINT:PRINT "Option ";X-2;" CURRENTLY HAS STATUS CODE: ";:PRINT USING
     "\\";STATUS$(X)
7210 PRINT "DO YOU WISH TO CHANGE THIS STATUS CODE REMEMBERING C=CAPITAL,E=EXPEN
SED,        N=NEITHER (Y/N) ? ";
7220 CS$=INKEY$:IF CS$<>"Y" AND CS$<>"y" AND CS$<>"N" AND CS$<>"n" THEN 7220
7230 IF CS$="N" OR CS$="n" GOTO 7400
7240 INPUT "CHANGE TO (C/E/N) ";STATUS$(X)
7250 IF STATUS$(X)<>"C" AND STATUS$(X)<>"E" AND STATUS$(X)<>"N" THEN 7240
7260 GOTO 7400
7270 REM CHANGE COSTS FOR NON-OPTIONS
7280 LOCATE 10,1
7290 PRINT INVDESCRIP$(X);" COST IS CURRENTLY: ";INVCOST(X)
7300 PRINT "DO YOU WISH TO CHANGE THIS COST (Y/N) ? ";
7310 DC$=INKEY$:IF DC$<>"Y" AND DC$<>"y" AND DC$<>"N" AND DC$<>"n" THEN 7310
7320 IF DC$="N" OR DC$="n" GOTO 7340
7330 INPUT "CHANGE TO ";INVCOST(X)
7340 REM CHANGE STATUS CODES FOR NON-OPTIONS
7350 PRINT:PRINT:PRINT INVDESCRIP$(X);" STATUS CODE IS CURRENTLY: ";STATUS$(X)
7360 PRINT "DO YOU WISH TO CHANGE THIS STATUS CODE REMEMBERING C=CAPITAL,E=EXPEN
SED,        N=NEITHER (Y/N) ? ";
7370 DS$=INKEY$:IF DS$<>"Y" AND DS$<>"y" AND DS$<>"N" AND DS$<>"n" THEN 7370
7380 IF DS$="N" OR DS$="n" THEN 7400
7390 INPUT " CHANGE TO (C/E/N) ";STATUS$(X)
7400 NEXT X
7410 RETURN
7999 REM ***********************************************************************
8000 REM SUBROUTINE TO PRINT INVESTMENT WORKSHEET ON LINE PRINTER
8010 REM LPRINT HEADINGS
8020 LPRINT CHR$(12):LPRINT TAB(30) "INVESTMENT WORKSHEET"
8030 LPRINT:LPRINT "DESCRIPTION" TAB(28)"COST" TAB(40) "STATUS" TAB(51) "10% TAX
" TAB(61) "5 YEAR" TAB(71) "EXPENSED"
8040 LPRINT TAB(38) "C=CAPITAL";TAB(51)"CREDIT";TAB(59)"DEPRECIABLE";TAB(72) "AM
OUNT"
8050 LPRINT TAB(38) "E=EXPENSED";TAB(61) "AMOUNT"
8060 REM LPRINT ROBOT COSTS
8070 LPRINT "I. ROBOT COST"
8080 FOR X=1 TO 2
8090 LPRINT INVDESCRIP$(X) TAB(27);:LPRINT USING "######";INVCOST(X);:LPRINT TAB
(43);:LPRINT USING "\\";STATUS$(X);:LPRINT TAB(51);:LPRINT USING "#####";TAXCRED
IT(X);:LPRINT TAB(61);:LPRINT USING "######";DEPREC(X);
8100 LPRINT TAB(72);:LPRINT USING "######";EXPENSED(X)
8110 NEXT X
8120 FOR X=3 TO 8
8130 LPRINT "Option";X-2;:LPRINT USING "\            \";INVDESCRIP$(X);:LPRINT
 TAB(27);:LPRINT USING "######";INVCOST(X);:LPRINT TAB(43);:LPRINT USING "\\";ST
ATUS$(X);
8140 LPRINT TAB(51);:LPRINT USING "#####";TAXCREDIT(X);:LPRINT TAB(61);:LPRINT U
SING"######";DEPREC(X);:LPRINT TAB(72);:LPRINT USING "######";EXPENSED(X)
8150 NEXT X
8160 FOR X=9 TO 11
8170 LPRINT INVDESCRIP$(X) TAB(27);:LPRINT USING "######";INVCOST(X);:LPRINT TAB
(43);:LPRINT USING "\\";STATUS$(X);:LPRINT TAB(51);:LPRINT USING "#####";TAXCRED
IT(X);:LPRINT TAB(61);:LPRINT USING "######";DEPREC(X);
8180 LPRINT TAB(72);:LPRINT USING "######";EXPENSED(X)
8190 NEXT X
8200 LPRINT "TOTAL ROBOT COST" TAB(27);:LPRINT USING "######";ROBOTCOST
8210 REM LPRINT TOOLING COSTS
8220 LPRINT:LPRINT "II. TOOLING COSTS
8230 FOR X=12 TO 14
8240 LPRINT INVDESCRIP$(X) TAB(27);:LPRINT USING "######";INVCOST(X);:LPRINT TAB
(43);:LPRINT USING "\\";STATUS$(X);:LPRINT TAB(51);:LPRINT USING "#####";TAXCRED
IT(X);:LPRINT TAB(61);:LPRINT USING "######";DEPREC(X);
8250 LPRINT TAB(72);:LPRINT USING "######";EXPENSED(X)
8260 NEXT X
8270 LPRINT "TOTAL TOOLING COSTS" TAB(27);:LPRINT USING "######";TOOLINGCOST
8280 REM LPRINT INSTALLATION COSTS
```

```
8290 LPRINT:LPRINT "III. INSTALLATION COSTS
8300 FOR X=15 TO 17
8310 LPRINT INVDESCRIP$(X) TAB(27);:LPRINT USING "######";INVCOST(X);:LPRINT TAB
(43);:LPRINT USING "\\";STATUS$(X);:LPRINT TAB(51);:LPRINT USING "#####";TAXCRED
IT(X);:LPRINT TAB(61);:LPRINT USING "######";DEPREC(X);
8320 LPRINT TAB(72);:LPRINT USING "######";EXPENSED(X)
8330 NEXT X
8340 LPRINT "TOTAL INSTALLATION COSTS" TAB(27);:LPRINT USING "######";INSTALLATI
ONCOST
8350 REM LPRINT ENGINEERING COSTS
8360 LPRINT:LPRINT "IV. ENGINEERING COSTS
8370 FOR X=18 TO 21
8380 LPRINT INVDESCRIP$(X) TAB(27);:LPRINT USING "######";INVCOST(X);:LPRINT TAB
(43);:LPRINT USING "\\";STATUS$(X);:LPRINT TAB(51);:LPRINT USING "#####";TAXCRED
IT(X);:LPRINT TAB(61);:LPRINT USING "######";DEPREC(X);
8390 LPRINT TAB(72);:LPRINT USING "######";EXPENSED(X)
8400 NEXT X
8410 LPRINT "TOTAL ENGINEERING COSTS" TAB(27);:LPRINT USING "######";ENGINEERING
COST
8420 REM LPRINT COLUMN SUMS
8430 LPRINT TAB(27) "------";TAB(51) "------";TAB(61) "------";TAB(72) "------"
8440 LPRINT "TOTALS";TAB(27);:LPRINT USING "######";TOTALINVESTMENT;:LPRINT TAB(
51);:LPRINT USING "######";TOTALTAXCREDIT;:LPRINT TAB(61);:LPRINT USING "######"
;TOTALDEPREC;:LPRINT TAB(72);:LPRINT USING "######";TOTALEXPENSED
8450 REM LPRINT INVESTMENT SUMMARY INFORMATION
8460 LPRINT:LPRINT "TOTAL INVESTMENT" TAB(27);:LPRINT USING "######";TOTALINVEST
MENT
8470 LPRINT "INVESTMENT TAX CREDIT" TAB(27);:LPRINT USING "######";TOTALTAXCREDI
T
8480 LPRINT "NET INVESTMENT" TAB(27);:LPRINT USING "######";NETINVESTMENT
8490 REM LPRINT DEPRECIATION SUMMARY INFORMATION
8500 LPRINT:LPRINT "TOTAL DEPRECIABLE 5 YEARS" TAB(27);:LPRINT USING "######";TO
TALDEPREC
8510 LPRINT "DEPRECIABLE FRACTION" TAB(27);:LPRINT "   .95"
8520 LPRINT "NET DEPRECIABLE" TAB(27);:LPRINT USING "######";NETDEPREC
8530 REM LPRINT EXPENSED SUMMARY
8540 LPRINT:LPRINT "TOTAL EXPENSED" TAB(27);:LPRINT USING "######";TOTALEXPENSED

8550 RETURN
8999 REM ********************************************************************
9000 REM SUBROUTINE TO PERFORM CALCULATIONS FOR ANNUAL SAVING/COSTS WORKSHEET
9010 REM CALCULATE DEPRECIATION AS A COST
9020 DEPRECIATIONASACOST=NETINVESTMENT/8
9030 REM CALCULATE TOTAL ANNUAL OPERATING COSTS
9040 ANNUALCOST=DEPRECIATIONASACOST
9050 FOR X=1 TO 10
9060 ANNUALCOST=ANNUALCOST+ANNUALCOST(X)
9070 NEXT X
9080 REM CALCULATE TOTAL ANNUAL SAVINGS
9090 ANNUALSAVINGS=0
9100 FOR X=11 TO 21
9110 ANNUALSAVINGS=ANNUALSAVINGS+ANNUALCOST(X)
9120 NEXT X
9130 REM CALCULATE ANNUAL PRODUCTION CAPACITY EFFECT
9140 CAPACITYEFFECT=(ANNUALCOST(22)-ANNUALCOST(23))*ANNUALCOST(24)
9150 REM CALCULATE TOTAL ANNUAL RETURN
9160 TOTALANNUALRETURN=-ANNUALCOST+ANNUALSAVINGS+CAPACITYEFFECT
9170 RETURN
9999 REM ********************************************************************

10000 REM SUBROUTINE TO PRINT ANNUAL SAVINGS/COSTS WORKSHEET
10010 REM CLEAR SCREEN AND PRINT HEADINGS
10020 CLS:PRINT TAB(26) "ANNUAL SAVINGS/COSTS WORKSHEET"
10030 PRINT "DESCRIPTION";TAB(25) "ANNUAL COSTS";TAB(41) "DESCRIPTION";TAB(63) "
ANNUAL SAVINGS"
10040 REM PRINT FIRST FOUR COSTS AND FIRST FOUR SAVINGS INCLUDING DESCRIPTIONS
10050 FOR X=1 TO 4
10060 PRINT ANNUALDESCRIP$(X) TAB(31);:PRINT USING "######";ANNUALCOST(X);:PRINT
 TAB(41) ANNUALDESCRIP$(X+10) TAB(71);:PRINT USING "######";ANNUALCOST(X+10)
10070 NEXT X
10080 REM PRINT DEPRECIATION AS A COST AND FIFTH SAVINGS ITEM
10090 PRINT "Depreciation-cost (computed)" TAB(31);:PRINT USING "######";DEPRECI
ATIONASACOST;:PRINT TAB(41) ANNUALDESCRIP$(15) TAB(71);:PRINT USING "######";ANN
UALCOST(15)
10100 REM PRINT SIX OPTIONAL COSTS AND SIX OPTIONAL SAVINGS INCLUDING OPTION NAM
ES
10110 FOR X=5 TO 10
10120 PRINT "Other";X-4;:PRINT USING "\                     \";ANNUALDESCRIP$(X);
:PRINT TAB(31);:PRINT USING "######";ANNUALCOST(X);
10130 PRINT TAB(41);"Other";X-4;:PRINT USING "\                     \";ANNUALDESC
RIP$(X+11);:PRINT TAB(71);:PRINT USING "######";ANNUALCOST(X+11)
```

```
10140 NEXT X
10150 REM PRINT TOTAL ANNUAL OPERATING COST AND TOTAL ANNUAL SAVINGS
10160 PRINT "TOTAL OPERATING COSTS";TAB(31);:PRINT USING "######";ANNUALCOST;:PR
INT TAB(41);:PRINT "TOTAL ANNUAL SAVINGS";TAB(71);:PRINT USING "######";ANNUALSA
VINGS
10170 REM PRINT PRODUCTION CAPACITY EFFECT SECTION
10180 PRINT:PRINT "PRODUCTION CAPACITY EFFECT"
10190 FOR X=22 TO 24
10200 PRINT ANNUALDESCRIP$(X);TAB(31);:PRINT USING "######.##";ANNUALCOST(X)
10210 NEXT X
10220 REM PRINT TOTAL CAPACITY EFFECT AND TOTAL ANNUAL RETURN
10230 PRINT "TOTAL CAPACITY EFFECT";:PRINT TAB(31);:PRINT USING "######";CAPACIT
YEFFECT
10240 PRINT:PRINT "TOTAL ANNUAL RETURN";TAB(31);:PRINT USING "######";TOTALANNUA
LRETURN
10250 REM ASK AT THE BOTTOM OF THE WORKSHEET IF THE USER WISHES TO CHANGE ANY SA
VINGS, COSTS, OR PRODUCTION CAPACITY EFFECT DATA ON THE ANNUAL SAVINGS/COSTS WOR
KSHEET
10260 LOCATE 24,1:PRINT "THESE ARE THE CURRENT VALUES. DO YOU WISH TO CHANGE, AD
D, OR DELETE DATA (Y/N)?";
10270 YN$=INKEY$:IF YN$<>"Y" AND YN$<>"y" AND YN$<>"N" AND YN$<>"n" THEN 10270
10280 IF YN$="Y" OR YN$="y" THEN ANNUALCHANGES$="Y" ELSE ANNUALCHANGES$="N"
10290 IF ANNUALCHANGES$="Y" THEN 10340
10300 REM NO CHANGES. ASK USER IF A PRINTOUT IS DESIRED.
10310 LOCATE 24,1:PRINT "WOULD YOU LIKE A PRINTOUT OF THIS ANNUAL SAVINGS/COSTS
WORKSHEET (Y/N)?              ";
10320 YY$=INKEY$:IF YY$<>"Y" AND YY$<>"y" AND YY$<>"N" AND YY$<>"n" THEN 10320
10330 IF YY$="Y" OR YY$="y" THEN PRINTANNUAL$="Y" ELSE PRINTANNUAL$="N"
10340 RETURN
10999 REM *********************************************************************

11000 REM SUBROUTINE TO CHANGE ANNUAL SAVINGS/COSTS WORKSHEET
11010 REM ASK FOR CHANGES IN EACH DATA ITEM
11020 FOR X=1 TO 24
11030 CLS
11040 LOCATE 10,1
11050 REM ONLY 5-10 AND 16-21 HAVE CHANGABLE DESCRIPTIONS
11060 IF X<5 OR X>21 GOTO 11260
11070 IF X>10 AND X<16 GOTO 11260
11080 REM CHANGE COST AND SAVINGS DESCRIPTIONS
11090 IF X<11 THEN PRINT "COST ";X-4;
11100 IF X>15 THEN PRINT "SAVINGS ";X-15;
11110 PRINT "IS CURRENTLY NAMED:";ANNUALDESCRIP$(X)
11120 PRINT:PRINT "DO YOU WISH TO CHANGE THIS NAME (Y/N) ? ";
11130 CN$=INKEY$:IF CN$<>"Y" AND CN$<>"y" AND CN$<>"N" AND CN$<>"n" THEN 11130
11140 IF CN$="N" OR CN$="n" GOTO 11160
11150 INPUT " CHANGE TO";ANNUALDESCRIP$(X)
11160 PRINT:PRINT
11170 REM CHANGE COSTS OF SAVINGS AND COST ITEMS WITH CHANGABLE DESCRIPTIONS
11180 IF X<10 THEN PRINT "COST ";X-4;
11190 IF X>15 THEN PRINT "SAVINGS ";X-15;
11200 PRINT "CURRENTLY EQUALS:";ANNUALCOST(X)
11210 PRINT "DO YOU WISH TO CHANGE THIS VALUE (Y/N) ? ";
11220 CC$=INKEY$:IF CC$<>"Y" AND CC$<>"y" AND CC$<>"N" AND CC$<>"n" THEN 11220
11230 IF CC$="N" OR CC$="n" GOTO 11360
11240 INPUT "CHANGE TO";ANNUALCOST(X)
11250 GOTO 11360
11260 REM CHANGE VALUES FOR COSTS AND SAVINGS FOR ITEMS WHOSE DESCRIPTIONS CAN N
OT BE CHANGED
11270 LOCATE 10,1
11280 IF X<11 THEN PRINT "OPERATING COST SECTION"
11290 IF X>10 AND X<22 THEN PRINT "ANNUAL SAVINGS SECTION"
11300 IF X>21 THEN PRINT "PRODUCTION CAPACITY EFFECT SECTION"
11310 PRINT:PRINT ANNUALDESCRIP$(X);" CURRENTLY EQUALS: ";ANNUALCOST(X)
11320 PRINT "DO YOU WISH TO CHANGE THIS VALUE (Y/N) ? ";
11330 DC$=INKEY$:IF DC$<>"Y" AND DC$<>"y" AND DC$<>"N" AND DC$<>"n" THEN 11330
11340 IF DC$="N" OR DC$="n" GOTO 11360
11350 INPUT "CHANGE TO ";ANNUALCOST(X)
11360 NEXT X
11370 RETURN
12000 REM SUBROUTINE TO PRINT ANNUAL SAVINGS/COSTS WORKSHEET ON LINE PRINTER
12010 REM LPRINT HEADINGS
12020 LPRINT CHR$(12):LPRINT TAB(26) "ANNUAL SAVINGS/COSTS WORKSHEET"
12030 LPRINT:LPRINT "DESCRIPTION" TAB(32) "COST"
12040 REM LPRINT ANNUAL OPERATING COSTS
12050 LPRINT:LPRINT "I. ANNUAL OPERATING COSTS"
12060 FOR X=1 TO 4
12070 LPRINT ANNUALDESCRIP$(X) TAB(31);:LPRINT USING "######";ANNUALCOST(X)
12080 NEXT X
12090 LPRINT "Depreciation (as a cost)" TAB(31);:LPRINT USING "######";DEPRECIAT
IONASACOST
```

```
12100 FOR X=5 TO 10
12110 LPRINT "Other";X-4;:LPRINT USING "\                    \";ANNUALDESCRIP$(X
);:LPRINT TAB(31);:LPRINT USING "######";ANNUALCOST(X)
12120 NEXT X
12130 REM PRINT TOTAL OPERATING COSTS
12140 LPRINT "TOTAL OPERATING COSTS";TAB(31);:LPRINT USING "######";ANNUALCOST
12150 REM LPRINT ANNUAL SAVINGS
12160 LPRINT:LPRINT "II. ANNUAL SAVINGS"
12170 FOR X=11 TO 15
12180 LPRINT ANNUALDESCRIP$(X) TAB(31);:LPRINT USING "######";ANNUALCOST(X)
12190 NEXT X
12200 FOR X=16 TO 21
12210 LPRINT "Other";X-15;:LPRINT USING "\                    \";ANNUALDESCRIP$(
X);:LPRINT TAB(31);:LPRINT USING "######";ANNUALCOST(X)
12220 NEXT X
12230 REM LPRINT TOTAL ANNUAL SAVINGS
12240 LPRINT "TOTAL ANNUAL SAVINGS";TAB(31);:LPRINT USING "######";ANNUALSAVINGS

12250 REM LPRINT PRODUCTION CAPACITY EFFECTS
12260 LPRINT:LPRINT "III. PRODUCTION CAPACITY EFFECT"
12270 FOR X=22 TO 24
12280 LPRINT ANNUALDESCRIP$(X);TAB(31);:LPRINT USING "######.##";ANNUALCOST(X)
12290 NEXT X
12300 REM LPRINT TOTAL PRODUCTION CAPACITY EFFECT
12310 LPRINT "TOTAL CAPACITY EFFFECT";TAB(31);:LPRINT USING "######";CAPACITYEFF
ECT
12320 REM LPRINT TOTAL ANNUAL RETURN
12330 LPRINT:LPRINT "TOTAL ANNUAL RETURN";TAB(31);:LPRINT USING "######";TOTALAN
NUALRETURN
12340 RETURN
12999 REM ***********************************************************************

13000 REM SUBROUTINE TO CALCULATE VALUES FOR RETURN ON INVESTMENT WORKSHEET
13010 REM ASSIGN EXPENSED INVESTMENT IN YEAR 1 EQUAL TO TOTAL EXPENSED FROM INVE
STMENT WORKSHEET
13020 ROIEXPENSED(1)=TOTALEXPENSED
13030 REM CALCULATE DEPRECIATION FOR TAXES
13040 TAXESDEPREC(1)=.15*NETDEPREC
13050 TAXESDEPREC(2)=.22*NETDEPREC
13060 TAXESDEPREC(3)=.21*NETDEPREC
13070 TAXESDEPREC(4)=.21*NETDEPREC
13080 TAXESDEPREC(5)=.21*NETDEPREC
13090 REM CALCULATE TAXABLE INCOME FOR EACH YEAR
13100 FOR X=1 TO 8
13110 TAXABLEINCOME(X)=TOTALANNUALRETURN-ROIEXPENSED(X)+DEPRECIATIONASACOST-TAXE
SDEPREC(X)
13120 NEXT X
13130 REM CALCULATE TAXES
13140 FOR X=1 TO 8
13150 TAXES(X)=TAXABLEINCOME(X)*TAXRATE
13160 NEXT X
13170 REM CALCULATE NET AFTER TAX
13180 FOR X=1 TO 8
13190 NETAFTERTAX(X)=TOTALANNUALRETURN-TAXES(X)
13200 NEXT X
13210 REM CALCULATE UNDISCOUNTED PAYBACK
13220 UNDISCOUNTEDPAYBACK(0)=NETINVESTMENT*-1
13230 FOR X=1 TO 8
13240 UNDISCOUNTEDPAYBACK(X)=UNDISCOUNTEDPAYBACK(X-1)+NETAFTERTAX(X)
13250 NEXT X
13260 REM CALCULATE PAYBACK PERIOD
13270 FOR X=1 TO 8
13280 IF UNDISCOUNTEDPAYBACK(X)>=0 THEN GOTO 13320
13290 NEXT X
13300 PAYBACK=9
13310 GOTO 13330
13320 PAYBACK=X-(UNDISCOUNTEDPAYBACK(X)/NETAFTERTAX(X))
13330 REM ITERATE TO CALCULATE RETURN ON INVESTMENT
13340 TESTVALUELOW=.00001:TESTVALUEHIGH=100:TESTVALUE=50
13350 REM CHECK TO SEE IF ROI IS WORSE THAN .00001 (SAME AS .001%). IF IT IS SET
 ROI EQUAL TO 0 AND QUIT SUBROUTINE.
13360 ROITEST=TESTVALUELOW
13370 GOSUB 14000
13380 IF RESULT<0 THEN ROI=0:GOTO 13620
13390 REM CHECK TO SEE IF ROI IS BETTER THAN +100 (SAME AS 1000%). IF IT IS SET
ROI EQUAL TO 101 AND QUIT SUBROUTINE.
13400 ROITEST=TESTVALUEHIGH
13410 GOSUB 14000
13420 IF RESULT>0 THEN ROI=101:GOTO 13620
13430 REM HAVING BOUNDED THE ROI BETWEEN .00001 AND 100 PERFORM ITERATION TO DET
ERMINE ROI TO THE TENTHOUSSNTH DECIMAL PLACE.
```

```
13440 ROITEST=TESTVALUE
13450 GOSUB 14000
13460 IF RESULT=0 THEN ROI=ROITEST:GOTO 13590
13470 IF RESULT>0 THEN TESTVALUELOW=TESTVALUE:TESTVALUE=(TESTVALUEHIGH+TESTVALUE
LOW)/2
13480 IF RESULT<0 THEN TESTVALUEHIGH=TESTVALUE:TESTVALUE=(TESTVALUEHIGH+TESTVALU
ELOW)/2
13490 IF TESTVALUEHIGH-TESTVALUELOW<.00001 THEN GOTO 13510
13500 GOTO 13440
13510 REM SEE IF TESTVALUEHIGH OR TESTVALUELOW IS CLOSER TO THE CORRECT ROI
13520 ROITEST=TESTVALUEHIGH
13530 GOSUB 14000
13540 RESULTHIGH=RESULT
13550 ROITEST=TESTVALUELOW
13560 GOSUB 14000
13570 RESULTLOW=RESULT
13580 IF ABS(RESULTHIGH)<ABS(RESULTLOW) THEN ROI=TESTVALUEHIGH ELSE ROI=TESTVALU
ELOW
13590 REM NOW THAT ROI IS KNOWN GET FINAL DISCOUNT RATES AND DISCOUNT NETS
13600 ROITEST=ROI
13610 GOSUB 14000
13620 RETURN
13999 REM ****************************************************************
14000 REM SUBROUTINE THAT CALCULATES DISCOUNT RATES AND DISCOUNTED NET AFTER TAX
ES FOR EACH YEAR
14010 DISCOUNTRATE(1)=1/(SQR(1+ROITEST))
14020 FOR X=2 TO 8
14030 DISCOUNTRATE(X)=DISCOUNTRATE(X-1)*(1/(1+ROITEST))
14040 NEXT X
14050 FOR X=1 TO 8
14060 DISCOUNTEDNET(X)=NETAFTERTAX(X)*DISCOUNTRATE(X)
14070 NEXT X
14080 REM AS RESULT APPROACHES ZERO THE ROI IS NARROWED IN ON
14090 RESULT=NETINVESTMENT*-1
14100 FOR X=1 TO 8
14110 RESULT=RESULT+DISCOUNTEDNET(X)
14120 NEXT X
14130 RETURN
14999 REM ****************************************************************
15000 REM SUBROUTINE TO PRINT RETURN ON INVESTMENT WORKSHEET ON THE SCREEN
15010 REM CLEAR SCREEN AND PRINT HEADINGS
15020 CLS:PRINT TAB(25)"RETURN ON INVESTMENT WORKSHEET"
15030 PRINT:PRINT "DESCRIPTION" TAB(16) "YEAR-1  YEAR-2  YEAR-3  YEAR-4  YEAR-5
YEAR-6  YEAR-7  YEAR-8"
15040 PRINT:PRINT "ANNUAL RETURN";
15050 FOR X=1 TO 8
15060 PRINT TAB(7+(X*8));:PRINT USING "#######";TOTALANNUALRETURN;
15070 NEXT X:PRINT
15080 PRINT "-EXPENSED";
15090 FOR X=1 TO 8
15100 PRINT TAB(7+(X*8));:PRINT USING "#######";ROIEXPENSED(X);
15110 NEXT X:PRINT
15120 PRINT "+DEPREC.(COST)";
15130 FOR X=1 TO 8
15140 PRINT TAB(7+(X*8));:PRINT USING "#######";DEPRECIATIONASACOST;
15150 NEXT X:PRINT
15160 PRINT "-DEPREC.(TAX)";
15170 FOR X=1 TO 8
15180 PRINT TAB(7+(X*8));:PRINT USING "#######";TAXESDEPREC(X);
15190 NEXT X:PRINT
15200 PRINT "=TAXED INCOME";
15210 FOR X=1 TO 8
15220 PRINT TAB(7+(X*8));:PRINT USING "#######";TAXABLEINCOME(X);
15230 NEXT X:PRINT
15240 PRINT "xTAX RATE";
15250 FOR X=1 TO 8
15260 PRINT TAB(7+(X*8));:PRINT USING "####.##";TAXRATE;
15270 NEXT X:PRINT
15280 PRINT "=ANNUAL TAXES";
15290 FOR X=1 TO 8
15300 PRINT TAB(7+(X*8));:PRINT USING "#######";TAXES(X);
15310 NEXT X:PRINT
15320 PRINT:PRINT "NET AFTER TAX";
15330 FOR X=1 TO 8
15340 PRINT TAB(7+(X*8));:PRINT USING "#######";NETAFTERTAX(X);
15350 NEXT X:PRINT
15360 IF ROI=101 OR ROI=0 THEN PRINT:PRINT:PRINT:PRINT:GOTO 15490
15370 PRINT "xDISCOUNT RATE";
15380 FOR X=1 TO 8
15390 PRINT TAB(7+(X*8));:PRINT USING "###.###";DISCOUNTRATE(X);
15400 NEXT X:PRINT
```

```
15410 PRINT "=DISCOUNT NET";
15420 FOR X=1 TO 8
15430 PRINT TAB(7+(X*8));:PRINT USING "#######";DISCOUNTEDNET(X);
15440 NEXT X:PRINT
15450 PRINT:PRINT "PAYBACK";
15460 FOR X=1 TO 8
15470 PRINT TAB(6+(X*8));:PRINT USING "+#######";UNDISCOUNTEDPAYBACK(X);
15480 NEXT X:PRINT
15490 PRINT:PRINT "NET INVESTMENT" TAB(27);:PRINT USING "######";NETINVESTMENT
15500 PRINT "TOTAL RETURN AFTER TAXES" TAB(27);:PRINT USING "#######";UNDISCOUNT
EDPAYBACK(8)+NETINVESTMENT
15510 IF ROI=101 THEN PRINT "RETURN ON INVESTMENT" TAB(27) "GREATER THAN 10000%"
:GOTO 15540
15520 IF ROI=0 THEN PRINT "RETURN ON INVESTMENT" TAB(27) "ZERO% OR NEGATIVE":GOT
O 15540
15530 PRINT "RETURN ON INVESTMENT" TAB(26);:PRINT USING "####.##";ROI*100;:PRINT
"%"
15540 IF ROI=0 OR ROI=101 THEN PRINT "PAYBACK PERIOD NOT CALULATED"
15550 PRINT "PAYBACK IN YEARS" TAB(26);:PRINT USING "######.#";PAYBACK
15560 REM ASK AT BOTTOM OF SCREEN IF USER WISHES TO CHANGE TAX RATE AND TURN ON
FLASHING CURSOR
15570 LOCATE 24,1:LOCATE ,,1:PRINT "THESE ARE THE CURRENT VALUES. DO YOU WISH TO
CHANGE THE TAX RATE (Y/N) ? ";
15580 YN$=INKEY$:IF YN$<>"Y" AND YN$<>"y" AND YN$<>"N" AND YN$<>"n" THEN 15580
15590 IF YN$="Y" OR YN$="y" THEN ROICHANGES$="Y" ELSE ROICHANGES$="N"
15600 IF ROICHANGES$="N" THEN 15650
15610 REM CHANGE TAX RATE
15620 LOCATE 24,1:PRINT "
                                                    ";
15630 LOCATE 24,1:INPUT "CHANGE TAX RATE TO WHAT PERCENTAGE BETWEEN .01 AND 1.00
";TAXRATE
15640 GOTO 15690
15650 REM NO CHANGES ASK USER IF A PRINTOUT IS DESIRED.
15660 LOCATE 24,1:PRINT "WOULD YOU LIKE A PRINTOUT OF THIS RETURN ON INVESTMENT
WORKSHEET (Y/N)?           ";
15670 YY$=INKEY$:IF YY$<>"Y" AND YY$<>"y" AND YY$<>"N" AND YY$<>"n" THEN 15670
15680 IF YY$="Y" OR YY$="y" THEN PRINTROI$="Y" ELSE PRINTROI$="N"
15690 RETURN
15999 REM **************************************************************
16000 REM SUBROUTINE TO LPRINT RETURN ON INVESTMENT WORKSHEET
16010 REM LPRINT HEADINGS
16020 LPRINT CHR$(12):LPRINT TAB(25)"RETURN ON INVESTMENT WORKSHEET"
16030 LPRINT:LPRINT "DESCRIPTION" TAB(16) "YEAR-1   YEAR-2   YEAR-3   YEAR-4   YEAR-
5   YEAR-6   YEAR-7   YEAR-8"
16040 LPRINT:LPRINT "ANNUAL RETURN";
16050 FOR X=1 TO 8
16060 LPRINT TAB(7+(X*8));:LPRINT USING "#######";TOTALANNUALRETURN;
16070 NEXT X:LPRINT
16080 LPRINT "-EXPENSED";
16090 FOR X=1 TO 8
16100 LPRINT TAB(7+(X*8));:LPRINT USING "#######";ROIEXPENSED(X);
16110 NEXT X:LPRINT
16120 LPRINT "+DEPREC.(COST)";
16130 FOR X=1 TO 8
16140 LPRINT TAB(7+(X*8));:LPRINT USING "#######";DEPRECIATIONASACOST;
16150 NEXT X:LPRINT
16160 LPRINT "-DEPREC.(TAX)";
16170 FOR X=1 TO 8
16180 LPRINT TAB(7+(X*8));:LPRINT USING "#######";TAXESDEPREC(X);
16190 NEXT X:LPRINT
16200 LPRINT "=TAXED INCOME";
16210 FOR X=1 TO 8
16220 LPRINT TAB(7+(X*8));:LPRINT USING "#######";TAXABLEINCOME(X);
16230 NEXT X:LPRINT
16240 LPRINT "xTAX RATE";
16250 FOR X=1 TO 8
16260 LPRINT TAB(7+(X*8));:LPRINT USING "####.##";TAXRATE;
16270 NEXT X:LPRINT
16280 LPRINT "=ANNUAL TAXES";
16290 FOR X=1 TO 8
16300 LPRINT TAB(7+(X*8));:LPRINT USING "#######";TAXES(X);
16310 NEXT X:LPRINT
16320 LPRINT:LPRINT "NET AFTER TAX";
16330 FOR X=1 TO 8
16340 LPRINT TAB(7+(X*8));:LPRINT USING "#######";NETAFTERTAX(X);
16350 NEXT X:LPRINT
16360 IF ROI=101 OR ROI=0 THEN LPRINT:LPRINT:LPRINT:LPRINT:GOTO 15490
16370 LPRINT "xDISCOUNT RATE";
16380 FOR X=1 TO 8
16390 LPRINT TAB(7+(X*8));:LPRINT USING "###.###";DISCOUNTRATE(X);
16400 NEXT X:LPRINT
```

```
16410 LPRINT "=DISCOUNT NET";
16420 FOR X=1 TO 8
16430 LPRINT TAB(7+(X*8));:LPRINT USING "#######";DISCOUNTEDNET(X);
16440 NEXT X:LPRINT
16450 LPRINT:LPRINT "PAYBACK";
16460 FOR X=1 TO 8
16470 LPRINT TAB(6+(X*8));:LPRINT USING "+#######";UNDISCOUNTEDPAYBACK(X);
16480 NEXT X:LPRINT
16490 LPRINT:LPRINT "NET INVESTMENT" TAB(27);:LPRINT USING "#######";NETINVESTME
NT
16500 LPRINT "TOTAL RETURN AFTER TAXES" TAB(27);:LPRINT USING "#######";UNDISCOU
NTEDPAYBACK(8)+NETINVESTMENT
16510 IF ROI=101 THEN LPRINT "RETURN ON INVESTMENT" TAB(27) "GREATER THAN 10000%
":GOTO 15540
16520 IF ROI=0 THEN LPRINT "RETURN ON INVESTMENT" TAB(27) "ZERO% OR NEGATIVE":GO
TO 15540
16530 LPRINT "RETURN ON INVESTMENT" TAB(26);:LPRINT USING "####.##";ROI*100;:LPR
INT "%"
16540 IF ROI=0 OR ROI=101 THEN LPRINT "PAYBACK PERIOD NOT CALULATED"
16550 LPRINT "PAYBACK IN YEARS" TAB(26);:LPRINT USING "######.#";PAYBACK
16560 RETURN
16999 REM *************************************************************
17000 REM SUBROUTINE TO FILL LASTBOT.DTA WITH NEW DATA
17010 REM FIRST SET ALL 85 DATA INTO VALUEB$ ARRAY
17020 REM SET INVESTMENT WORKSHHET OPTION NAMES INTO VALUEB$ ARRAY
17030 FOR X=1 TO 6
17040 VALUEB$(X)=INVDESCRIP$(X+2)
17050 NEXT X
17060 REM SET ANNUAL OPERATING COST OPTIONS' NAMES INTO VALUEB$ ARRAY
17070 FOR X=7 TO 12
17080 VALUEB$(X)=ANNUALDESCRIP$(X-2)
17090 NEXT X
17100 REM SET ANNUAL SAVINGS OPTIONS' NAMES INTO VALUEB$ ARRAY
17110 FOR X=13 TO 18
17120 VALUEB$(X)=ANNUALDESCRIP$(X+3)
17130 NEXT X
17140 REM SET COSTS FROM INVESTMENT WORKSHEET INTO VALUEB$ ARRAY.  THIS REQIRES
FIRST CONVERTING THEM INTO STRING VARIABLES
17150 FOR X=19 TO 39
17160 VALUEB$(X)=MKS$(INVCOST(X-18))
17170 NEXT X
17180 REM SET COSTS FROM ANNUAL SAVINGS/COSTS WORKSHEET INTO VALUEB$ ARRAY.  THI
S REQIRES FIRST CONVERTING THEM INTO STRING VARIABLES
17190 FOR X=40 TO 63
17200 VALUEB$(X)=MKS$(ANNUALCOST(X-39))
17210 NEXT X
17220 REM SET TAX RATE FROM RETURN ON INVESTMENT WORKSHEET INTO VALUEB$ ARRAY.
THIS REQIRES FIRST CONVERTING IT INTO A STRING VARIABLE.
17230 VALUEB$(64)=MKS$(TAXRATE)
17240 REM SET INVESTMENT WORKSHEET STATUS CODES INTO VALUEB$ ARRAY
17250 FOR X=65 TO 85
17260 VALUEB$(X)=STATUS$(X-64)
17280 NEXT X
17300 REM OPEN FILE LASTBOT.DTA, LEFTSET STRINGS AND STORE ON DISK
17310 OPEN "LASTBOT.DTA" AS #3
17320 FIELD #3, 25 AS DA$
17330 FOR RECORD=1 TO 85
17340 LSET DA$=VALUEB$(RECORD)
17345 PUT #3,RECORD
17350 NEXT RECORD
17360 CLOSE
17370 RETURN
17371 POWER OFF
17372 INSERT DOS 1.1 DISK
17373 TURN POWER ON
17374 ENTER CURRENT DATE AND TIME
17375 AT PROMPT A>
17376 TYPE BASIC
17377 ENTER
17378 REMOVE DOS DISK
17379 INSERT ROBOTJUSTIFICATION DISK
17380 TYPE LOAD" ROBOT
17381 OK
17382 TYPE RUN (F2)
```

6

ROBOTS—A MANUFACTURING TOOL

THE ROLE OF MANUFACTURING

Robots are just one tool to improve America's competitiveness and productivity. As Joseph Engelberger, president of Transition Research Corporation, and former president of Unimation, has stated, "No one needs a robot," but America does need to improve its manufacturing operations. These improvements are based on the near-term need to be more competitive in world markets. An understanding of the U.S. history of manufacturing is important as a framework for the implementation of change, whether it is driven by robots, teamwork, data exchange standards, or computer-integrated manufacturing. The United States' productivity performance has improved as a result of implementing better manufacturing processes and tools, such as robots, but our historical analysis indicates that we must invest more in people, manufacturing processes, and tools. Without a longer-term manufacturing investment focus, the United States will fall behind our competitors in producing products and will become a second-rate producer, as we are fast becoming in consumer electronics and automobiles. This chapter provides an issues oriented review of manufacturing technology and the role robotics can play in improving our competitive position.

COMPETITIVE MANUFACTURING

Robots are one tool for enhanced productivity but should not be viewed as the total solution. We must understand the big picture in manufacturing and focus on the significant changes that can improve our competitiveness. This chapter provides a broad overview of new ideas in manufacturing and how these concepts will impact the work force and the utilization of robots in our industrial base.

For U.S. manufacturing, an extended period of world dominance in manufacturing innovation, process engineering, productivity, and market share has ended. Other countries have become leaders in certain industries, the U.S. market is being flooded by manufactured imports, and U.S. manufacturers are faced with relatively low levels of capacity utilization and declining employment. The reasons for this fundamental change are complex. Improved capabilities and competence of foreign manufacturers are partly responsible, and either government interference or the lack of government support has been blamed. Cultural disadvantages are often cited, and many economists explain the relative decline of U.S. manufacturing simply as economic evolution, with the United States moving toward a service economy. These and other factors have been held responsible for the relative decline of U.S. manufacturing, and all are legitimate partial explanations. The truth remains, however, that U.S. manufacturing is not performing as well as that of many foreign competitors and has lost competitiveness in many industries. Regardless of why the environment has changed, the managerial practices, strategies, and organizational designs applied by U.S. manufacturers have not adapted sufficiently to the changed competitive environment, and consequently U.S. manufacturing has not been as successful as that of other countries.

The term competitiveness is subject to a variety of definitions. In simplest form, an industry is competitive if the price, quality, and performance of its products equal or exceed that of competitors and provide the products demanded by customers. International competitiveness is somewhat more complicated because price is heavily influenced by exchange rates, which cannot be controlled by an individual producer. Many economists would claim that the recent high rate of the dollar has been responsible for any lost competitiveness of U.S. manufacturing, and recent adjustments to the dollar will restore competitiveness. This may or may not be true, however, because exchange rates are only one determinant of product price, and price is only one determinant of competitiveness. Price is also determined by production costs, and quality and performance, including innovation, unique or superior design, and reliability, are in many cases more important determinants of competitiveness than price. If U.S. manufacturers can produce (as shown in Fig. 6-1) high-quality goods with less labor, materials, overhead, and inventory than foreign producers, then competitive production can be ensured. These are the areas in which U.S. manufacturers have fallen behind—improvements in the use of these resources, as well as product quality and performance, are the requirements for improved competitiveness.

These changes in relative manufacturing strength are occurring at the same time that many technological innovations, such as robots, promise to revolutionize products and processes in manufacturing. Just as major technological breakthroughs spurred industrial development in the mid-eighteenth century (steam power and new engine-driven machinery) and the development of the modern factory system in the late nineteenth century (electricity, the telephone, and mass production techniques), current breakthroughs in robotics, electronics, materials, and communications are creating another revolution in manufacturing. Just as earlier changes forced new directions in manufacturing man-

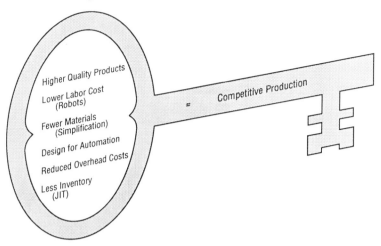

Figure 6-1 Keys to competitiveness.

agement, production strategies, and national policies for maximizing competitiveness, the competitive and technological changes affecting manufacturing today should create new goals, new priorities, and new expectations in U.S. industry. Many manufacturing managers and national policymakers, however, have been slow to recognize the implications of these developments. United States manufacturing is in danger of being unprepared to compete in the coming age, a failure that would cause rapid erosion of the nation's manufacturing base.

Effective response to the changes in manufacturing depends on a clear understanding of the new environment. Although specific developments are difficult to predict with certainty and the types of changes will vary tremendously among industries, likely trends can be identified. Competition will continue to increase both at home and abroad. New products will proliferate; many products will have shorter life cycles and development cycles. Some industries will have smaller production volumes, with more product customization and variety. New technologies, especially those based on microprocessors, will optimize control of the production process and offer entirely new capabilities. Fewer production workers and middle managers will be needed, but the remaining jobs will require higher skill, more technical knowledge, and greater responsibility. Managers will need to manage manufacturing as a system and base decisions on new, nontraditional factors. Direct labor costs will decrease significantly, and the costs of equipment, materials, distribution, energy, and other overhead will grow in importance. Quality, service, and reliability will receive much more emphasis as determinants of competitive production.

These trends indicate that competition, both international and domestic, will be more intense and that the factors determining competitiveness will differ substantially from past experience. Strategies and priorities designed to enhance competitiveness in the mid-twentieth century will be far less effective in the future. The new manufacturing environment will be sufficiently familiar to permit many firms to continue to use traditional approaches, but these firms will lose market share, profits, and the ability to compete. In the new environment, it will not be sufficient to do the same old things better. Companies will need to adopt new management techniques, organizational structures, and operational procedures to strengthen their international competitiveness. Government policies must also ensure that U.S. manufacturers receive the infrastructural support they will need to compete effectively.

HISTORICAL PERSPECTIVE ON UNITED STATES MANUFACTURING

For much of the twentieth century, U.S. manufacturers were unchallenged in an environment in which conservative approaches to both process technology and managerial techniques produced successful results. Foreign competition was minimal, the vast domestic market encouraged product standardization and economies of scale, and the preeminence of Yankee ingenuity was unchallenged. Companies modified strategies and processes in minor ways in response to shifting economic circumstances, but mostly the system worked and they had little incentive to change. The relative stability of the manufacturing environment was unsustainable, however; a series of changes has gradually converted the traditional strategies to handicaps.

One change has been in the way companies justify new investment in manufacturing. During the 1950s and 1960s, the emphasis in manufacturing was on providing substantial additional plant capacity that was needed just to keep up with market growth. The addition of capacity provided the opportunity to incorporate process improvements that otherwise were rarely implemented. Beginning in the early 1970s, the rate of growth slowed (Table 6-1), in many cases eliminating the need for additional capacity. Companies needed to develop new justifications for reinvestment in manufacturing, which many have been slow to do.

Another major change in the manufacturing environment was in the process of developing and implementing new innovations. The first Industrial Revolution in the 1800s produced a series of significant innovations in process and product technologies that represented an integration of several types of technologies. In contrast, during the early to mid-1900s, manufacturers, except perhaps electronics and chemical manufacturers, increasingly refined proven technologies rather than developing and integrating new and diverse technologies to

Table 6-1

Average Annual Percentage Changes in U.S. Manufacturing Output[a]

Period	Total	Durable goods	Nondurable goods	Percentage of total output [b] (average)
1950–1983	3.1	3.0	3.1	24.4
1950–1973	4.0	4.0	4.0	24.6
1973–1983	0.9	0.7	1.1	24.1
Slowdown	3.1	3.3	2.9	0.5

From: U.S. Bureau of Labor Statistics (1985).

[a] Gross product originating in manufacturing in constant dollars.

[b] Gross national product in constant dollars.

accomplish, or even eliminate, traditional tasks. This apparent trend toward a more stable, conservative approach to process technology in a broad range of U.S. industries combined with a variety of other factors—such as changing labor demographics, higher energy prices, and lower expenditures on research and development—to cause a shift toward more modest improvements in productivity. United States industries in which new technology did seem to offer great potential focused predominantly on product engineering at the expense of process engineering. (The semiconductor, chemical, and biotechnology industries are exceptions—most of the breakthroughs in their products depend on breakthroughs in process capabilities.) Since manufacturers had their hands full in simply adding capacity of a known type, they saw no pressing need to add new process technologies at the same time. Consequently, many U.S. firms spent incremental dollars on product technology and very little on new process technology. Generally speaking, U.S. manufacturers left process development to equipment suppliers and allowed their own skills at such development—and its link with product technologies and product quality—to decline.

CURRENT ROLE OF THE MANUFACTURING FUNCTION

These historic trends illustrate aspects of the manufacturing environment that have shaped the strategies of U.S. managers. For these and a variety of other reasons rooted in the history of industrial development, many managers have focused on increasing the productivity of the manufacturing function by emphasizing production volume instead of product quality and reliability and process development. They believe that manufacturing, at best, can simply provide adequate support for competitive advantages in marketing or design engineering. It is true that many firms, particularly those in the Fortune 500, do enjoy substantial advantages in manufacturing owing to economies of scale and degrees of specialization that they have been able to achieve as large organizations. Generally, however, the charge to manufacturing even in these companies has been "Make the product—without any surprises."

The traditional view in many U.S. firms is that manufacturing is a problem that can be solved with a given process at a given time. That process is then operated efficiently, with little incremental upgrading, until a significant improvement or new technology is implemented by competitors. This command-and-control view of manufacturing is based on the premise that smart people should be able to determine the optimal solution (process) for handling the tasks of the manufacturing function and then control the process and organization for maximum stability and efficiency until some external event forces change. Since the time between changes varies, the repercussions of this view may not be readily apparent. The key point is that it is a reactive view that overlooks the potential contributions of the manufacturing function to overall competitiveness.

Such an approach can erode the strength and competitive advantage provided by manufacturing. Quality, reliability, and delivery problems get blamed on manufacturing—the plan is assumed to be good, so the people in production must have failed to deliver. The organization increasingly refines the detailed measures of manufacturing by removing degrees of freedom. Scientific management techniques were developed to measure, predict, and control all the aspects of production in an effort to limit change, or at least eliminate surprises, and achieve maximum productivity. Advances in production planning, project evaluation, and operations research offered new tools for maintaining stability and increasing productivity. The introduction of computers and manufacturing information systems in the late 1960s and early 1970s was hailed as finally giving manufacturing a tool that could be used to pursue the command-and-control approach to operations. Although these detailed measurements and sophisticated control tools are designed to ensure stability in daily operations, too often they become ends in themselves and impediments to process changes.

The consequence of this approach to manufacturing has been increased tuning and refining of a set of resources that were outdated and increasingly inappropriate. The individual firm often slipped into a debilitating spiral: additional investment was withheld because the current investment was not performing as expected; those operating the current investment simply tried to minimize the problem in the near term rather than looking for long-term solutions they knew would not be approved and supported.

RECENT PERFORMANCE OF UNITED STATES MANUFACTURING

The repercussions of this command-and-control approach, with its reactive nature and short-term focus, are not difficult to find. The United States has experienced a steady erosion of competitiveness and overall manufacturing strength over the past two decades that must be attributed at least partly to deficiencies in standard management practices in manufacturing. Individual companies have adapted to the new environment and fared well, but overall the picture has been bleak. Declining growth trends in manufacturing output have already been cited. Other indicators include:

- Growth in manufacturing productivity (output per man-hour) in the United States during the past 25 years has been among the lowest in the industrial world (Table 6-2). Although manufacturing productivity in this country

Table 6-2
Output per Hour in Manufacturing (Average Annual Percentage Change)[a]

Country	1960–1973	1973–1983
Japan	10.5	6.8
France	6.5	4.6
West Germany	5.7	3.7
United Kingdom	4.3	2.4
Canada	4.7	1.8
United States	3.4	1.8

[a] From U.S. Bureau of Labor Statistics.

Table 6-3
Foreign Labor Cost Components in Relation to U.S. Producers[a]

Country	1970	1975	1980	1981	1982	1983	1984
		Average hourly compensation					
France	41	72	92	75	68	63	56
West Germany	56	97	125	97	90	85	75
Italy	42	73	81	68	63	62	58
Japan	24	48	57	57	49	50	50
Korea	N.A.[b]	6	11	10	10	10	10
United Kingdom	36	51	75	65	58	51	46
United States	100	100	100	100	100	100	100
		Output per hour					
France	65	70	82	81	85	86	87
West Germany	66	71	79	78	79	79	78
Italy	56	60	70	70	71	68	69
Japan	44	52	72	74	79	79	84
Korea	N.A.[b]	15	17	18	18	17	18
United Kingdom	41	43	42	43	44	45	44
United States	100	100	100	100	100	100	100
		Unit labor costs					
France	63	103	112	92	80	74	65
West Germany	85	136	157	123	114	107	95
Italy	75	123	115	96	89	91	84
Japan	53	92	79	77	62	63	60
Korea	N.A.[b]	39	63	57	59	60	56
United Kingdom	86	120	177	151	132	115	105
United States	100	100	100	100	100	100	100

[a] From Data Resources, Inc. (1985). U.S. dollar values based on average annual exchange rates.
[b] N.A. indicates data not available.

remains the world's highest, it has been virtually equaled in recent years by Japan, France, and West Germany. Based on average hourly compensation and output per hour, unit labor costs in U.S. manufacturing have been higher than those of our major competitors (Table 6-3).

- In contrast to the growth in manufacturing trade surpluses enjoyed by Japan and West Germany, U.S. performance over the past 15 years has been highly erratic, with significant deficits, as shown in Table 6-4.
- By 1984, manufacturing output was 8 percent above the previous peak in 1979. Defense production, however, accounted for more than 40 percent of that increase; nondefense output has risen less than 1 percent annually since 1979, compared with 3.5 percent annually from 1973 to 1979.
- Recent employment trends have been unfavorable in most durable goods manufacturing industries, particularly import-competing industries (Fig. 6-2).
- Capital investment as a percentage of output in U.S. manufacturing has increased slightly over the past 10 years (Table 6-5), but the composition of investment has tended to neglect traditional industries and new factory construction. Although U.S. manufacturing investment has shown some improvement, it has continued to be below that in other countries.
- A major reason for the level and types of investment in manufacturing, cited by other reports on U.S. manufacturing, is the high cost of invest-

Table 6-4
Trade Balance in Manufacturing (Billions of U.S.
Dollars)[a]

Year	United States	Japan	West Germany
1970	3.4	12.5	13.3
1971	0.0	17.1	15.0
1972	−4.0	20.3	17.7
1973	−0.3	23.3	28.7
1974	8.3	38.0	42.4
1975	19.9	41.7	38.7
1976	12.5	51.2	42.1
1977	3.6	63.0	46.9
1978	−5.8	74.2	53.5
1979	4.5	72.0	59.2
1980	18.8	93.7	63.1
1981	11.8	115.6	61.7
1982	−4.3	104.0	67.5
1983	−31.0	110.3	58.7
1984	−87.4	127.9	60.5
1985	−107.5	107.7	59.5

[a] From U.S. Department of Commerce, Bureau of Economic Analysis (1985), and International Trade Administration (1986).

ment capital. The cost of capital in this country is far higher than in other nations, and the return on manufacturing assets has not kept pace with the return on financial instruments (Table 6-6 and Fig. 6-3). In addition to the obvious impact this differential has on investment costs, lower capital costs and different sources of capital allow some foreign competitors to succeed with much lower rates of after-tax profit on sales than U.S. firms (1–2 percent versus 5–6 percent for U.S. firms). This difference effectively provides extra funds for capital investment or research and development expenditures.

There are a myriad of explanations for these troubling trends in U.S. manufacturing. Management, labor, and government all share responsibility. Macroeconomic factors such as domestic interest rates, exchange rates, the availability and cost of labor, foreign and domestic trade policies, and the constant seesaw of business cycles all have had an impact. Uncertainty about government spending, tax, and regulatory policies and changes in the relative attractiveness of nontechnological (even nonmanufacturing) investments have deterred risky investments in new process technologies and bred caution in managers. Pressure from stockholders, standard financial evaluation procedures, and the disruptive effect that new technology can have on short-term operational efficiency also have caused managers to give priority to maximizing returns on existing assets.

Because of the diversity of the manufacturing sector and the factors affecting manufacturing output and trade, there is little agreement among economists and policymakers that U.S. manufacturing is losing competitiveness. Some authors have used economic data to demonstrate that U.S. manufacturing remains generally strong despite the problems of a few industries. Many reports have addressed the issue by using macroeconomic data, but they have had little impact on either policymakers or the general public.

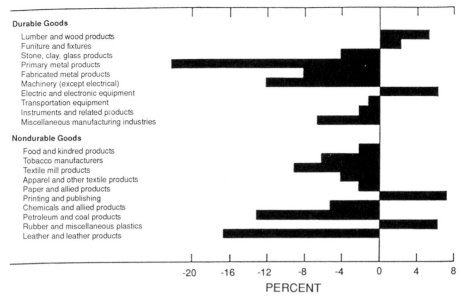

Figure 6-2 Change in manufacturing employment in selected industries from July 1981 to May 1984 (based on seasonally adjusted data for private manufacturing; includes only payroll employees). From U.S. Department of Labor, Bureau of Labor Statistics, establishment survey data (1985).

Table 6-5
Capital Investment as Percentage of Output[a] in Manufacturing for Selected Countries, 1965–1982[b]

Period	France	West Germany	Japan	United Kingdom	United States
1965–1982	15.1	12.8[c]	21.2	13.6	10.5
1965–1973	16.5	14.3	25.3	14.3	10.0
1974–1982	13.6	11.2[d]	17.1	13.0	11.1

[a] Fixed capital and output measured in constant dollars.
[b] From U.S. Bureau of Labor Statistics (1985).
[c] 1965–1981.
[d] 1974–1981.

Table 6-6
Average Weighted Cost of Capital to Industry, 1971–1981 (in percent)[a]

Country	1971	1976	1981
United States	10.0	11.3	16.6
France	8.5	9.4	14.3
West Germany	6.9	6.6	9.5
Japan	7.3	8.9	9.2

[a] From U.S. Department of Commerce, "Historical Comparison of Cost of Capital" (April 1983).

Figure 6-3 United States real return on manufacturing assets and industrial bond yield, 1960–1983. (From Quarterly Financial Reports of Mining, Manufacturing and Trade Corporations, Federal Trade Commission (1960–1961); Census Bureau (1981–1984); inflation data from Economic Report of the President (1984); Moody's Industrial Bond Yield from Survey of Current Business (July 1984); and Business Statistics (1979, 1982).)

Statistics on the manufacturing sector tend to be inconclusive because of the complex, transient economic factors that affect the data. Other indicators, however, show that at least some U.S. companies have perceived both eroding competitiveness and a basic change in the nature of the manufacturing environment. These data tend to be anecdotal and industry specific and can be illustrated by a few examples.

- Through improved management, changed work rules, large investments in automation, and a variety of other measures, the three major U.S. automobile manufacturers have reduced their break-even volume for domestic production by more than 30 percent since 1980. Despite this dramatic improvement, estimates of the cost advantage of Japanese producers have grown. Based on consumer surveys, U.S. cars also have lagged behind Japanese makes in perceived quality. United States producers have launched new projects—General Motors' Saturn, Chrysler's Liberty, and Ford's Alpha—to eliminate these gaps by rethinking management concepts, employee relations and compensation, and technology. All three companies also are aggressively pursuing joint ventures with foreign producers and captive imports of finished vehicles and parts from several countries to offset the cost disadvantage of domestic production. The companies' approaches differ, but these programs clearly indicate that senior managers in the U.S. automobile industry recognize both the shortcomings of traditional practices and the opportunities that new technologies, such as robotics, and new management approaches will provide. Although these efforts may solve current competition problems with Japan, in many cases they will not become operational until about 1995. By that time, other disadvantages and new competitors may have emerged that U.S. firms will be ill-equipped to address.

• Companies in other industries also have aggressively pursued a strong competitive position only to be confronted by intensified competition. Black and Decker Corporation, for example, has devoted significant effort to reducing costs and increasing efficiency by pursuing new investments, increasing automation, reducing its work force, and standardizing parts and product lines across its international operations. Despite these long-term efforts, the company faced growing competition in the world power tool market from Makita Electric Works, Ltd., of Japan and lost a significant part of its market share. Since 1980, Black and Decker has spent $80 million on plant modernization, cut its work force by 40 percent, and adopted new manufacturing practices. The company has regained a 20 percent share of the world market in power tools at the cost of reduced profits resulting from price pressures from the Japanese company. The efforts by Black and Decker indicate the kinds of commitment that are absolutely necessary to maintain a worldwide competitive position.

• The Japanese are not always the prime competitors. Chaparral Steel Company, a minimill operation based in Midlothian, Texas, figures that if it can produce steel at a labor cost per ton no higher than the per-ton cost of shipping steel to this country from Korea, it can out compete Korean producers. In achieving this goal, the company has invested in some of the most modern steel plants in the world and can produce steel using 1.8 man-hours per ton, compared with 2.3 for the Koreans and 6+ for integrated U.S. producers. Although its capacity and range of products are more focused than that of large integrated producers, Chaparral illustrates two important aspects of the new manufacturing environment. First, the company's experience (and that of other minimill operations, such as Nucor Corporation) has shown that U.S. producers can be world leaders and can pose more of a threat to traditional U.S. manufacturers, albeit in a relatively narrow product line, than foreign competitors. Second, traditional competitive targets, such as matching the production costs of competitors, may not be enough to ensure long-term competitiveness; other targets, such as the shipping costs used by Chaparral, may need to be considered.

• A final example comes from the computer disk drive industry. Floppy disk drives are used in lower-end home computers and personal computers, whereas rigid disk drives are used most often in advanced personal computers and engineering workstation products. The disk drive industry was created by U.S. electronics firms from technology developed by International Business Machines and Control Data Corporation. Several smaller firms entered the field in the mid-1970s and quickly grew to substantial size. In recent years, however, the status of U.S. disk drive manufacturers has changed considerably. The leading U.S. maker of floppy disk drives in 1980 was Shugart Associates. Xerox Corporation, the owner of Shugart, has since announced the closing of the unit as a disk drive manufacturer. In 1984, more than 20 Japanese firms manufactured floppy disk drives; no U.S. manufacturers did so. While the United States retains a strong position in rigid disk drives, the Japanese are likely to dominate the next-generation technology, which is optical disk drives. Developments in this industry show that being the first to market, even with high-technology products, is not a long-term advantage. Constant improvement in both products and processes is needed to ensure survival.

As these examples illustrate, pervasive and potentially damaging change is overtaking U.S. manufacturing across the spectrum of industries from traditional to "high tech." Industries as diverse as motorcycles, consumer electronics, and semiconductor memories also have been subject to lost leadership and declining market shares. Many firms recognize the change and are responding, though often in limited ways. Many more do not recognize the problem or think that it does not apply to them or their industries. Still others attribute their difficulties to the recent high value of the dollar and are looking forward to the benefits of the recent dollar depreciation.

Factors such as interest and exchange rates and unfair foreign competition do have significant effects on industrial health. Unfavorable trends in these areas, however, provide easy scapegoats and disguise other important factors that are changing the manufacturing world. A majority of U.S. manufacturers need to recognize that lowering the cost of the dollar in international currency markets, while important, will not solve all their competitive problems—the price elasticities of many important U.S. imports and exports will determine the long-term effect of the recent decline in the dollar. Although some U.S. commodity exports, such as timber, coal, and some agricultural goods, are likely to increase as the dollar declines, exports of capital goods and major imports of items such as machine tools, automobiles, and consumer electronics may change little as the dollar's value changes, at least in the near term. Many consumers continue to prefer foreign goods because of perceived quality and reliability advantages over their U.S. counterparts. Furthermore, many foreign companies in a range of industries have advantages in production costs that permit them to offset even unexpectedly large devaluations of the dollar by limiting price increases in the U.S. market.

More U.S. firms need to join the minority that recognize the challenges emerging in manufacturing and are devoting resources to meet them. Although competitive challenges are spreading to more and more products and industries, too few companies are making the essential commitment to competitive manufacturing operations in the United States. The rising competition from previously weak or nonexistent sources is prompting a response, but it is insufficient. The initial, and natural, reaction is to do everything better. Redoubled efforts are nearly always beneficial; it is a rare company that does not have room to improve. Doing things better than yesterday or better than competitors today, however, will not necessarily ensure long-term competitiveness.

Another response has been to move production facilities offshore, through foreign direct investment, outsourcing, joint ventures with foreign producers, or other mechanisms. While such arrangements have clear short-term advantages in terms of foreign market penetration and labor cost containment, the long-term repercussions of offshore production strategies are not clear. In some industries, firms must move constantly in search of even lower wage rates; in others, host countries insist on domestic content, technology transfers, and domestic equity positions that lead to independent, competitive production capabilities. Factors vary across industries, and some firms in labor-intensive industries may have no choice but to move production offshore or purchase components or products from abroad. As technological developments yield effective alternatives to offshore production and conditions for foreign direct investment become more stringent, a better understanding is needed about the effects of offshore production strategies on the long-term interests of individual firms and the domestic industrial base.

Another response from U.S. manufacturers has been based on the widely held idea that technology alone will solve the problem. Advanced manufacturing technology, such as robotics, can provide dramatic improvements in operations, but only if the groundwork is laid. The benefits of new technology will not be fully achieved if the organizational structure and decision-making process are not changed to take advantage of available system information, if the work force is not prepared for the changes brought by the technology, and if potential bottlenecks created by automating some operations but not others are not foreseen and avoided. Managers need to understand that technology is both a tool for responding to competitive challenges and a factor causing change in manufacturing.

Recent economic data and the experiences of specific industries suggest that a strong case can be made that U.S. manufacturers, with the exception of a handful of enlightened companies, are not responding adequately or entirely appropriately to new competitive challenges, even as those challenges intensify. The first corrective step is to convince managers that they face a manufacturing problem that new technology, offshore production, changes in exchange rates, and redoubled efforts cannot resolve. The next step is to indicate the kinds of changes in manufacturing organizations that will be needed to maintain competitiveness.

The changes needed can be described broadly as a shift from the traditional management goal of maximizing stability, productivity, and return on investment in the short term to the new goal of maximizing flexibility to a rapidly changing market, with long-term competitiveness as the first priority. A number of authors have detailed the changes that are necessary in the management of the manufacturing function. Robert Hayes and Steven Wheelwright, for example, describe the needed changes as a shift from an "externally neutral" role for the manufacturing function, in which the firm only seeks to match the process capabilities of its competitors, to an "externally supportive" role, in which process improvements are continually sought and implemented in an effort to maintain a lead over competitors, and manufacturing is viewed as a significant contributor to the firm's competitive advantage. This shift cannot be made overnight, and it is far too easy to backslide once a new plateau is reached. The shift requires changes in organizational structure and decision-making processes, and it demands new skills: managers must learn to manage change.

IMPACT ON UNITED
STATES ECONOMY

Because manufacturing remains crucial to national economic and defense interests, the repercussions of declining competitiveness could be devastating. Many economists argue that continued erosion of the domestic industrial base is limited because manufactured goods are the major component in international trade. The United States will remain a major manufacturer because world markets may not tolerate a constant large U.S. trade deficit. They believe that exchange rates will adjust to ensure that the United States can export manufactured goods. Alternatively, the United States will suffer a recession that will dampen demand for imports and alleviate the trade deficit. Recent historical evidence for this argument, however, is ambiguous at best: the United States managed only small surpluses in manufactured goods during the late 1970s, when the dollar was relatively weak, and had a small deficit in the recession year of 1982 (see Table 6-4). Particularly because exchange rates increasingly react more to financial flows than to flow of goods, the sustained process of devaluation of the dollar necessary to maintain the competitiveness of U.S. manufacturers would be difficult to accomplish.

Recessions and shifts in currency value can be painful ways for the nation to reach equilibrium in its manufacturing trade. An alternative is for U.S. manufacturers to implement the organizational, managerial, and technical changes necessary to maintain a strong manufacturing sector. Competitiveness would be based on leadership in product performance and quality rather than on a declining exchange rate. The resulting strength would provide the basis for continued economic growth and provide crucial advantages in areas of national importance, such as:

- Defense—Counter to conventional ideas that a strong industrial production base is necessary to meet U.S. defense commitments, some economists have argued that these commitments can be met without broad support for manufacturing. Although it may be possible to meet them through selective policies designed to support specific defense industrial production instead of entire industries, such an approach would be inadvisable for two major reasons. The first is that it would not provide the productive capacity needed for surges or mobilization in the event of a prolonged conventional military engagement. The second reason is that selective policies would hinder the ability of defense contractors to maintain broad technological superiority. This in turn would limit their flexibility in response to new defense needs. Production capacity and the technological level of weapons systems are closely linked. Advanced weapons that maintain the qualitative advantage built into the U.S. defense posture require complex manufacturing processes and advanced production equipment, which in turn require broad-based manufacturing capacity. Both the weapons and the production processes are most effectively developed and implemented in the broad context of a healthy manufacturing sector.
- Living standards—Although an absolute decline in the manufacturing base might be countered in the short term by growth in the service sector, services are unlikely to be able to absorb a large percentage of unemployed

manufacturing workers at their customary level of wages and benefits. Few economists disagree about the validity of projections of a shrinking middle class, but declining manufacturing employment would certainly have a large impact on total wage and benefit packages. The increased competition for jobs in services, as well as the likely increase in competition among firms in that sector, would moderate wage growth in services.

International competition in services also can be expected to intensify and moderate wage levels. Apart from the effect of this competition on wages, sufficient growth in services is not at all ensured because many services are tied to manufacturing; if manufacturing decays, these services will decline too. Furthermore, there is no guarantee that the United States can maintain a comparative advantage and large trade surplus in services that would be necessary to pay for manufactured goods. It is not at all clear that the nation's long-term economic strength lies in services or that potential strength in services is greater than its potential strength in manufacturing. Given these considerations, the extent to which services can absorb workers displaced from a declining manufacturing sector and drive overall economic growth remains in doubt.

A technologically advanced manufacturing sector also would result in displacement of workers, but in a competitive, dynamic economy that should be much more successful at creating new jobs. The development of new products, technologies, and support needs would create whole new industries with job opportunities that would be unlikely to develop in a stagnating manufacturing sector.

- National economic and political goals—In the domestic economy, regional concentration of manufacturing activity creates the potential for economic disruption from a declining manufacturing sector that would be disproportional to its share of the gross national product. The decline of whole communities dependent on a single factor is, of course, not a new phenomenon, but past experience has clearly shown that the necessary adjustments are difficult and costly. Services in those regions and communities tend to depend on manufacturing and are ill-equipped to provide employment and generate income in the face of a declining industrial infrastructure. The decline of U.S. manufacturing would have a severe adverse effect on these regions, and the national policies that would be necessary to support them would be politically difficult to enact. These patterns of regional strength and weakness serve to exacerbate the national economic dilemmas posed by a decline in U.S. manufacturing.

On an international scale, the sheer size of the domestic market is a major driver of economic development, competition, and continued advances as a growing number of foreign manufacturers compete for a share of the U.S. market. A declining ability of the United States to supply its own manufactured goods, however, would fundamentally change the relationship between this country and foreign manufacturers. Domestic companies would have less revenue and incentive to pursue strong research and development programs, leading to less innovation and invention and fewer patents. The lack of manufactured goods to trade and of manufacturing income to purchase foreign goods would reduce the bargaining position of U.S. producers and the attractiveness of the U.S. market.

These points illustrate the importance of a strong manufacturing sector and the danger of considering the demise of U.S. manufacturing in purely economic terms. Clearly, each individual industry need not survive, but manufacturing as an economic activity is too important to let decay. Changes in management, process technology, corporate organization, worker training, motivation and involvement, and government policies are necessary to ensure that resources continue to flow to manufacturing. Changing traditional ideas about education, the role of workers, investment in research, development, and innovation, and overall attitudes toward manufacturing will require input and active participation from a variety of sources. The transition will not be painless. Job displacement, plant closures, and changing industrial patterns will be the norm, as they always have been. But these events will take place in a dynamic economy and, therefore, will be accepted and resolved as smoothly as possible. The result will be a competitive manufacturing sector, far different from today's, that will be a leader in the new era in manufacturing.

WORLD CLASS COMPETITIVENESS

Worldwide robot sales passed the $1 billion mark in 1981 and are expected to top $5 billion in 1990. Worldwide production is increasing at a consistent rate, and the number of robots produced worldwide increased almost sevenfold between 1980 and 1985, with most of the increase taking place in Japan, which accounts for more than half of world robot production and use. The United States accounts for 13–15 percent of world production, and Western Europe makes up a third market of roughly the same magnitude as the United States.

Competition in world markets for sophisticated industrial robots is concentrated among Japan, the United States, Sweden, West Germany, France, the United Kingdom, and a few other European nations. Japan has by far the largest domestic robot production base, with a total of some 300 firms producing robots, 100 of them for in-house use only. There are approximately 50 firms in the United States producing robots; nearly the same number operate in Europe. On a worldwide basis the number of firms offering a robotic product for export is estimated to be on the order of 300 firms.

Trade in robots has grown at least as rapidly as the industry itself. The proliferation of international marketing agreements that characterize the world robot market has resulted in a rapid increase in international shipments of industrial robots and their parts. Since the U.S. market for industrial robots is the single largest market outside of Japan, a large proportion of these shipments have been absorbed by the United States, resulting in a surge in U.S. robot imports beginning in 1983. Most of these imports, as noted earlier, originate in Japan.

Japan established an early lead in the world robot market with some very basic hardware that has been upgraded over time into a relatively complex technology. Until recently, the emphasis in Japan has been to put in place, as quickly as possible, as many industrial robots as Japanese industry could be induced to absorb. This strategy caused the Japanese market for industrial robots to grow dramatically and has enabled Japanese firms to establish at least a 5-year lead over firms in other robot-producing countries in production of industrial robots. Japanese robotics firms export an average of 30 percent of their annual production.

The foreign sector plays a prominent role in European countries as well. Sweden exports 90 percent of its robot production, and has enjoyed a trade surplus in robots, as have Norway and Italy. France and the United Kingdom are net importers of robots.

COMPETITIVE ROBOTICS

A recent study by the Society of Manufacturing Engineers asked robot users to rank eight purchasing factors in order of their importance in their purchasing decisions. Robot cost was ranked as a critical factor by all purchasers, as were performance, design, and ease of maintenance. Foreign purchasers of U.S.-produced robots based their decision primarily on design and performance features, with the cost of the robot ranking behind these considerations. In contrast, U.S. buyers purchased foreign robots primarily because of their lower cost. Table 6-7 compares these rankings.

United States robot producers are at a disadvantage relative to foreign producers regarding the low end of the robot market, where cost is an important purchasing consideration. However, they are competitive with, or have an advantage over, foreign producers in the production of high-performance, multipurpose robots. Marketing and distribution networks and quality control considerations are also important competitive factors in the robot market.

Robot Costs

The price for a U.S.-produced robot can run as much as one-third to one-half more than the final sales price of a foreign robot of equal capacity. Part of this price differential is accounted for by relatively high U.S. production costs. The high domestic cost of capital has been a major disadvantage to U.S.-based producers. Costs of capital to U.S. producers rose substantially in

Table 6-7
Buyer Rankings of Robotic Purchasing Factors[a]

Factors	Foreign buyers of U.S. robots	U.S. buyers of foreign robots
Design	1	3
Performance	2	2
Cost	3	1
Maintenance	4	4
Warranties	5	6
Financial terms	6	7
Delivery terms	7	5
Other	8	8

[a] From *Industrial Robots, Forecasts and Trends, Delphi Study.* Society of Manufacturing Engineers, The University of Michigan (1985).

1981 and 1982, relative both to previous levels in the United States and to the level in other countries. The situation has improved somewhat in the past years; real U.S. interest rates have declined fairly steadily since 1984. Capital costs still place U.S. producers at a disadvantage relative to robot producers in Japan, but the difference is much less than it was in 1982, when U.S. interest rates were at their peak.

A second reason for the price differential between foreign and domestically produced robots is the fact that production in the United States has never reached a level where economies of scale create substantial cost savings, as is the case for Japanese firms. Many U.S. suppliers have focused their development and marketing efforts on low-volume systems with a high engineering content, or on systems integration—both high-cost areas of the overall robot market.

Virtually all the high-volume orders for industrial robots worldwide come from the automotive industries in the United States, Europe, and Japan. Japanese robotics firms dominate in this world market segment, specifically in the areas of spot welding and finishing/coating robots. Prices are generally declining in these market segments, in large part because of the cost advantages that Japanese firms enjoy because of their high production volume relative to U.S. and European robotics firms.

Finally, some of the price difference between the average U.S.-produced robot and its Japanese competitor can be traced to the difference in complexity of the robot mechanism itself. A large proportion of Japanese robots currently sold in foreign markets were originally developed for in-house use by Japanese manufacturers. These robots are intended for a comparatively narrow range of applications and are generally less sophisticated—and less expensive—than U.S.-produced robots. Overall, the special-purpose mechanisms and manipulators favored by Japanese robot producers are less expensive to produce than the general-purpose mechanisms on which many U.S. robotics firms have focused their development and marketing efforts.

Since early 1985, it has been difficult to interpret the effect of the decline of the dollar on U.S. robotics firms. The dollar has depreciated by nearly 40 percent against the Japanese yen, a change that should have stimulated a decline in the price of U.S.-produced robots relative to those produced in Japan. However, major U.S. robotics firms depend to a substantial extent on imports from Japan of basic robot mechanisms, to which they add various accessories and peripherals that enhance the mechanism's capabilities. The depreciation of the dollar against the yen could increase the price of these imports, with a negative effect on final U.S. prices.

Performance Features

In the early stages of the development of the world robot market, the tendency of U.S. producers to focus on technically complex, high-performance robots worked to their disadvantage, both in the domestic market and overseas. Early generations of U.S.-produced robots were typically complex in design, expensive, and required frequent maintenance. In contrast, robots being produced in Japan and Europe were mechanically simpler, less expensive, and therefore easier for users to justify as capital expenditure items. These robots appealed to a much wider range of potential users than the more sophisticated U.S.-developed robots.

As robot users become more sophisticated, and robot applications expand into assembly and material-handling operations, a growing market for high-performance robots has developed. United States firms have an advantage over foreign producers in the production of high-performance robots with substantial value-added peripherals and accessories. The total installed cost of an advanced robot with integrated process control, vision and sensor interaction, and communications capabilities is often lower than that of a simpler robot in cases where manufacturing requirements vary substantially depending on the product in production. In the short run, however, this product and system focus incurs high costs—in research and development, in marketing, and in the extensive customer support services that must accompany custom installations of robot systems.

Marketing and Distribution

The single most striking characteristic of the international robot market is the extent and variety of cooperative arrangements between robot-producing firms of different nationalities. These arrangements run the gamut from marketing accords to licensing agreements to full-fledged joint ventures. Many of these arrangements involve pairings of U.S. and Japanese or U.S. and European firms. They have provided Japanese and European firms with unprecedented access to the U.S. market, but have not afforded U.S. firms equivalent benefits in foreign markets. Figure 6-4 outlines the range of technology, marketing, and other agreements characteristic of the robotics industry.

Japanese robotics firms are involved in over 100 international agreements in 13 nations. Nearly 70 percent of these agreements are marketing/sales agreements, which have given Japanese firms quick access to foreign markets with immediate sales and service support. Japanese firms are involved in comparatively few joint venture or parent/subsidiary relationships with foreign firms. The major joint venture between a Japanese and a foreign firm is GMF. There has been virtually no penetration of the domestic Japanese market by foreign firms, even those operating jointly with Japanese firms.

In contrast to the Japanese approach to international agreements in robotics, nearly 70 percent of the arrangements formed by U.S. firms are either parent/subsidiary arrangements or joint ventures. The balance are licensing agreements—either manufacturing/sales or marketing/sales arrangements. The majority of these agreements involve U.S. firms operating in their home market, as opposed to overseas. Selected U.S. manufacturers have established themselves in the European market through these types of arrangements.

Quality Control

From a technical standpoint there is little quality difference among robots manufactured by the major supplier countries. Robotics technology has spread rapidly internationally, and the major suppliers in Europe, Japan, and the United States have established product lines of relatively equal quality. However, Japanese producers do have an advantage over other robot producers in applications testing of their robots, because of their large internal robot market. Many of the robots marketed by Japanese firms were first developed for in-house use, and robot manufacturers' factories still serve as extensive testing beds for robot development. Emphasis is placed on reliability and predictability

GMF Robotics Corporation. Joint venture between General Motors Corporation and Fanuc Limited of Japan.

Domestic Production → Painting robot
Offshore Arrangement ← The remaning product line is manufactured by Fanuc, Japan, with significant value added domestically.

Cincinnati Milacron
Domestic Production   Entire product line
→ Cincinnati; Japan
→ Cincinnati; Europe; Austrian plastic plant
← Japanese firm, will operate as OEM for new product line.

Automatix
Domestic Production   None
Offshore Arrangements
← Marketing and sales, Hitachi Ltd., Japan
← Marketing and sales, KUKA, W. Germany
← Marketing and sales Hirata, Japan
← Marketing and sales Yaskawa, Japan

DeVilbiss
Domestic Production   Paint-spray robot
← Marketing and sales, American Cimflex
Offshore Arrangements ← Licenses, manufacturing, and sales, Trallfa, Norway (ASEA)
← Matsushita, Japan

ASEA   Assembly and some machining in United States; reports 50 percent U.S. content
Domestic Production
Offshore Arrangement ← Parent company, ASEA Robotics, Sweden, controls holdings of U.S. subsidiary

IBM
Domestic Production   One prototype of assembly robot
Offshore Arrangements ← Licenses, manufacturing, and sales, Sankyo Seiki, Japan
↔ Joint Venture, Selenia, Elsag Spa, Italy
→ Licensing agreement, Thorn EMI, U.K.

General Electric
Offshore Arrangement ← Licenses, manufacturing, and sales, Hitachi Ltd., Japan
← Marketing and sales, Nachi Fuji Koshi, Japan

Prab Robots Inc.
Domestic Production   Produces a limited domestic product line
Offshore Arrangements → Licenses, manufacturing, and sales, Canadian English Company, Canada
→ Licenses, manufacturing, and sales, Murata Machinery, Japan
→ Licenses, manufacturing, and sales, Fabrique Nationale, Belgium
→ Licenses, manufacturing, and sales, EKE, Finland
→ Recent arrangement with ASEA, Sweden

Cimflex Tecknowledge Corporation   Entire product line; also has and arrangement with
Domestic Production   DeVilbiss for marketing paint-spray units
Offshore Arrangements → Licenses, manufacturing, and sales, Daikin Industries, Japan
→ Licenses, manufacturing, and sales, Rediffusion Robots, LTM, United Kingdom

Adept Technologies Inc. ← Joint venture, Westinghouse, purchased 15 percent 1984, $1.5 million.
Domestic Production ← Joint venture, Cummins Engine Co., 1984, $1.6 million.
Offshore Arrangement ← Arrangement with Kawasaki, Japan

Graco Robotics
Domestic Production   Paint spray
Offshore arrangement   None

Figure 6-4 Domestic production and offshore arrangements of major U.S. robot suppliers. Arrow direction indicates flow of hardware or technology.

in robot motion. Japanse firms have a large base of experience in both robot production and use, experience that assists them in their quality control efforts. This is most evident in arc welding and coating/finishing robots, where Japanese-built robots have a better reputation than their U.S.-built counterparts.

Quality control has been more difficult for U.S.-based robot producers. All the U.S. auto producers have been plagued by problems with inadequate robot load capacity, failures in robot mechanisms, or at the very least robots that do not perform as expected. Part of the problem stems from the fact that the U.S. robotics industry has no standard measure of basic robot operational characteristics such as speed or repeatability. This leaves users open to the risk that the robots that they purchase will require extensive debugging prior to implementation. This inherent risk explains the preference that many U.S. users have for retaining the services of a systems integrator, whose responsibility it is to provide an operational robot system customized for a particular user's needs.

The inclination of new robot users to rely on firms with systems integration capabilities may work to the advantage of U.S. robot producers as robotics spreads outside of its conventional circle of end-users—the automotive, aerospace, and electronics industries. Some domestic producers have already restructured their operations to include turnkey and systems integration services. Other U.S. robot producers are selling their robots to third-party systems integrators. In the worldwide competitive marketplace, robots have become an effective manufacturing tool to provide flexibility, enhanced quality, and reduced labor for the industrial base.

7

ROBOTS AND PEOPLE

IMPACT OF ROBOTICS

It is important to understand that robots by themselves will not solve our manufacturing problems. The impact of people and organizational issues will provide far more productivity enhancement than the installation of a robot. Therefore, this chapter provides a review of the significant interface issues involved in the enhanced operation of our manufacturing organizations in which robots will be utilized as part of the system solution.

This chapter will provide an awareness of the impact of robots on people and vice versa. We will discuss key issues, including our responsiveness to technological change, flexibility as a tool for market domination, concern regarding quality improvement and cost reduction, how people can function effectively in organizations, the major impact of teamwork in changing the way we work, employment security issues and incentives, and their potential impact on jobs today and tomorrow.

Responsiveness to Technological Change

An organization's response to change varies with specific circumstances, such as the structure of the industry, the relations with the work force, the particular product line, the market in which the product is sold, and the firm's competitive emphasis. Because of the many permutations of external factors and possible responses, the important requirement is not a strategy for every contingency but the ability to pursue a range of strategies aimed at particular combinations of circumstances. Much improvement in responsiveness can be achieved by reevaluating the company's operations, particularly in design, engineering, and manufacturing, to determine handicaps, improve functional cooperation, enhance teamwork, and strengthen common goals. Cooperation and even integration of the many functions in the entire manufacturing system will need to be pursued aggressively to achieve many of the necessary improvements in productivity, quality, and responsiveness. In the future, these efforts will be strengthened by the capabilities embodied in advanced manufacturing technologies, such as robotics. When combined with effective organizational changes, advanced manufacturing technologies will be powerful tools for achieving enhanced responsiveness to many external factors that affect design and production.

The technologies that can help maximize responsiveness, such as robotics, will vary among firms and product types, and an enormous amount of tailoring will be involved. A major consideration will be the degree to which the firms' competitive strategy depends on price leadership or product differentiation. A low-price strategy implies the ability to offer the combination of performance and quality demanded by customers at the lowest possible price, yet still respond to demand changes, variations in input availability and relative costs, and changes in competitors' capabilities. A product differentiation strategy, on the other hand, aims to supply a range of price and performance options that covers most consumer demands. A firm with a low-price strategy may benefit more from improved production, material handling, and inspection technologies, whereas a product differentiation strategy may demand more emphasis on robotics, computer-aided design, flexible manufacturing systems, and new materials and processing techniques.

Manufacturers in the future are likely to find that the flexibility provided by robots is a necessary competitive advantage. Application of robotics will introduce new bases for competition and may change the economic environment in many industries. Competition will be based on management and labor skills, organizational effectiveness, the price and quality of the final product, speed of delivery, and serviceability of the design, including appropriateness of materials used, functionality, ease of repair, and longevity. Since robot technology is readily available, market success will depend on proprietary refinements to the robot system and how well it is used. The manufacturer who can use robots not only to respond quickly to new manufacturing requirements but also to minimize total labor resource requirements will have a competitive edge.

Flexibility

Responsiveness, as discussed here, refers to a manufacturer's ability to react quickly to changes in external conditions; flexibility is really an extension of that concept to internal factors. In fact, one can distinguish several types of flexibility:

- Process flexibility is the ability to adapt processes to produce different products without major investments in machines or tooling for each product. This type of flexibility is the cornerstone of robot applications that allow optimal matching of materials to product applications, the ability to use various materials, and the ability to produce a variety of product designs.
- Program flexibility allows process path modifications, adaptive control and self-correction, unattended operations, and backup capabilities to maintain production even when some part of the process fails. This type of flexibility addresses the need to optimize equipment use and run multiple workshifts (some unattended).
- Price–volume flexibility provides the ability to maintain economic production in a wide range of market conditions resulting from cyclical and

seasonal changes in demand. (This type of flexibility concerns external circumstances, but the firms' internal flexibility will determine the success of the response.)

• Innovation flexibility refers to the ability to implement new technologies as they become available. This type of flexibility depends on a modular approach to manufacturing systems integration that is essential to an evolving design and process capability.

Manufacturers have always confronted the problems these various types of flexibility address and to solve them have relied on compromises between production capabilities and costs. The costs of increased flexibility traditionally have included higher inventory, increased tooling and fixturing requirements, lower machine utilization, and increased labor costs. By reducing some of these costs through robotics, simplified product designs, streamlined organization, better functional cooperation, just-in-time inventory control systems, material requirement planning, and other mechanisms, future manufacturers have the opportunity to reduce the need for many of the traditional cost–flexibility compromises. Cost–flexibility trade-offs will always exist, however, and the advantages of specific technologies will vary tremendously among industries and product lines.

For many mass production industries, conventional hard automation will remain the most efficient production process. Hard automation—that is, transfer machine lines—is relatively inflexible; it is generally product specific. Advances in design capabilities, sensors, materials, robotics, material-handling systems, and automated inspection technologies should introduce a degree of flexibility into these operations, but efficient production will still tend to depend on economies of scale and product standardization. For traditional batch part manufacturers, flexible automation technologies will change many of the historic cost–flexibility compromises. In some applications, manufacturing facilities with flexible fixtures can be expected to reduce setup times to near zero, allowing smaller and smaller lots produced on demand to become both economically feasible and competitively necessary. In other applications, group technology, designing for producibility, and efforts to speed changeovers will increase flexibility at less cost and with greater effectiveness than elaborate installations.

Although the flexibility of the process equipment on the factory floor will differ between mass producers and batch manufacturers, both will benefit from the flexibility embodied in new manufacturing systems. The ability to gather and manipulate data in real time as orders are received and products are made will provide a degree of control over the manufacturing process that has not been possible in the past. It is in this context that the issues and benefits of flexibility become particularly relevant to a competitive production strategy.

No manufacturer could afford and no technology could provide infinite flexibility, and increasing investments in advanced technologies will not necessarily correlate with increasing flexibility in production. As an extreme example, a machine shop using manual machine tools and expert craftsmen may be more flexible in producing a broad range of parts and may be better able to improvise to produce prototypes than a more modern machine shop using numerical control (NC) machine tools. The manual shop, however, is likely to be less cost-effective and slower, have more scrap and rework, and, most importantly, be ill prepared to take advantage of other computer-based technologies that could improve control over and the effectiveness of the total production process. The NC shop may have a narrower product line, but it is likely to have quicker response times, more consistent tolerances, better repeatability, and greater ability to integrate other computer-based technologies, such as CAD, and use them effectively. Strictly from a production perspective, the manual shop could be described as more flexible, but from a total operations perspective, the NC shop is more flexible. Its potential for introducing new design and production technologies, particularly enhanced data-handling capabilities, is incomparably greater than that of the manual shop. Neither approach is indisputably correct, however; each is based on value judgments and trade-offs made by the owners in response to their circumstances. This example, although extreme, illustrates the unavoidable cost–capability compromises that will always be confronted in the pursuit of greater production flexibility.

Determination of an optimal level of flexibility for a given plant must include not only the cost effects of different ranges of product mix and quality relative to production capacity, but also the cost effects of fluctuations in demand. The greater the investment in production facilities and the associated fixed costs, the higher the break-even rate of capacity utilization. Consequently, cost savings expected from more capital-intensive production systems at high levels of utilization must be balanced against higher average unit costs as seasonal and cyclical fluctuations reduce average capacity utilization. This dilemma involves price–volume flexibility, but the lesson is applicable to all four types of flexibility. Significant planning is required to achieve optimum flexibility; ad hoc programs and investments will be counterproductive.

Although cost–flexibility compromises will continue to apply, the basic flexibility provided by new technology will be much greater than with current NC machining and turning centers. Effective implementation of these technologies will require adjustments from managers, engineers, and customers. The trade-offs between cost and flexibility will also vary among industries and products. Advanced systems will not be infinitely flexible because flexibility will depend on management practices and organizational effectiveness, as well as software, tooling, and material availability. In general, however, both mass production and batch manufacturing industries that can take advantage of advanced manufacturing technologies, such as robotics, can expect a degree of flexibility unknown in the past, with benefits in responsiveness, competitiveness, and total production costs that outweigh the cost of the technology itself.

Cost and Quality

Advanced manufacturing technologies will give managers new tools to help them minimize use of total resources and thereby reduce product life cycle costs. Whether competitive strategy emphasizes low price or product differentiation, price competition in the future is likely to be severe. Reducing life cycle costs and maximizing quality for every product line will be an important determinant of competitiveness and profitability. Cost minimization must not be pursued, however, at the expense of responsiveness and flexibility, as many manufacturers may be tempted to do. The best way to avoid overemphasis on costs is to think in terms of minimizing use of total resources, not only in production but also in purchasing, design, distribution, finance, marketing, and service. Nevertheless, the attention given to individual production factors will continue to depend to a great extent on relative factor costs and the shifting importance of factors in particular industries.

Because new manufacturing technologies will be developed and implemented at various rates, the effect of technology on relative factor costs is difficult to predict. For some manufacturers, new robot technology is likely to have only a limited effect on direct labor costs and, indeed, will be applied for reasons other than labor savings. The potential savings from low labor rates abroad would need to be balanced against the costs of coordinating demand, production, and delivery. Timely production and delivery will be important in avoiding loss of orders and inventory costs that may not be faced by competitors. These factors will require manufacturers with offshore facilities to use significant forward planning to align production with demand. Advanced technologies will allow manufacturers to handle data in ways that should help to ameliorate the disadvantages of offshore operations, but these gains may not be sufficient to offset the transportation costs, delays, and relative isolation entailed by distant production facilities.

For many manufacturers, advanced technology can be expected to allow more rapid reduction of direct labor inputs, although again, labor savings may not be the major motivation for the investments. It also will introduce entirely new elements to the manufacturer's cost structure, alter traditional ways of measuring costs, and eliminate some major portions of traditional factory costs. It will be possible, for example, to reduce direct labor to insignificant levels or eliminate it in some applications. With no direct labor inputs, some measurements of labor productivity and cost allocation based on direct labor will be irrelevant. New cost accounting systems will be a major need.

Elimination of direct labor is not the same as eliminating labor costs. Technicians, engineers, and programmers will be needed in increasing numbers to maintain and implement robot systems. Salaries for these employees are likely to exceed wages for direct labor, and their productivity may be more difficult to measure. Even with higher individual salaries, however, labor costs should decline as a share of total production costs because of the capital investments required to keep a robot system up-to-date.

It is difficult to predict the effects of investments in new technology on capital costs as a proportion of total costs. Firms will need to monitor the production capabilities of their competitors, as well as those demanded by the market; timely updates of the design and production system will be a competitive necessity. Greater return can be expected and less total capacity may be needed, however, because robotics is expected to allow more workshifts and more optimal use of productive equipment through flexible process plans, less scrap and rework, higher-quality production, and lower product life cycle costs. Justification and amortization of technology purchases should be based on total system performance, which implies a significant shift in the measurement and allocation of capital costs.

Developments in new materials and material processing will have a significant impact on material costs and availability, especially vis-à-vis product performance and quality. Advanced material-handling systems should have a major effect on the costs of moving and storing materials. New materials such as high-temperature ceramic superconductors, high-strength resins, composites, and ceramics will create new options in product development, providing significant improvements in performance while reducing material requirements. Ceramic engine parts, for example, are under development by virtually all major combustion engine manufacturers and will allow simplified engine design and fewer total parts. Once the material and processing problems are overcome, the effects on material costs and requirements will be substantial. Similar effects can be expected with other materials and applications. Even with more traditional materials (e.g., metals), progress in ultraprecision machining will reduce material requirements and improve product performance.

There is some evidence that, as a result of responsiveness, flexibility, and quality concerns, future trends in factory locations, particularly for component manufacturers, will be toward a proliferation of smaller factories closer to final markets and greater use of contiguous manufacturing, in which progressive manufacturing operations are located in close proximity to each other. New technologies will make both of these strategies easier to pursue for many industries, and market demands may make them a necessity. For some industries, the concept of the microfactory will become important: small factories, highly automated and with a specialized, narrow product focus, would be built near major markets for quick response to changing demand. Because of the unique circumstances of each industry, in terms of technology availability, labor requirements, cost structures, and competitive circumstances, it is difficult to predict how strong each of these trends will be, but they are representative of new options available to manufacturers in their efforts to maximize competitiveness.

All of these considerations imply that manufacturers will have a very different cost structure in the future than they have today. The most important factor in improving responsiveness, flexibility, costs, and quality will be the effectiveness of management practices, organizational design, and decision-making criteria. As the capabilities and advantages of new manufacturing technologies progress, they will become increasingly important to managers' future strategies for improving competitiveness. Changes and adjustments to the manufacturing system will be based on each company's market situation, product line, and customer base, so many of these capabilities will be internally developed and proprietary. Along with the management aspects of the manufacturing organization, they will determine competitive advantage in the manufacturing environment of the future.

This view of manufacturing technology is very different from the traditional technical view. Robots and advanced manufacturing technologies are not going to solve all the problems of production. Instead, they will give managers many more options. Managers will have an even greater need to focus the goals of the firm and then assess the needs of the manufacturing function and how technology can best address them. Once choices are made, managers will not have the luxury of running the technology for long periods while they focus on product design, marketing, or some other function to maintain a competitive position. Dynamic, continuous, day-by-day improvement of manufacturing capabilities will become essential to long-term success.

People and Organizations

The competitive market pressures and technological capabilities of robots discussed in this book are two dimensions of the changes that can be expected in the future manufacturing environment. This chapter also addresses changes in the management of people and organizational design that future manufacturers will need to pursue to be successful. Such changes can strengthen the competitiveness of many companies regardless of the technology employed, and in virtually every case, modifications in both the internal and external relationships of the business are a prerequisite to effective use of new technology.

The changes needed in people and organizations will be a difficult aspect of the revolution in manufacturing. They require a dramatic refocus of the traditional culture in the factory, away from hierarchical, adversarial relations and toward cooperative sharing of responsibilities. With such fundamental changes, progress will be slow, the degree of change will vary among companies, and the full transition is likely to be accomplished by a relatively small number of companies. However, the demands placed on manufacturers to be effective in an increasingly competitive marketplace can be expected to push managers and workers in the directions described in this chapter.

Much depends on the size and culture of the firm and the commitment of managers and workers. Many manufacturing enterprises need changes not only in broad organizational areas and management philosophy but also in employee behavior, union policies, and customer and supplier relations. Every stakeholder—managers, employees, owners, suppliers, and customers—must recognize the challenge and be prepared to change traditional practices. Furthermore, people who may not have a direct stake in manufacturing—government officials, educators, researchers and scientists, and the general public—will need to understand the importance of manufacturing to future prosperity, recognize the evolving role of manufacturing in the U.S. economy, and support the many social and cultural changes that will both result from and encourage continued progress in U.S. manufacturing.

The Team Approach

Part of the problem with U.S. manufacturing is that the common definition has been too narrow. Manufacturing is not limited to the material transformations performed in the factory. It requires a team encompassing design, engineering, purchasing, quality control, marketing, and customer service as well as material transformation; the operations of subcontractors and the whims of customers are also important parts of the system. The team approach is a key principle not only for manufacturing technology but also for organizational structure, supplier relations, and human resource management. Such a concept has been foreign to most U.S. managers (although embraced by Japanese managers), and the result has been a lack of responsiveness and declining competitiveness in many industries. Managing manufacturing as a unified system will profoundly affect every activity involved; it is the only way to take advantage of the many opportunities in both products and processes that the future will bring.

An aggressive team approach in a company should eliminate many of the functional distinctions that can introduce inefficiencies into the production process. Instead of the labyrinth of functional departments that is common in many firms, the operations function is likely to become the focus. Ancillary and supportive functions will be reintegrated into operations. Maintenance and process design, for example, will no longer be distinct entities with separate schedules and staffs; instead, employees in operations will be responsible for maintaining equipment or modifying the process as the need arises. Such reintegration will mean that management structures are likely to be more streamlined and that many job classifications will be eliminated to allow employees to perform multiple tasks. Job design and classification will be based on broad operational functions rather than narrowly defined activities.

Functions such as product design, manufacturing, purchasing, marketing, accounting, and distribution will require close cooperation and tight coordination. Eliminating them as separate departments would be impractical—the various types of expertise will still be needed—but, with increasing computerization and communication capabilities, information on each area will be widely available and close teamwork will be essential. This cooperation may often be accomplished through working groups of people from different departments. They will include permanent groups to ensure long-term integration of ideas and temporary groups designed to address specific projects. Techniques such as comprehensive job rotation may be used to eliminate interdepartmental barriers. The process of integrating the data bases and process technologies in the factory also will help to eliminate artificial barriers between functions, but the major tools for change will be the guidance of senior managers and the initiatives of employees.

In external relations, a systems concept calls for reassessment of the mechanisms used to specify, order, manufacture, and deliver subcontracted parts. Because production by suppliers will be viewed as the initial step in the manufacturing system, major customers will need to take a strong interest in the capabilities of their suppliers and institute programs to raise those capabilities through gentle persuasion, direct assistance, or reselection. As an example of the changes that can be expected, customers' design equipment will be able to communicate directly with suppliers' production equipment. Substantial investments will be made in communication linkages to allow extensive sharing of data on design, production scheduling, material requirements planning, costs, and training.

These types of arrangements will be essential for flexible management of the manufacturing system, but they imply significant change in supplier relations. More subcontracts will be for longer terms, and the number of captive shops supplying one customer can be expected to increase substantially. The investment in communication links by the customer and the corresponding investment that the customer will expect of the supplier will make long-term contracting desirable for both parties. Since long-term contracts weaken the threat of changing suppliers if standards are not met, a strong commitment to close cooperation will be a necessity. Problems will need to be solved as they arise, just as with in-house production, because the cost of failed relationships will be high. Both parties will lose independence in the subcontracting process, but the advantages of an integrated, highly efficient manufacturing system will outweigh the costs.

Participation and Ownership

A key step in the evolution of human resource management in manufacturing will be to broaden participation in the company's decision-making process. Employees at all levels should be given an opportunity to contribute ideas, make decisions, and implement them in areas that may affect operations beyond the individual's formal responsibilities. The principle involved is intellectual ownership: if all employees can feel a degree of ownership in decisions that affect them and the company, they are likely to support those decisions more enthusi-astically, resulting in a highly motivated work force and a more responsive, effective company. Extensive, even universal, participation in decision making gives all employees a stake in the company, beyond financial considerations, that may be essential for continued competitiveness in a rapidly changing envi-ronment.

For most manufacturers, such a decentralized decision-making process will require a major cultural shift and a number of prerequisites to avoid disorder. The most fundamental requirement is a well-understood, common set of goals and a high level of commitment to them from both managers and employees. Beyond that, both management and labor must meet certain responsibilities.

Management cannot expect employees to contribute ideas and participate in decision making without the necessary knowledge and expertise. Vehicles will be needed to facilitate the rapid flow of information within the organization and to ensure that the proper intellectual resources are available at all levels. Close links between upper management and operatives on the factory floor will be required for rapid information exchange and responsiveness. Information must flow both upward and downward in the organization. Employees must under-stand fully the goals and priorities of the firm to make consistent, effective decisions. Managers need to be assured that the correct decisions are being made. This type of cooperative, two-way exchange represents a radical shift for many firms that may cause significant cultural disruptions.

Information linkages are currently provided by several layers of middle management that serve primarily as an information conduit. With decision-making responsibility pushed to the lowest possible level, the extra layers of middle management are likely to be both unnecessary and unaffordable. The result in most cases probably will not be mass layoffs of middle managers; instead, the change will become manifest as a gradual blurring of the distinctions between operatives and managers. Middle managers will be reduced in number and merged into new roles that allow direct access between upper management and floor workers. Knowledge requirements, authority, and responsibility will tend to converge, resulting in much flatter organizations. This fundamental change in organizational structure already is happening in a number of com-panies.

Progress in factory communications technology also can be expected to facilitate information flows and contribute to the elimination of management layers. Wide, if not universal, access to all types of information, from part designs and scheduling to accounting data and marketing plans, will reduce the need for personal exchanges of information. Both upper managers and opera-tives will have direct access to the information needed to make effective deci-sions. With the process of flattening the organizational structure and creating direct communication channels between operatives and upper management well under way, advanced data-tracking and communications systems will be far more effective. Without the efficiencies introduced by wide participation and shared responsibility, a manufacturer might be overwhelmed by the volume of information provided by the new technologies. As with most aspects of the new manufacturing environment, organizational and technological changes comple-ment each other and cannot be separated without tremendous costs in corporate effectiveness.

Effective decision making depends on trained personnel. Employees not only must be competent in their own jobs, but also must understand the relation-ship of their jobs to overall corporate operations and goals. Developing the required knowledge will require extensive training by a variety of mechanisms and a significant amount of job rotation at every level of employment. As new technology is implemented, substantial training can be expected from equip-ment vendors, but the broader scope of job responsibilities is likely to require off-site classroom courses, companywide seminars, and on-the-job training. Training will need to be extended to every employee as a corporate necessity, and it will account for a much higher percentage of working time and total costs than it has traditionally. Job rotation also can be expected to be far more extensive than has been common in U.S. firms. Short-term efficiency will be lost to a degree as employees rotate into unfamiliar jobs, but the long-term benefits, in terms of systems knowledge and a greater sense of a corporate team, will be indispensable for competitive operations.

Employment Security

Creation of a company-wide environment suited to competitive production with advanced technology will require a strong commitment to employment security—the ability of a firm to retain its employees even though changing market conditions or advancing technology may significantly change the content of the jobs they do. There is little doubt that manufacturing will no longer be a strong source of employment for the unskilled and semiskilled. Factories will employ fewer people in these groups in particular, but the number of people employed among skilled workers and managers will also decline. The remaining jobs, however, may be challenging, rewarding, and in demand. Competition for those jobs and competition for good people will make strong job security an interest of both employee and employer.

Information systems, training programs, and changes in organizational structures will represent huge investments in human capital. Cyclical layoffs or unnecessary turnover would severely limit the return on that investment and risk a complete breakdown in the company's operations. Employment security is crucial to engendering commitment of workers as true stakeholders. In-creased responsibility and participation will improve the attractiveness of manu-facturing jobs, but employees are not likely to feel a strong stake in the company unless they believe it has a stake in them. From the perspective of both company and employees (unionized or not), job security is a critical principle to pursue, which in itself will represent a significant change in the attitude of management and labor.

Although various mechanisms will be used in pursuit of a stable work force, absolute job security is likely to remain both elusive and a source of contention. Some companies recently have been very successful in relocating unskilled and semiskilled workers to other plants and in retraining them to perform new and varied tasks in the automated factory. Many senior employees will be unable to adapt to a new environment that requires more skills, knowledge, and responsi-bility. Following this shakeout, however, it will be feasible and advantageous for employers to provide strong job security for a core group of employees. This core group would be capable of handling daily operations, and subcontracted temporary workers would be hired to meet surge demands. These temporary crews would perform specific duties that do not require extensive knowledge of the company's operations. They would be managed by the operatives usually responsible for those tasks to maintain continuity in decision making. This approach will insulate the core staff from fluctuations in market demand (essentially making the core labor a fixed cost), will provide employment opportunities for previously displaced workers, and, if widely used, may change the nature of unemployment trends in the macroeconomy. The approach is already used extensively in the airframe industry.

Job security also may be strengthened by the trend to perform previously subcontracted work in-house, although this trend will vary across industries and firms depending on size, available technology, and product mix. No company can do everything well, and in many industries subcontracting is a way to share risks, costs, and expertise. In some industries, however, advanced process technologies are likely to provide sufficient capacity and flexibility to encourage firms to initiate subcontracted production in-house. The advantages in quality control, production scheduling control, and design change would reinforce the job security benefits of such a strategy. In fact, the trend can be seen already in the domestic mainframe computer industry. In other industries, the advantages of small, focused factories may create more subcontracting than has been traditional. Despite these variations, many companies will find that the advantages of in-house production outweigh the disadvantages, particularly in maximizing return on the large investment in human capital.

Incentives, Evaluations, and Decision Criteria

Traditional measures of success in manufacturing will be inadequate for tomorrow's manufacturing environment. New measurements, as well as new rewards, will be needed to manage production effectively, maintain employees' motivation, justify new investments, and stimulate stockholders' interest.

In the area of factory operations, managers will need new criteria on which to base operational decisions. Mechanisms for improving factory effectiveness, such as precise inventory control systems, material requirements planning, in-house production of previously subcontracted work, production process planning, and the many aspects of factory automation, will change the operations of the future factory. The criteria that managers have traditionally used to make operational decisions will change and, in many cases, the decisions will change. A factory using just-in-time inventory control, for example, will have less input inventory on hand than a manager may have been accustomed to having. As another example, changes in production processes and work flows will change the criteria used to judge effective machine utilization rates, manning levels, acceptable work-in-process inventory, and tooling requirements. Managers will need retraining to alter their thinking about the effective operation of the factory to prevent old habits from inhibiting potential cost savings, quality improvements, and overall effectiveness.

Evaluations of individuals—both managers and workers—are likely to be much more subjective than they have been traditionally. Quantifiable improvements in individual performance, such as increasing output per hour or shift, will not be applicable to automated, integrated production with emphasis on project teams. Objective indicators of performance will remain in areas such as quality, delivery, process system costs, customer satisfaction, and company earnings, but these will reflect more on group efforts or the total work force than on individuals. Consequently, individuals' pay is expected to shift from hourly wages to salaries; pay will entail a greater emphasis on bonuses based on improvement in short-term results, long-term improvements in the total system, and achievement of the goals of that particular level of the organization. The "profit center" and "cost center" focus used in the past as a basis for judging individual performance can be expected to be replaced by a systems focus. Subjective assessments of individuals' skills and competence by their peers will affect salary decisions at least indirectly. Promotions will remain a form of recognition and opportunity for increased responsibility, but increased use of project teams and job rotation is expected to diminish the importance and obvious benefits of promotions; the elimination of most middle management positions will reinforce this trend.

At the company level, evaluation of performance will depend largely on a meaningful management accounting system. Traditional methods that aggregate data, allocate costs based on direct labor, and compute data over long intervals (usually monthly) will be ineffective and counterproductive in the new environment. New accounting systems will give manufacturers the accurate, timely data they need to respond rapidly to changing conditions. The availability of more relevant data will give almost everyone in the business a clear perspective on total performance and its response to key decisions on matters such as investment, personnel, subcontracting, and research and development expenditures.

Changes in accounting procedures will contribute to the strong trend toward balancing short-term results against long-term prospects in determining the health of a manufacturing firm. New criteria will be developed to give stockholders and investors a basis for assessing the steps a firm is taking to ensure its long-term competitiveness. These criteria may include research and development expenditures, the amount and kinds of investment over a given period, training and recruitment patterns, and the activities of major competitors. None of these indicators will be conclusive, but as a package they will give stockholders more information than is common at the present.

Future Focus

In the new manufacturing environment, efficiency alone will not ensure success. Foresight will be the ultimate competitive weapon, because market share and profit margins are likely to be small for the followers. A long-term, future-oriented focus, extending beyond the next quarter or year, will be a competitive necessity. Manufacturers will need to devote an increasing amount of time, money, and energy to those parts of the business that will have a preponderant impact in the future, particularly product and process research and development.

The pace of change is expected to be rapid, so emphasis on strong in-house research and development will be a necessity for firms seeking a leadership position. Manufacturers will need to accept the risks inherent in long-range research. Investments in scientific and engineering personnel, laboratories, and computers are expected to be a significant portion of total capital budgets. At the same time, the need to implement new technologies, introduce new products, and attract talented personnel will be expensive. Some companies will share costs by participating in research consortia, which in fact may be the only viable method of research in some industries. Other companies will save research costs by using licensing agreements, but as product life cycles shorten, the value of licensing as a relatively inexpensive way to enter new markets can be expected to diminish. Companies will face difficult choices in striking a balance between spending for future and immediate competitiveness. Similar circumstances exist today. The major difference is that future manufacturers will probably have much less ability to milk profits from new products because competing entrants will be close behind. The costs of being a follower will be more apparent, so the weight given to future-oriented investments should be much greater than it has been traditionally.

With these changes in the human and organizational components of manufacturing, the factory will become a much different factor in society. Although opportunities for unskilled or semiskilled labor will diminish, the jobs that will be created are expected to be challenging and of high quality. Also, manufacturing jobs will be in demand among graduate engineers, who do not generally prize them today, and there may be too few to go around. Firms will have such large investments in people that they will make extraordinary efforts to retain employees, which will limit job creation at existing plants. This constraint may be countered somewhat by the trend in some industries toward microfactories, although the labor requirements of such facilities may be quite small. Employment opportunities also will arise in industries that will produce goods yet to be invented and in the variety of services that can be expected to develop to support future manufacturers.

These changes in the factory will permeate the social and economic fabric of the nation. Changes in internal factory operations will affect relations with unions, subcontractors, wholesalers and retailers, producers of services, and other economic activities outside but closely related to factory operations. The expectations and opportunities of workers at all levels will be affected by the cultural revolution that has already begun in manufacturing. For many companies, the rate and direction of change will be determined through the collective bargaining process; for other firms, less formal approaches of labor–management cooperation will be used. None of the changes will be sudden, however, and no two industries will progress at the same pace.

In fact, there may very well be a backlash from both managers and workers who have a strong stake in traditional relationships and organizational structures. Consequently, the changes in people and organizations will, at best, proceed in fits and starts, but the benefits in terms of manufacturing effectiveness and profitability are expected to be so clear that these difficult cultural changes will be implemented. The specifics of these changes are difficult to predict because they are based on individual decisions in a vast variety of circumstances. The direction of change, however, is becoming increasingly clear, and the repercussions will be wide-ranging.

Plan for Tomorrow

Manufacturing has already entered the early stages of revolutionary change caused by the convergence of three powerful forces:

- The rapid spread of manufacturing capabilities worldwide has created intense competition on a global scale.
- The emergence of advanced manufacturing technologies, such as robots,

is dramatically changing both the products and processes of modern manufacturing.
- There is growing evidence that changes in traditional management and
labor practices, organizational structures, and decision-making operations
provide new sources of competitiveness and introduce new strategic opportunities.

The effects of these forces are already being felt by the U.S. manufacturing
community. Domestic markets that were once secure have been challenged by a
growing number of foreign competitors producing high-quality goods at low
prices. New technologies are helping U.S. manufacturers compete, but many
technical and social barriers remain before advanced technologies have a major,
widespread impact on manufacturing operations. Unfortunately, foreign competitors may well have overcome some of these barriers first and are now using
new technologies to increase their competitiveness.

As these points indicate, the three trends now affecting manufacturing are
closely interrelated. Increased competition has demonstrated the need for U.S.
manufacturers to reexamine traditional human resource practices and their use
of new product and process technologies. Corrective measures, however, cannot focus exclusively on either area, since technology will not be effective
without changes in human resource practices, and the benefits from those
changes are limited without the productive thrust offered by new technologies.
Meanwhile, the competition intensifies, current production must be maintained,
and the resources available to make the required changes always seem inadequate.

All of this poses a difficult dilemma for manufacturers who have depended
on stability to maintain competitive production. Many manufacturers recognize
the need to adapt, but do not know what changes are necessary or how to
implement them. More than anything else, the key problem is that the forces
affecting manufacturing require that managers think and act differently to bring
about change in a systems context and that workers accept new roles and
responsibilities.

The major roadblocks to more competitive U.S. manufacturing are in the
attitudes, practices, decision-making criteria, and relationships of both managers and workers. This new vision means that hierarchical, adversarial management structures will handicap attempts to improve competitiveness. Employees at all levels of the organization will need to be viewed as a resource, and
the organization will need to be structured so that everyone will have the
opportunity and responsibility to make the maximum contribution. Furthermore, the importance of the manufacturing function in the total corporate
context will need to be recognized. Functional integration based on a clear
understanding of the manufacturing systems concept will be a major key to
competitive success. This way of thinking about manufacturing is foreign to
most managers, workers, and educators in this country, and it may be overly
optimistic to expect such a dramatic shift in attitudes and culture. Ingrained
attitudes will be difficult to change and may require a generational shift.

This book provides some direction, but not a solution. Circumstances vary
too much to try to prescribe specific actions, but the direction for change should
be clear. The use of new advanced manufacturing technologies such as robots is
insufficient. The key is to focus on evaluating traditional managerial practices,

relationships, decision-making criteria, and organizational structures to determine specific strengths in responding to competitive pressures. The renewed organization will be in a better position to implement new technologies and further strengthen competitiveness. For some companies, however, attempts to implement new technologies will force labor and management changes. Managers will need to realize that implementation of advanced manufacturing technologies to automate existing processes will yield suboptimal results. Efforts to optimize the technologies will demand creative thinking to take advantage of the opportunity to redesign many processes, simplify many designs, and change the flow of work on the factory floor. This creative thinking and the necessary cultural changes will be the major obstacles to attaining improved competitiveness.

Government should play a significant role in encouraging and supporting the changes in manufacturing, but the impetus must come from private companies. In general, the main responsibility for government is threefold: (1) to recognize the importance of a strong manufacturing sector as a source of goods for international trade and as a crucial factor in continued economic prosperity and strong defense; (2) to support the process of change in manufacturing; and (3) to stay abreast of the changes taking place in manufacturing and adapt government tax policies and programs to maximize their effectiveness in the new environment. In addition, some specific government activities, for instance in education, research, and tax incentive programs, will need to be particularly sensitive to manufacturing requirements and ensure that necessary resources remain available.

To summarize, U.S. manufacturers are facing a crucial challenge. Traditional markets are being attacked by imports and traditional practices are not producing adequate results. Changes in labor and management attitudes, organizational design, and the role of the manufacturing function in the total corporate system are needed to regain and maintain competitiveness. New technologies, such as robots, will help this process, but manufacturing strategies will need to be evaluated to ensure both that the right technologies are used and that the full potential of those technologies is realized. Manufacturing in the United States is on the threshold of an exciting new era—the challenges are daunting but the opportunities are unprecedented.

8

A GLIMPSE OF
THE FUTURE

MARKET TRENDS AND
COMPETITIVENESS

Despite rapid growth in robot sales this year, the U.S. robotics industry remains a small, low-volume industry, still dependent on the automotive and light manufacturing electronics industries for the majority of its revenues. The industry has not grown as rapidly as expected because the automotive industry has cut back on their capital spending plans. At present the automobile industry's share of robotics orders booked annually runs about 55 percent, down substantially from the beginning of the decade. As a result of the decline in automotive-related capital expenditures between 1985 and 1990, the robotics industry has increased research and development in vertical applications that will allow other industries, such as light manufacturing, to apply robotics technology to their manufacturing processes.

Light manufacturing application advancements, such as those made during 1990 in surface-mount and through-hole technologies, will reduce the robotic industry's dependence on orders from the automotive industry. These types of applications particularly suit the revitalized U.S. electronics and appliance industries. Also, the flexibility, total quality control, productivity, and automation requirements of today's manufacturing manager ensure expanding use of robotics in the factory of the future. The robotic industry's recent profitability will enable U.S. producers to devote more time, attention, and funding to vertical specific industry application research.

The fastest-growing markets for robotics are in light manufacturing assembly operations. The electronics industry has seen significant recent growth, which was influenced by developments in robot sensors, artificial intelligence, network communications, enhanced accuracy, and system integration.

Between 1987 and 1994, U.S. robot revenues could have a compound annual growth rate of 9.7 percent and may reach $879 million. The light manufacturing use of robots has been increasing despite the overall situation in the robot market. Revenues for light industrial robots are expected to exceed 50 percent of the total U.S. robot market by 1994. Table 8-1 shows the total shipments of complete robots, robot accessories, and components.

Internationally, the world market for robots was $2.83 billion in 1987 and may reach $4.93 billion in 1994. Imports of robots are estimated to be at least 30 percent of domestic consumption, and Japan is the source of more than 80 percent of these imports. Japan is still the dominant force in the world in the manufacture of robots, producing more than half the total. The United States and Europe each produce about 20 percent of the world total. There are about 300 firms producing robots in Japan, one-third of which are for in-house use only.

One of the reasons that the Japanese control the world robot market is due to support by the Japanese government. Government incentives include funded research and development programs, low-interest loans, tax incentives, and a government-funded robot leasing company. European governments have also encouraged robot manufacturers, but have not been nearly as successful as the Japanese in promoting industry growth. In general, the U.S. government has not been directly involved in promoting or broadening the commercial aspects of robots. Most funding has been directed at space and military applications.

The growth of robots in American industry is tied to the level of long-term investment by industry in new manufacturing methods and automation in general. In comparison to some of the other leading industrial nations, investment has been dismally low in the United States, and U.S. corporate management must make a long-term commitment to develop the productivity and quality improvements possible with industrial robots and other forms of automation.

Assuming that management does make this commitment, the U.S. robotics industry will change markedly over the next decade in response to demand shifts. The spread of robots to a wider range of light manufacturing industries will make the industry less dependent on capital spending cycles in the automotive sector. The rise in assembly and material-handling applications for robots will bring an increase in demand for robot systems, as opposed to stand-alone machines. Future success in the U.S. market appears to lie with the supplier that can provide a complete turnkey system to meet users' needs. The application of peripherals and systems software for the more complex factory automation solutions will become an increasingly important focal area for domestic producers. Growth in robotics in the next 10 years will also be affected by software developments, diversification of application areas, systems integration including CIM, and developments in robot intelligence and sensors.

Robotics firms in the United States will remain dependent on offshore components in the manufacture and assembly of robot systems. The source for these imports may well shift as the European Community appears ready to challenge the Japanese share of the world market. Based on foreign business practices and past interactions we can only assume tougher competition both in the domestic market and in overseas markets in the future. The Western European nations have recently worked out agreements to share in the cost of research and development, and this type of joint effort will expedite closing gaps in technology where they exist. More importantly, it will reduce the costs associated with research and development for a number of companies and allow them to spread their research over a wider base.

It has been projected that within the next 20 years, about one-third of all blue-collar jobs could be handled by robots. Japan has already developed several fully unmanned factory systems. In the United States, metalworking industries are experiencing an attrition rate in the neighborhood of 15% annually; the overall rate of increase of blue-collar workers is declining; productivity rates are decelerating; and OSHA and EPA regulations are essentially removing certain types of jobs from human involvement. In other words, industrial robots are facing a ready market.

Technological developments that enhance robot capabilities will be a major driving force in the robotics industry worldwide. The spread of these developments will take place through the large number of international marketing and technical exchange agreements currently in place among major producers of different nationalities. Progress in the development of standards, both national and international, will also play a role in the direction of change in the industry. The future competitiveness of the U.S. robotics industry depends on the level of effort that firms apply in each of these areas.

KEY MARKET IMPACT ISSUES

It is generally agreed that there are five key elements impacting the future market for robots: (1) sensor technology, (2) cost, (3) size reduction, (4) system integration, and (5) market acceptance. Until recently, progress in any one of these areas was largely neutralized by relative stagnation in another. What is now propelling the industry is the fact that each of these five elements, is synergistic.

Sensor Technology

For robots to be truly useful across a wider breadth of markets, they must be able to adjust automatically to production setups. "Blind" robots are adequate in highly organized factory environments where parts positions are changed relatively infrequently or where extensive software packages have already essentially recorded positions of all parts. The majority of American industry is not so ordered. Therefore, for the purpose of opening the market to growth throughout the widest span of industry applications, robots must be automatically adaptive, capable of recognizing, reorienting, and then manipulating disordered parts. For many assembly and installation procedures, this adaptive ability will be essential.

A considerable amount of research is currently being devoted to the area of machine vision and tactile sensing. For example, "artificial skin" for robots has been developed that could adapt to their environment through using the sense of touch to register varying amounts of pressure. A number of visual systems have been developed and are being utilized to accomplish pattern recognition in two or three dimensions. Industry sources generally agree that sufficient refinements in terms of processing speed and cost will occur during the decade to allow robots to accomplish complex assembly operations.

Table 8-1
Typical Total Shipments of Complete Robots, Robot Accessories, and Components

Product description	Number of companies[a]	Quantity[a] (units)	Value (thousands of dollars)
Robots, robot accessories, and components	56	(X)	249,912
Robots (complete)	X	4,273	187,507
Servo-controlled robots	25	2,459	175,960
Point-to-point type:			
Welding, soldering, brazing, and/or cutting (welding type)	5	476	43,944
Foundry, forging, and/or heat treating	1		
Inspection, measuring, gauging, and/or sorting	2		
Metal bending, shearing, and/or forming	—	28	3,412
Plastics molding and/or forming	1		
Machine tool loading and/or unloading	3		
Drilling and/or cutting (machine type)	2		
Assembly, for nonelectronic products	6	535	19,573
Assembly, for electronic products	6		
Material handling and/or parts transfer	8	713	43,016
Other point-to-point type	3		
Continuous path type:			
Welding, soldering, brazing and/or cutting (welding type)	5	110	9,020
Spraying, painting, gluing, and/or sealing	9	297	41,348
Fettling, grinding, polishing, and/or deburring	1	300	15,647
Other continuous path type	6		

Nonservo-controlled robots	11	215	8,153
Foundry, forging, and/or heat treating	1		
Metal bending, shearing, and/or forming	—		
Plastics molding and/or forming	2		
Machine tool loading and/or unloading	1	125	5,948
Inspection, measuring, gauging, and/or sorting	4		
Assembly, for nonelectronic products	1		
Assembly, for electronic products	2		
Other nonservo-controlled robots	1		
Materials handling and/or parts transfer	8	90	2,205
Other robots	6	1,599	3,394
Educational, hobby, and experimental robots	5	1,599	3,394
Other robots	2		
Robot accessories, subassemblies, components, and parts (sold separately)	44	X	62,405
End-of-arm tooling for robots	12	X	5,936
Vision, sonic, force, tactile, and proximity sensors	15	X	15,604
Interface modules	2	X	
Compliance devices	3	X	815
Joint locating and guidance systems for welding	3	X	
Guarding and safety devices	4	X	3,989
Robot accessories, subassemblies, components, and parts	26	X	36,061
Miscellaneous receipts:			
Research and development, testing, and evaluation of systems and components (receipts and billings not reported as shipments of specific products)	7	X	8,437

Source: U.S. Department of Commerce, *Current Industrial Robots (Shipments)* (1987), MA35X(87)-1, issued August 1988.

[a] (—) Represents zero; X, not applicable.

Cost

Until fairly recently, the use of industrial robots has been paralyzed because of their high cost relative to other available labor or machinery. Increasing labor costs (health care, benefits, and direct labor cost) and semiconductor advancements have now changed the economics of robots. Further, the range of prices for robots available for a given task has begun to broaden on the lower end. International competition has driven down the unit robot costs significantly over the past 5 years, and continued development of smaller and simpler vertical market electrical robots will aid the overall cost reduction for broad application of robots.

Size Reduction

High-technology industrial robots have been largely dominated by machines with work envelopes of up to 1000 cubic feet and load capacity of over 350 pounds in the mid-1980s. To be introduced into factory environments, robots of this size and reach generally require the displacement of existing machinery or even entirely new manufacturing configurations. Certain factory setups are ideally suited to these heavy-duty robotic devices.

However, during the late 1980s, electric-driven versus large hydraulic robots have been the market growth leaders for light manufacturing assembly operations. Smaller robots, with a reduced work envelope and payload, can more readily adapt to the vast majority of industry uses. Even in the automotive industry, where nearly half of the heavy-duty robots have been installed, it is estimated that 90 percent of the parts in the average automobile weigh less than 3.1 pounds. Smaller robots can, of course, also be removed from a production line for maintenance and off-line programming without taking down the whole line.

Systems Integration

Manufacturers are showing increasing interest in the concept of flexible manufacturing systems (FMS) for greater manufacturing efficiency. Briefly, this concept ties together previously independent numerical control machine tools, robots, transfer mechanisms or parts-handling devices, and a coordinating control system to deal with the mid-volume range of production that represents the majority (around 70 percent) of production. So-called flexible manufacturing systems or computer-integrated manufacturing (CIM) facilities have as their primary aim that of combining efficient levels of output over a wide range of families of components with the flexibility to change what had previously been achievable only by a sharp reduction in output. Successful robotics manufacturers have shifted their marketing emphasis from sales of isolated pockets of individual robots to that of vertical market application systems design whereby robots can be intrinsically linked into a total computer-integrated manufacturing process.

Market Acceptance

The fifth, and in some ways the most important, of the five primary elements directing the future growth of industrial robots is that of aggressive marketing and product acceptance. Now that robots are accepted and have become effective "tools," robot manufacturers, the majority of whose backgrounds are in the engineering and technical fields, are facing a positive market. Early science fiction images of walking and talking robots as the total solution to our manufacturing productivity have been replaced by an understanding of the value and proper application of industrial robots as another "tool" rather than a "toy" to play with.

INTERNATIONAL INTERDEPENDENCE

Although the international interdependence of robot producers facilitates the spread of new technology, gaps exist in several areas between the United States and its foreign competition. United States firms lead their foreign competitors in a number of areas associated with robot peripherals and applications of the more complex robot functions. However, it appears that as a whole they have been slow to apply these technologies in the production arena. Producers in Japan and Western Europe are concentrating on closing any technological gaps in areas where they lag U.S. producers, and in some forms of technology they are extending their lead over U.S. suppliers. Our international competitive opportunity is driven by robot capabilities, research and development, standards, and international agreements, which are discussed in the following sections.

Robot Capabilities

The potential for substantial advances in robot capabilities is perhaps greatest in the areas of sensors and artificial intelligence. Sophisticated sensing technology, such as machine vision, provides a robot with the "intelligence" necessary to recognize an object, determine its orientation, direct the movement of the object, perform work on it, and inspect it for defects. Machine vision-equipped robots represent the state of the art in robot application-oriented development. American producers have the potential to maintain a decisive technological lead in this area, but they will be directly challenged by Japanese producers, who have also begun to focus their research efforts on machine vision systems and on semiautonomous robots that can operate without human intervention. These artificial intelligence-supplemented robots will be the factory tools of 2020.

Research and Development

Japanese and European robotics firms allocate a substantial portion of their own funds to research and development (R&D), as do U.S. firms. Foreign producers benefit substantially from government R&D programs that are generally closely geared to developing technologies with commercial applications. In the area of international manufacturing automation, primary emphasis is placed on cooperative research by pooling the resources of industry, government, and universities. While both U.S. industry and the U.S. government are supporting some research efforts in the area of manufacturing automation technologies, these efforts are largely contained within individual firms or government research laboratories. Many research efforts currently under way in the United States in robotics are underfunded and lack direct commercial applicability.

Continuation of this trend could translate into diminished competitiveness for U.S. firms.

The National Cooperative Research Act of 1984 has cleared away what many U.S. companies had perceived to be the main barrier to cooperative research—the risk of antitrust liability. Companies are starting to join together in various associations to support research in which they share a common interest. Current legislation is attempting to bring these cooperative opportunities to the manufacturing production phase. By working together, U.S. companies are able to upgrade their technological bases at lower risk, and thus have a better chance of staying ahead of foreign competitors. The use of cooperative research and development programs in the United States is consistent with the recommendations of the President's Commission on Industrial Competitiveness.

Standards

The development of standards for interfacing robots with other types of automation equipment will be a critical factor in determining the speed with which robot use spreads across a broad range of manufacturing industries both internationally and in the United States. Cost is a critical factor in how a system or cell is assembled and that cost is directly related to how easily the various machines or components can be married together. Standard interfaces between robot system elements reduce costs by providing savings in system integration, installation, and maintenance of the user's production equipment.

The Robotic Industries Association issued a standard for industrial robots and robot systems safety requirements in conjunction with the American National Standards Institute. The association has also developed standards in the areas of electrical interface, mechanical interface, performance, communication/information, human interface, and terminology for robot systems.

General Motors and a number of others in the manufacturing sector have joined in an effort to establish factory automation standards. They are requiring that products purchased for their manufacturing facilities meet a set of standards included under their Manufacturing Automation Protocol (MAP). Through these efforts, the private sector has already established a very positive beginning for dealing with standards problems.

The movement toward standardization will affect the U.S. robotics industry and its competitiveness in world markets. Widespread acceptance of standards will expand the domestic robot market and assist U.S. producers in attaining economies of scale in production. Software standards could also enhance U.S. suppliers' principal advantage in the high end of the robot market, permitting systems designers to focus their efforts on increasing robot capabilities through more complex programming rather than having to write code to support data conversion from one system component to another.

International Agreements

The robotics industry is becoming increasingly internationalized through a proliferation of joint business ventures and agreements among robot producers and manufacturer/users. Present trends indicate that the lower value-added portion of the industry will be located offshore (Japan and Europe) and that the

U.S. producers will focus on specialized equipment and the higher value-added segments of the robot market. International agreements give U.S. firms access to lower-cost, foreign-produced generic robots, which are then equipped in the United States with domestically produced controls, end-effectors, sensors, and other peripheral devices. United States firms can also benefit to a certain degree through technology absorption. The drawback to this method of production, which involves relying on foreign suppliers for the basic robot mechanism, is the loss of full domestic production capability and therefore technology leadership.

TECHNOLOGY TRENDS

Robots in the year 2000 will be smarter, smaller, quicker, lighter, stronger, more ingenious, easier to operate, more intelligent, and less expensive than they are now. Table 8-2 forecasts key technology development areas in the future of robot development.

The technology for robot miniaturization, modularization, high-speed operation, and computer control has advanced to the point where it is now technically accepted as a reliable manufacturing tool. Technology for part recognition and position determination is currently available; however, technology for color and behavior recognition, unattended automated assembly, and operational smart robots will not achieve widespread utilization until the first half of the 1990s.

One of the greatest advantages of robotics and automation occurs in the cases where their use greatly increases equipment utilization. A robot arc welder cannot weld faster than a human, but by keeping its torch on the work about 90 percent of the time, versus no more than 30 percent of the time for a human, it can turn out three times as much work in the same time. If through automation more work shifts can be worked, productivity is even further increased.

In the next few years, welding robots will be sufficiently sophisticated to work from plans stored in computer memory and to correct errors that may occur during the job. Welding robots will then be able to work nights and weekends completely without human supervision. At that point, productivity improvements of severalfold over present methods will become possible.

By 1990, robot sensory and control capabilities will improve to the point where unattended robots can find and load unoriented parts or pick parts out of a bin filled with randomly oriented parts lying on top of each other. This may improve productivity several times over because it will make it possible to install robots in many existing plants without major engineering or revision of production methods.

Robots will eventually have a significant impact on mechanical assembly, and there has been a great deal of research effort spent on robot assembly. On the one hand, robots cannot compete with classical so-called "hard automation" in assembly of mass-produced parts. General-purpose machines, like robots, are still too slow and too expensive to be economical for mass production assembly tasks. On the other hand, CIM systems utilizing robots still cannot compete with human assembly workers in small-lot assembly for very flexible production requirements. Nevertheless, progress is being made and will

Table 8-2
Forecast of Robot Technology Development

Materials
Lighter and stronger materials (composites) for robot structures will be developed. These will include both organic and nonorganic substances. As a consequence, the size and weight of robots will decrease.

Power Sources
Small, high-capacity power sources will allow robots greater freedom of location and movement. Electric drive will be the predominant robot power source.

Actuators
Smaller, high-performance actuators will appear.

Sensors
Small, reliable, high-performance, low-cost artificial eyes, ears, and tactile sensors will be developed and even low-cost robots will have sophisticated sensor capability.

Control Systems
Advances in computer technology will dramatically improve robot control. Control systems costs will be greatly reduced. Enhanced network systems will be common.

Communications Systems
Remote control of robots will be enhanced through development, normal use of fiber optics, and wireless communications.

Processing Methods
Nonmechanical processing methods such as laser beam cutting, welding, and other high-energy processing methods will reduce the processing load on robots and make the design work for them simpler.

Robot Body Structure
Utilization of biomechanical concepts will result in superior robot structures. Robot designs will be more stylish.

Software
Robot use will become easier through the development of standardized robot languages. Self-diagnosing will be widely applied. Modular software will contribute to reducing the design work needed on each robot installation.

Integrated Systems
Better techniques for integrating production systems encompassing humans, machines, and robots as well as their peripheral devices will be developed. Further, their design processes will be computerized.

continue. Robot capabilities will gradually increase, and sensory systems will become more sophisticated and less expensive. The cost of computer hardware is continuing to drop, but software costs are likely to be the major impediment to robot development in the foreseeable future. However, even these obstacles will slowly yield to the techniques of structured modular programming, natural language processing, and other high-level languages.

Eventually, extremely fast, accurate, dexterous, robots will be programmed using CAD graphics data bases that describe the shape of the parts to be made and the configuration of the assemblies to be constructed. Robots will be able to respond to a wide variety of sensory cues, to learn by experience, and to acquire skills by self-optimization. Such skills can then be transferred to other robots so that learning can be propagated rapidly throughout the robot labor force.

By the mid-1990s, investment in robot technology in the U.S. will have increased to the degree necessary to produce the totally automated factory. In such factories, robots will be able to perform most, if not all, of the operations that now require human skills. There will be totally automatic inventory and tool management, and automatic machining, assembly, finishing, and inspection systems. As in Japan, computer-integrated manufacturing facilities will reproduce themselves, that is, automatic factories will make the components for other automatic factories. Once this occurs, productivity improvements will propagate from generation to generation. Each generation of machines will produce machines less expensive and more sophisticated than themselves. This will bring about an exponential decline in the cost of robots and automatic factories that may equal or exceed the cost/performance record of the computer industry. Eventually, products produced in automatic factories may cost only slightly more than the raw materials and energy from which they are made.

In summary, what we see emerging are robots with increasing intelligence, sensory capability, and dexterity. Initially, we will see an increasing use of off-line programming of computer-controlled robots, using improved robot command languages. Provision will be made to include the role of sensors, such as machine vision and touch sensors, in this programming. Later, self-planning will emerge as higher and more general commands are given to the robot. At this point, the marriage of robotics and artificial intelligence will be virtually complete. At the same time, robotic hands with improved dexterity and advanced control systems to support this dexterity will emerge. Robots will even have coordinated multiple arms and eventually legs supported by even more sophisticated control systems.

Recent developments in the laboratory have greatly expanded the use of artificial sensory perception. Machine vision systems are now commonplace among single robots, and the development and use of other sensors are proceeding at an astounding pace. Tactile, audio (reception and transmission), olfactory, proximity, range, magnetic-field, superconductor, and radioactivity sensors are all being developed and will be exploited as soon as they are commercially practical.

Artificial intelligence still represents a major problem area in that the knowledge assimilation and codification of new information still must be done by a human operator. Development and exploitation in the use of analog problem solving may augment stored operational parameters and assist in attaining true artificial intelligence.

It is predicted that widespread adoption of robotic units in the factory will affect employment. However, studies indicate that factory automation will provide a decrease in demeaning and/or hazardous jobs. Factory jobs will shift toward more skilled workers required for fewer jobs within the factory, and technical support jobs may offset some of these job losses. As this evolution progresses, information and intelligence will become the dominant factor in robots, with the manipulator devices shrinking in importance.

THE FUTURE OF ROBOTICS

Robots today are not extremely flexible devices. They still perform well only in structured situations and are not capable of adjusting to unpredictable events. The flexibility of the human worker is related to his or her high-order sensory and innate problem-solving capability. But in the area of efficiency robots outperform humans in purely mechanical areas such as strength, repetition, endurance, speed, precision, and dexterity. Robots are best suited to tasks requiring more dexterity but less flexibility, whereas humans, being highly flexible but inefficient, perform relatively poorly at highly structured tasks.

Future capabilities of the robot depend on the sensory and problem-solving capacities inherent in humans. If a robot is truly to be a replacement for a human, this mission will be totally dependent on the science and engineering research initiatives and their analysis of what human features make us productive workers. Unfortunately, this is presently a tall order since the robot is still relatively new and, for the most part, unable to respond in our world. Evolution has created a pattern for human development that we can only dream of duplicating in our artificial creatures on the factory floor. Complex vision, information processing, decision theory, coordinated motion (both hand to hand and mobility), adaptability, and flexibility are natural and accepted in humans, but so far cannot be reproduced in our robots. This is not to say that robots will not continue to expand into the workstations of the future factories, for they are already making a serious impact in a variety of chores.

What is certain about the future is that we will only be able to develop new work situations for robot exploitation if we can begin to give our robot more of the features that make us human, namely, those features previously mentioned. Do not expect R2D2 or C3PO to meet you at the factory door any time soon. For the most part, these developments will come in an evolutionary manner, much as we have evolved. And given the millions of years of evolution to create our species, robots have a ways to go.

The limitations of the robot will be the driving forces that create better systems in the future. Some of these improvements will correct or improve the capability that now exists, while other more challenging problems will remain in the laboratory to be puzzled over and poked by the scientists. There are many real difficulties that must be addressed first, because they will continue to be the weak link in the system. Regardless of where the evolutionary trends take the future robot, immediate needs will be examined first, and then having found acceptable solutions, the engineers will proceed to the truly "blue sky" imaginative initiatives in the works.

Year 2000

The ultimate goal in using a robot is to fully integrate it into a totally integrated, unmanned manufacturing facility. This goal views robot development as a machine tool component of that facility rather than a unique piece of "high-tech" equipment. Most recent developments have centered on improvements in computer control, programming, and integration, while continuing basic manipulator design.

If the present rate of growth of the robot industry continues into the mid-

1990s, they may be used in 10 percent of all manufacturing processes. While this number might appear smaller than expected, consider that the applications are only limited by some near-term problems being worked out now, and when they are put to rest the application scenarios will expand tremendously. Some of these nearer-term solutions are listed in the following paragraphs.

Elements of robot systems have been developed from strong, lightweight materials that yield smaller and lighter robots, some of which are already available but have not been widely used in the robot industry. New composites are being used in aircraft design (the B2 bomber) and lightweight structural elements of bridges. Plastics can be used to replace metals in many products as they continue to marry product and process development. There are even plastic engine components in use today and some designers think robots could one day be fabricated from plastic. Imagine the weight savings, with this approach, not to mention the potential cost savings that will come with it. As this trend continues, stronger lighter robots with higher capacities will eventually be in operation in the same size packages that exist today.

Given the development of the materials needed to make the robot stronger and lighter, the next challenge might be in increasing the robot's accuracy and speed. For now accuracy is limited by the unknowns of the workstation, that is, what the robot does not know because of its limited sensory input and its inability to perform optimally. To expect complex processing and accuracy in this world of few sensory inputs is unrealistic.

Speed and accuracy are not mutually exclusive parameters, for one cannot occur without some impact on the other. Lighter robot structures will reduce the stresses imposed and therefore improve the possibilities for more rapid movement, but the control of the movement will be the greater challenge in the future. Machine vision, touch sensors, scene analysis, and processing will gradually allow the sensory-deprived robot of today to enter a more sensory world where it can explore and comprehend the complexities of multisensory inputs.

Future developments in gripper technology will also permit more flexible work configurations. The real problem today is that there are too many different kinds of grippers in use, making standardization very difficult if not impossible. Flexibility in the design is needed and has been recognized as one area that requires significant emphasis if robots are to continue to replace humans in the work force. Even with the multiplicity of grippers available, most are incapable of sensing the pressure being applied and to match this pressure with the product to ensure a more humanlike handling for a variety of production items. New sensors and gripper materials need to be introduced from the laboratory and integrated into the robot.

Machine vision will continue to be added to many robots. The introduction of lightweight, low-cost camera systems will aid this developing capability, however, there will still be barriers to overcome. Cameras will need to be integrated into knowledge systems that can locate and recognize parts. This will require the ability to see color in three-dimensional space as the human does, and then after seeing to be able to make sense out of the scene presented. This apparently simple task, something we take for granted as humans, is the most vexing problem in developing more intelligent robots.

The constantly expanding electronics industry is a great aid to engineers and scientists in their quest for robot intelligence. Each year the microprocessor, the heart of artificial intelligence for future robots, gets more capable and less expensive. Scene analysis and pattern recognition will require even more from this industry if the complexities of intelligence are to be worked out within the next decade. Given these developments, one can more readily see how voice recognition and command can become part of the robot.

Mobility will be another challenge to the robot designers in the coming years. The ability to move from one point to another is just beginning to be exploited in the most basic ways. Some developers are currently pursuing mobile and semiautonomous robotic platforms that can be used in manufacturing production lines, while still others are using robots to operate in hazardous places, such as in ordinance disposal, prison security, nuclear power plants, and fighting fires. But all the progress so far has been in the more gross mobility aspects. Widespread use of robots on the assembly line will require orders of magnitude more capability from the industry. Today's robot is unable to wander farther from his workstation than its rigid base or track will permit. While one might envision the use of mobile robots to move materials from one place to another, it becomes more difficult to see this same robot performing the precision work processes involved in the current workstation at the same time.

Reliability will continue to be improved by the use of better electronics and new structural materials. Improved reliability will be traded off against a more complex and sophisticated robot. Self-diagnosis and fault isolation and training will become part of the software programming in the future.

Safety will play an important role in how future robots will develop. Obviously if we expect robots to become mobile and to be capable of human vision and limited understanding, we must also expect that some day the cages that keep them from us will have to come down. While there is some comfort in knowing that the robot of today can only harm humans if they enter the robot space, that same comfort will be lost if robots of the future will be free to roam as we are. Industrywide safety initiatives will be required to ensure the possibility of still further robot evolution. And even though most of the artificial intelligence and mobility problems are far from solved, the issue of safety may still be the central problem of the factory robot in the year 2000.

Future applications of robots will be driven by the standardization of communications and software protocols access that will allow the robot vendor community to incorporate computer-integrated manufacturing robotics and machine vision technology. Software is becoming a larger proportion of the overall robot cost and future systems cannot continue to include unique software each time a new model is introduced. Unfortunately, most users do not recognize the value and role of software even though the robot is next to worthless without it. As the robot continues to emerge in the next century, its abilities will suggest even more applications that are not even considered today. Therefore, improvement will always be an ongoing and necessary element of the future development for robots.

APPENDIX A: GLOSSARY OF TERMINOLOGY

Aberration   Failure of a machine vision imaging device to produce exact point-to-point correspondence between an object and its image.

Absolute accuracy   The difference between a point instructed by the control system and the point actually achieved by the manipulator, whereas repeat accuracy is the cycle-to-cycle variation of the manipulator arm when aimed at the same point. The extent to which a machine vision system can correctly interpret an image, generally expressed as a percentage to reflect the likelihood of a correct interpretation.

Absolute coordinates   Units measured from the origin point in the coordinate system (or some other fixed point), rather than expressed as relative to other objects or locations.

Accuracy   The degree to which actual position corresponds to desired or commanded position—thus the degree of freedom from error, which is frequently confused with precision. Accuracy refers to the degree of closeness to a "correct" value; precision refers to the degree of preciseness of a measurement. Accuracy involves the capability to hit the mark, or reach the point in space, or get the correct answer.

Active accommodation   Integration of sensors, control, and robot motion to achieve alteration of a robot's preprogrammed motions in response to sensed forces. Used to stop a robot when forces reach set levels, or to activate performance feedback tasks like insertions, door opening, and edge tracing.

Active illumination   On a robot machine vision system, illumination that can be varied automatically to extract more visual information from a scene. This can be done by turning lamps on and off, by adjusting brightness, by projecting a pattern on objects in the scene, or by changing the color of the illumination.

Actuators are often custom designed for each manufacturing need. (Courtesy of Parker Hannifin Corporation.)

Actuator In robots, a motor or transducer that converts electrical, hydraulic, or pneumatic energy into motion, for example, a cylinder, servomotor, or rotary actuator.

Adaptable Capable of making self-directed corrections—often accomplished in robots with the aid of visual, force, or tactile sensors.

Advanced manufacturing technology Advanced manufacturing technology tools differ from conventional automation primarily in their use of computer and communications technology. They are thus able to perform information processing as well as physical work, to be reprogrammed for a variety of tasks, and to communicate directly with other computerized devices. Advanced manufacturing technology is divided into three general categories: (1) computer-aided design; (2) computer-aided manufacturing (e.g., robots, computerized machine tools, flexible manufacturing systems); and (3) computer-aided techniques for management, such as management information systems and computer-

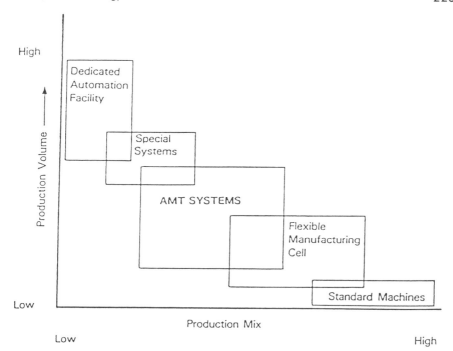

Unique production role for Advanced Manufacturing Technology.

aided planning. These systems are integrated by extensive computer-based coordination software. Because of its ability to perform a variety of tasks, advanced manufacturing technology is usually associated with batch production. However, it has been used extensively in mass production, and it could be useful in custom production as well.

AML Manipulator-oriented programming language for robot programming. Advanced Manufacturing Language (AML) is a product of IBM.

Analog control Control involving analog signal processing devices (electronic, hydraulic, pneumatic, and others).

Analog-to-digital (AD) converter An electronic device that senses a voltage signal and converts it to a corresponding digital signal (a string of 1's and 0's) for use by a digital computer system.

Android A robot resembling a human in physical appearance.

Anthropomorphic robot A robot with all rotary joints and motions similar to a human arm (also called jointed-arm robot). See top figure on page 226.

Arc In welding, an arc is a sustained continuous discharge of electricity between two electrodes or between an electrode and the work.

Arc brazing Brazing with an electric arc, usually with two nonconsumable electrodes.

Arc cutting Metal cutting with an arc between an electrode and the metal itself. The terms carbon-arc cutting and metal-arc cutting refer, respectively, to the use of a carbon or metal electrode.

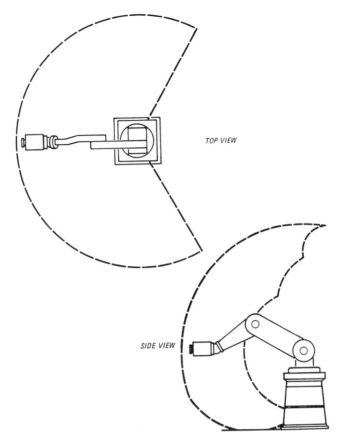

TOP VIEW

SIDE VIEW

Work envelope of an anthropomorphic robot, also referred to as a jointed-arm robot.

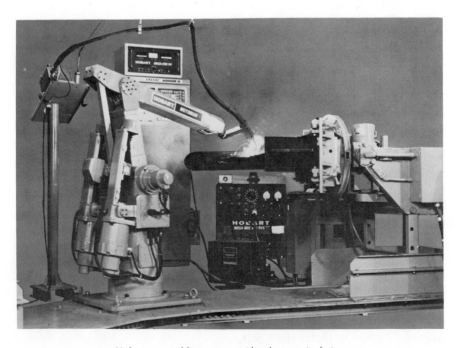

Hobart arc welding system with robot manipulation.

Arc welding Welding with an electric arc welding electrode. See bottom figure on page 226.

Arm An interconnected set of links and powered joints comprising a robot manipulator that supports and/or moves a wrist and hand or end-effector through space.

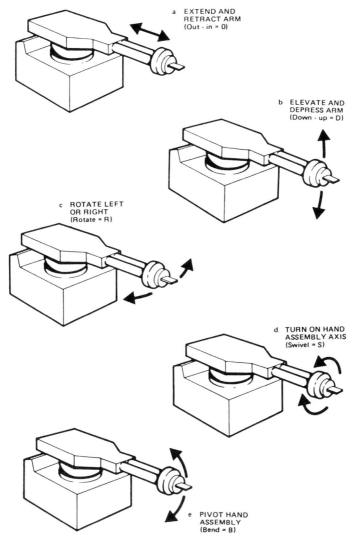

a EXTEND AND RETRACT ARM (Out - in = 0)

b ELEVATE AND DEPRESS ARM (Down - up = D)

c ROTATE LEFT OR RIGHT (Rotate = R)

d TURN ON HAND ASSEMBLY AXIS (Swivel = S)

e PIVOT HAND ASSEMBLY (Bend = B)

Typical articulations of a playback robot with point-to-point control. (From *Robotics in Practice* by Joseph F. Engelberger.)

Articulated robot Robots having rotary joints in several places along the arm that roughly correspond to the shoulder, elbow, and wrist in humans. They are usually mounted on a rotary base.

Assembly robot places components on a printed circuit board.

Assembly robot   A robot designed specifically for mating, fitting, or otherwise assembling various parts or components into either subassemblies or completed products. A class of generally small, lightweight, fast, accurate robots used primarily for grasping parts and mating or fitting them together.

Automatic operation   The time during which a robot is performing its programmed tasks through continuous program execution.

Axis   A general direction of relative motion between cutting tool and workpiece. The understanding of axes in rectangular coordinates is the basic keystone to understanding numerical control. A reference line of a coordinate system, for example, the *X, Y,* or *Z* axis of the Cartesian coordinate system. A direction along which a movement of a tool or workpiece occurs. Also, rotary or translational (sliding) joint in a robot.

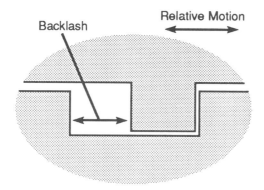

Illustration of backlash. (Source: NIST, *A Glossary of Terms for Robotics.*)

Backlash   Movement between interacting mechanical parts resulting from looseness. Free play in a power transmission system, such as a gear train, resulting in a characteristic form of hysteresis.

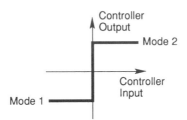

Illustration of one position or another for robot control. (Source: NIST, *A Glossary of Terms for Robotics.*)

Bang-bang robot   A non-servocontrolled, point-to-point robot that operates by "banging" into fixed stops to achieve the desired positions. Any robot in which motions are controlled by driving each axis against a mechanical stop.

Barrier   A physical means of safely separating persons from the robot-restricted work envelope.

Base   The platform or structure to which a robot arm is attached; the end of a kinematic chain of arm links and joints opposite to that which grasps or processes external objects.

Bilateral manipulator   A master–slave manipulator with symmetric force reflection, where both master and slave arms have sensors and actuators such that in any degree of freedom a positional error between the master and slave results in equal and opposing forces applied to the master and the slave arms.

Bin picking   The ability to remove individual parts from a bin in an oriented fashion.

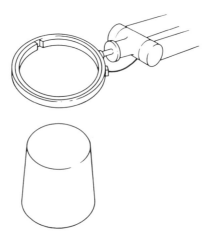

Expansion bladder hand. (From *Robotics in Practice* by Joseph F. Engelberger.)

Bladder hand   Large cylindrical vessels with flexible walls are difficult for mechanical hands and fingers to grasp, but an expandable bladder in the form of a cuff will do the job. A rigid backup ring supports the bladder. The illustrated plastic container with tapered walls represents a typical part for which the bladder is useful. Of course, a given bladder design will handle only one size of vessel. An alternative to the internally expanding (in ID) bladder shown is one that is expanded externally (in OD) after insertion into a vessel. Vacuum pickup can be another suitable alternative for an application such as this one.

Bridge configuration robot   A bridge configuration robot is a Cartesian robot that looks like a bridge crane and in which the traveling bridge lies on elevated rails.

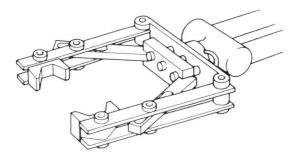

Illustration of cam-operated hand mechanism (From *Robotics in Practice* by Joseph F. Engelberger.)

Cam-operated hand   Heavy weights or bulky objects are handled easily by the cam-operated hand. More expensive than the standard hand, the cam-operated hand is designed to hold the part so that its center of gravity (CG) is kept very close to the "wrist" of the hand. The short distance between the CG and wrist minimizes the twisting tendency of a heavy or bulky object. To achieve this "close coupling" of hand and part, there is a sacrifice: a specific cam-operated hand design will accommodate only a very narrow range of object sizes.

Carousel A rotating work-in-process queuing system that delivers workpieces to a load/unload station that may be served by an operator or a robot.

Cartesian coordinate robot A robot whose manipulator arm degrees of robot freedom are defined primarily by Cartesian coordinates. A robot in which there are linear motions arrayed in mutually perpendicular directions, that is, east–west, north–south, and up–down, as well as rotary motions to change orientation. A robot with motions resulting from movement along horizontal and vertical tracks, rather than through the use of joints—often called an orthogonal robot.

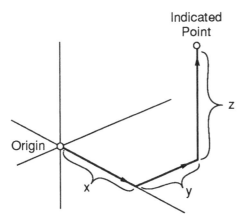

Illustration of relationship between origin and x, y, and z points in Cartesian Coordinate system. (From NIST, *A Glossary of Terms for Robotics.*)

Cartesian coordinate system A coordinate system whose axes or dimensions are three intersecting perpendicular straight lines and whose origin is the intersection.

Cell A manufacturing unit consisting of two or more workstations with the material-handling systems, storage buffers, and other items necessary to connect them. A computer graphic entity that is a rectangle or parallelogram. Its only aspect is color, which is specified as part of the associated output primitive.

Cell control A module in the control hierarchy that controls a cell. The cell control module is controlled by a center control module, if one exists, otherwise it is controlled by a factory control level.

Center of acceleration That point in a rigid body around which the entire mass revolves.

Center of gravity That point in a rigid body at which the entire mass of the body could be concentrated and produce the same gravity resultant as that for the body itself.

Central processing unit The arithmetic and logic unit and the control unit of a digital computer. Another term for processor. The hardware part (CPU) of a computer that directs the sequence of operations, interprets the coded instructions, performs arithmetic and logical operations, and initiates the proper commands to the computer circuits for execution.

Centripetal torque The torque term in dynamic equations that is proportional to the square of a robot joint velocity.

Fairchild Charge-Coupled Device (CCD) industrial camera.

Charge-coupled device camera (CCD)   A machine vision image sensor that uses camera (CCD) semiconductor arrays so that the electric charge at the output of one provides input stimulus to the next.

Clamp   The function of a pneumatic hand that controls grasping and releasing of an object.

Closed-loop control   Robot control that uses a feedback loop to measure and compare actual system performance with desired performance, and then makes adjustments accordingly.

Complex sensor   Vision, sonar, and tactile sensors that will enable a robot to interact with the work environment.

Compliance   Robot manipulator compliance is an indication of displacement in response to a force or torque. A high compliance means the manipulator moves a good bit when it is stressed and therefore would be termed spongy or springy. Low compliance would be characterized by a stiff system.

Computed path control   A control scheme wherein the path of the manipulator end is computed to achieve a desired result in conformance to a given criterion, such as acceleration limit or a minimum time.

Contact sensor   A device that detects the presence of an object or measures the amount of force or torque applied by the object through physical contact with it. Contact sensing of force, torque, and touch can be usefully combined with visual sensing for many material-handling and assembly tasks. The function of contact sensors in controlling manipulation can be classified into the following basic material-handling and assembly operations: searching— detecting a part by sensitive touch sensors on the hand exterior without moving the part; recognition—determining the identity, position, and orientation of a part, again without moving it, by sensitive touch sensors with high spatial resolution; grasping—acquiring the part by deformable, roundish fingers, with sensors mounted on their surfaces; and moving—placing, joining, or inserting a part with the aid of sensors.

Continuous path motion   A type of robot motion in which the entire path followed by the manipulator arm is programmed on a constant time base during teaching, so that every point along the path of motion is recorded for future playback.

Controlled path   A servodriven robot with a control system that specifies or commands the location and orientation of all robot axes. This allows the robot to move in a straight line between programmed points with the added benefit of real-time velocity.

ASEA robot driven by the ASEA controller.

Controller   A computer, or group of computers, used to control a machine tool, robot, or similar device or group of devices. They may be arranged in a hierarchy so that, for example, a workstation controller may issue ''commands'' to a robot controller or machine-tool controller. The robot brain that directs the motion of the end-effector so that it is both positioned and oriented correctly in space over time.

Coordinate reference   Robots can be classified according to the spatial reference system defining their three axes of motion (x,y,z). These three will produce vertical, horizontal, and in–out motion about the robot center of motion, normally its fixed base. There are presently four basic geometric configurations in use for robot motion, each of which offers more or less freedom of activity, with a corresponding cost dependency, the more agile being the more costly. The job will determine the choice most suitable for use. (1) Rectangular or Cartesian motion—moving in the classical up–down, left–right, in–out directions. The wrist can be controlled in height, width, and depth of operation with a great degree of accuracy. (2) Cylindrical or rotational motion—an extendable arm moves up and down as well as in and out from a central pole, and swivels angularly around the pole. (3) Polar or spherical motion—an extended arm mounted on a central pivot reaches above and below its pivot point and rotates angularly around the pivot. (4) Revolute or jointed-arm motion—a humanlike arm can bend and swivel at the shoulder and bend at the elbow. This motion allows the arm to move back close to the base, extending the work area of the robot.

Coordinated axis control   Control wherein the axes of the robot arrive at their respective end points simultaneously, giving a smooth appearance to the motion. Control wherein the motions of the axes are such that the end point moves along a prespecified type of path (line, circle, and so forth). Also called end-point control.

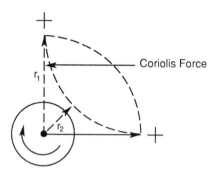

Illustration of coriolis forces in a robot. (Source: NIST, *A Glossary of Terms for Robotics.*)

Coriolis force   The coriolis force is the deflecting effect opposite the direction of rotation when the velocity of the robot arm is constant but the length of the arm is changed. An opposing torque (in the direction of rotation) must be applied to overcome this force.

Coriolis torque   The torque term in dynamic equations that is proportional to the product of joint velocities from two different links.

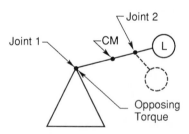

Illustration of coupling forces for a robot. (Source: NIST, *A Glossary of Terms for Robotics.*)

Coupling force   Coupling forces (torques) arise from the acceleration of the robot's net center of mass measured from one joint due to the accelerations of other joints. These factors have a much greater impact on the control of the arm than do centrifugal or coriolis forces.

Cycle   One complete sequence of robot motions from the start of one operation to the start of another.

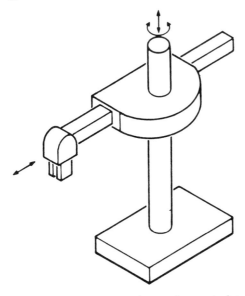

Illustration of cylindrical-coordinate robot manipulator.

Cylindrical coordinate robot   A robot whose manipulator arm consists of a primary vertical slide axis on a rotary axis. The vertical slide axis and a second slide are at right angles to one another in such a way that the shape traced by a point at the end of the farthest axis at full extension is that of a cylinder. A robot whose manipulator arm degrees of robot freedom are defined primarily by cylindrical coordinates.

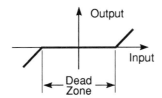

Illustration of no output in dead zone. (From NIST, *A Glossary of Terms for Robotics.*)

Dead zone   A range within which a nonzero input causes no output.

Degree of disorder   Inability of robots to operate in a disorderly environment. Parts to be handled or worked on must be in a known place and have a known orientation. For a simple robot, this must always be the same position and attitude.

Degree of freedom   One of a limited number of ways in which a point or a body may move or in which a dynamic system may change, each way being expressed by an independent variable and all required to be specified if the physical state of the body or system is to be completely defined.

Differential positioning   The position difference obtained by providing pulses of compressed air to the air motor in opposite directions, resulting in more accurate positioning.

Direct kinematics   Finding the position of the end of the manipulator given a particular amount of motion at each robot joint.

Distal   Away from the base, toward the end-effector of the robot arm.

Distance guard   The guard, used in robotics, may take the form of a fixed barrier or fence designed to prevent normal access to a danger area, or a fixed access tunnel that prevents access to a danger point because of the relationship of the opening dimensions of the guard to the length of tunnel.

Downtime   The period during which a production line robot, computer, communications line, or other device is malfunctioning or not operating correctly because of mechanical or electronic failure, as opposed to available time, idle time, or standby time.

Drift   The tendency of the robot to gradually move away from the desired response.

Drive power   The source or means of supplying energy to the robot actuators to produce motion.

Drum sequencer   A mechanical programming device that can be used to operate limit switches or valves to control a robot.

Eddy-current detector   Sensor that uses small coils in the robot manipulator that are stimulated when in the proximity of metal. The smaller the coil, the closer the manipulator must approach to effect a detection and, therefore, the more precise the location has become.

Effector   A robot actuator, motor, or driven mechanical device.

Elbow   The joint that connects the robot's upper arm and forearm.

Electrically actuated robot   Robots driven either by stepping motors or dc motors. They are generally quiet and take up less space than the other types of robots and have excellent accuracy and repeatability. They also tend to be less powerful and are more expensive than the other choices.

Electrostatic sensor   Sensors that can sense proximity but are susceptible to background conditions, including the electrostatic body charge of the operator, which can vary considerably from day to day depending on humidity. The capacitive effects of objects can also be detected by highly sensitive field effect devices, similar to those used in elevator buttons that are activated by touch, which react to the capacity of the human to ground.

Encoder   A transducer used to convert angular or linear position or velocity into electrical signals. A device used to convert one form of information into another. A feedback device that generates pulses as it rotates. The source of the pulses is often an interrupted light beam. Encoders are becoming popular with Computer Numerical Control (CNC) systems because of their digital quality that can be readily compared with the pulses generated by the CNC system. The robot system uses an incremental optical encoder to provide position feedback for each joint. Velocity data are computed from the encoder signals and used as an additional feedback signal to assure servostability.

Encoder accuracy   The maximum positional difference between the input to an encoder and the position indicated by its output. Includes both deviation from theoretical code transition positions and quantizing uncertainty caused by converting from a scale having an infinite number of points to a digital representation containing a finite number of points.

End-effector   A tool or gripping mechanism attached to the "wrist" of a robot to accomplish some task. While gripping mechanisms can be thought of as robotic "hands," end-effectors also include single-purpose attachments such as paint guns, drills, and arc welders.

End of axis control   Controlling the delivery of tooling through a path or to a point by driving each axis of a robot in sequence. The joints arrive at their preprogrammed positions in a given axis before the next joint sequence is actuated.

End-point control   Any control scheme in which only the motion of the manipulator end point may be controlled and the computer can control the actuators at the various degrees of freedom to achieve the desired result.

End-point rigidity   The resistance of the robot hand, tool, or end point of a manipulator arm to motion under applied force.

Envelope   The set of points representing the maximum extent or reach of the robot hand or working tool in all directions. The work envelope can be reduced or restricted by limiting devices that establish limits that will not be exceeded in the event of any foreseeable failure of the robot or its controls.

Exoskeleton   An articulated mechanism whose joints correspond to those of a human arm and, when attached to the arm of a human operator, will move in correspondence to his or her arm.

External sensor   A feedback device that is outside the inherent makeup of a robot system or a device used to effect the actions of a robot system that are used to source a signal independent of the robot's internal design.

Fail safe   Failure of a device without danger to personnel or damage to product or plant facilities.

Fail soft   Failure in performance of some component part of a system without immediate major interruption or failure of performance of the system as a whole and/or sacrifice in quality of the product.

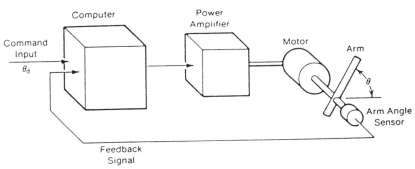

A feedback control system for controlling a single manipulator arm about one axis. (From *Robotics and Automated Manufacturing* by Richard C. Dorf.)

Feedback control   A type of system control obtained when a portion of the output signal is operated upon and fed back to the input to obtain a desired effect. A guidance technique used by robots to bring the end-effector to a programmed point.

Feedback device   Device installed to sense the positions of the various links and joints and transmit this information to the controller. These feedback devices may be simply limit switches actuated by the robot's arm or position-measuring devices such as encoders, potentiometers, or resolvers and/or tachometers to measure speed. Depending on the devices used, the feedback data are either digital or analog.

Findpath problem   The geometric problem of finding a path for a moving solid among other solid obstacles.

Fixed guard   A barrier not readily removable, to prevent entry of personnel into potentially dangerous areas.

Fixed stop robot   A robot with stop point control but no trajectory control, that is, each of its axes has a fixed limit at each end of its stroke and cannot stop except at one or the other of these limits. Such a robot with N degrees of freedom can therefore stop at no more than two N locations (where location includes position and orientation). Some controllers do offer the capability of program selection of one of several mechanical stops to be used. Often very good repeatability can be obtained with a fixed stop robot. Also called a non-servo robot.

Fixture   A device that holds a workpiece in position in a machine tool for machining. The workpiece must be held in a precise position, with no room for slippage, so if the shape is at all complex a special fixture is usually built to hold the piece. Device used to hold a part such that its reference axes are in a defined orientation with respect to the reference axes of a tool; may or may not be an integral part of a pallet.

Flexibility   The ability of a robot or other advanced manufacturing technology to perform a variety of different tasks.

Flexion   Orientation or motion toward a position where the joint angle between two connected bodies is small.

Force feedback   A sensing technique using electrical or hydraulic signals to control a robot end-effector.

Force sensor   A sensor capable of measuring the forces and torques exerted by a robot at its wrist.

Forearm   That portion of a jointed arm robot that is connected to the wrist.

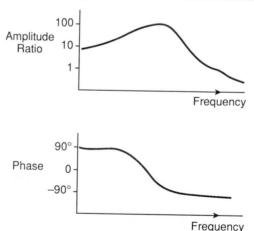

Illustration of gain and phase relationship curve of robot system output. (Source: NIST, *A Glossary of Terms for Robotics*.)

Frequency response   The output of a system with a periodic input. Frequency response may be defined in terms of the Fourier coefficients or the gain and phase at each multiple of the period. The characterization of system output to a continuous spectral input, according to a continuous plot of gain and phase as a function of frequency.

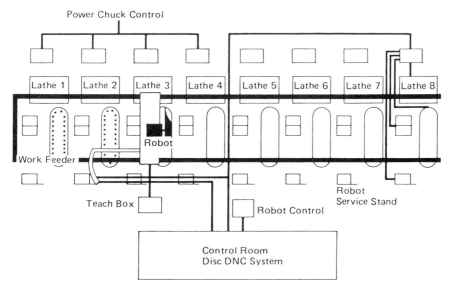

Diagram of an overhead gantry robot system. (From *Robotics in Practice* by Joseph F. Engelberger.)

Gantry robot   A bridgelike frame along which a suspended robot moves. A gantry creates a much larger work envelope than the robot would have if it were pedestal mounted.

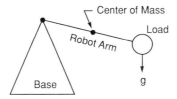

Illustration of gravity loading in a robot system. (Source: NIST, *A Glossary of Terms for Robotics.*)

Gravity loading   The force exerted downward, due to the weight of the robot arm and/or the load at end-of-arm. The force creates an error, with respect to position accuracy, at each joint in relation to the horizontal. The force exerted also creates an effective centroid of mass whereby a compensating torque can be computed. This is normally calculated by the robot controller, which brings the arm back to the desired position.

Gripper   An actuator, gripper, or mechanical device attached to the wrist of a manipulator by which objects can be grasped or otherwise acted upon.

Guard   A physical means of separating persons from danger from robots or hazardous machines.

Half-bridge robot   A half-bridge robot is a Cartesian robot in which there is a north–south axis and an up–down axis but no east–west axis.

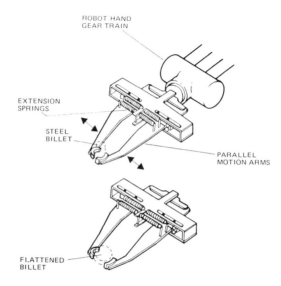

Special hand design for holding hot metal billets. (From *Robotics in Practice* by Joseph F. Engelberger.)

Hand   A clamp or gripper used to grasp objects that is attached to the end of the manipulator arm of an industrial robot.

Job	Typical hazards
Battery makers	Exposure to lead, alkali, sulfuric acid, cobalt, epoxy resins, mercury, nickel, solvents, pitch.
Electric appliance workers	Exposure to noise, ionizing radiation, acids, asbestos, chlorinated biphenyls, chlorinated naphthalenes, enamels, epoxy resins, phenolic resins, pitch, rubber, solder fluxes, solvents, varnishes.
Electronics workers, integrated circuits	Exposure to hydrofluoric, nitric, hydrochloric, phosphoric, and acetic acids; strong bases: arsenic; arsine; phosphine; fluorcarbons; solvents; infrared and ultraviolet radiation; laser light; x-radiation; noise
Electroplates	Exposure to acids, alkalis, benzene, chromic acid, heat, lime, nickel, potassium cyanide chlorinated waxes, zinc cyanide.
Machinists	Exposure to noice, antioxidants, aqueous cutting fluids, synthetic chlorinated cutting oils, chromates, germicides, greases, insoluble cutting oils, lubricants, rust inhibitors, soluble cutting fluids, solvents.
Welders	Exposure to heat, ultraviolet radiation, fluxes, metallic oxides, ozone, phosgene.

Typical industrial job hazards.

Hazard   A condition or changing set of circumstances that presents a potential for injury, illness, or property damage. The potential or inherent characteristics of an activity, condition, or circumstance that can produce adverse or harmful consequences.

Hazardous motion   Unintended or unexpected robot motion that may cause injury.

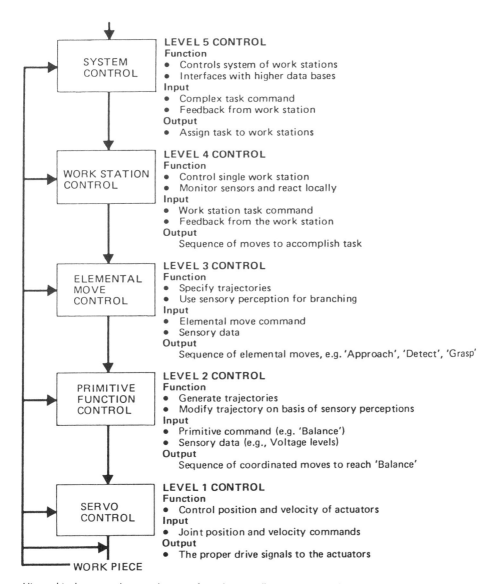

LEVEL 5 CONTROL
Function
- Controls system of work stations
- Interfaces with higher data bases

Input
- Complex task command
- Feedback from work station

Output
- Assign task to work stations

LEVEL 4 CONTROL
Function
- Control single work station
- Monitor sensors and react locally

Input
- Work station task command
- Feedback from the work station

Output
  Sequence of moves to accomplish task

LEVEL 3 CONTROL
Function
- Specify trajectories
- Use sensory perception for branching

Input
- Elemental move command
- Sensory data

Output
  Sequence of elemental moves, e.g. 'Approach', 'Detect', 'Grasp'

LEVEL 2 CONTROL
Function
- Generate trajectories
- Modify trajectory on basis of sensory perceptions

Input
- Primitive command (e.g. 'Balance')
- Sensory data (e.g., Voltage levels)

Output
  Sequence of coordinated moves to reach 'Balance'

LEVEL 1 CONTROL
Function
- Control position and velocity of actuators

Input
- Joint position and velocity commands

Output
- The proper drive signals to the actuators

System blocks: SYSTEM CONTROL, WORK STATION CONTROL, ELEMENTAL MOVE CONTROL, PRIMITIVE FUNCTION CONTROL, SERVO CONTROL, WORK PIECE

Hierarchical approach control system for robot installation. (From *Robotics in Practice* by Joseph F. Engelberger.)

Hierarchical approach   An approach to machine vision that is based on a series of ordered processing levels in which the degree of abstraction increases from the image level to the interpretation level.

Hierarchical control   A computer control scheme in which the data processing necessary to accomplish a task is split into discrete levels, with the outputs of higher levels being used as input commands for lower levels. Upper levels of the hierarchy split complex tasks into subtasks, and each subtask is similarly split up by a lower element in the hierarchy. Such systems tend to be fast and efficient, because they can be designed so that decisions are made no higher in the architecture than necessary.

Hydraulic motor   An actuator consisting of interconnected valves or pistons or vanes that converts high-pressure hydraulic or pneumatic fluid into mechanical shaft translation or rotation.

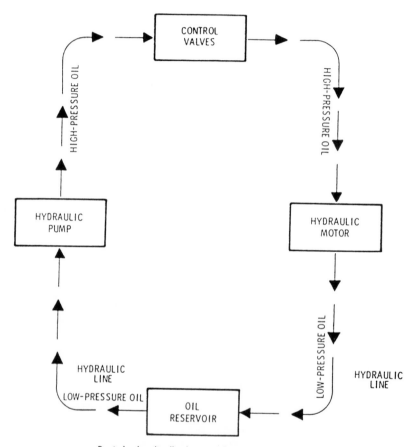

Basic hydraulically driven robot system elements.

Hydraulically driven robot   Robots that are mechanically simpler than their robot electrically driven counterparts and have both the physical strength and high speed essential in the most successful robots. While they use hydraulic servo valves and analog resolvers for control and feedback, digital encoders and modern resolvers can provide a very high repeatability and accuracy. This robot type normally includes a hydraulic power supply as either an integral part of the manipulator or as a separate unit. The hydraulic system consists of an electric-motor-driven pump, filter, reservoir, and usually a heat exchanger (either air or water). These robots normally operate on petroleum-based hydraulic fluid; however, most are available with special seals for operation on fire-retardant fluid.

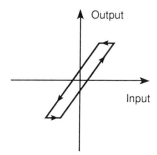

Illustration of hysteresis loop. (Source: NIST, *A Glossary of Terms for Robotics.*)

Hysteresis loop   Curve showing relationship between magnetizing force and magnetic induction in a material in a cyclically magnetized condition. For each value and direction of magnetizing force, there are two values of induction: (1) when the magnetizing force is increasing and (2) when the magnetizing force is decreasing. Result is actually two smooth curves joined at ends to form a loop.

Independent joint control   A control scheme in which the actuator for each joint receives feedback only from the sensor(s) for that joint.

Inductive sensor   The class of proximity switch using an Radio Frequency (RF) field, typically employing one-half of a ferrite core, whose coil is part of an oscillator circuit. When a metallic object enters this field, at some point the object will absorb enough energy from the field to cause the oscillator to stop oscillating. It is this difference between oscillating or not oscillating that is detected as the difference between an object being present or not present.

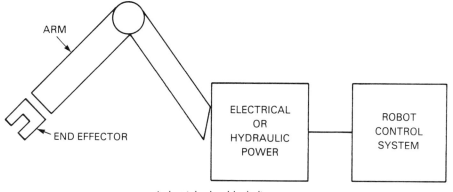

Industrial robot block diagram.

Industrial robot   A reprogrammable, multifunctional manipulator designed to move material, parts, tools, or specialized devices through variable programmed motions for the performance of a variety of tasks. The principal components of an industrial robot are (1) one or more arms, usually situated on a fixed base, that can move in several directions; (2) a manipulator, the working tool of the robot, is the "hand" that holds the tool or the part to be worked; and (3) a computer controller that gives detailed movement instructions.

Inertial torque The torque term in dynamic equations that is proportional to the robot joint accelerations.

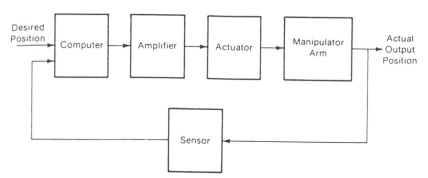

The computer control of an intelligent robot. (From *Robotics and Automated Manufacturing* by Richard C. Dorf.)

Intelligent robot A robot that can be programmed to make performance choices contingent on sensory inputs.

Interface A boundary between the robot and machines, transfer lines, or parts outside of its immediate environment. The robot must communicate with these items through input or output signals provided by sensors.

Interlock A safety device that prevents the robot from operating further until some condition has been satisfied.

Internal sensor A feedback device in the robot manipulator arm that provides data to the controller on the position of the arm.

Interrupt A break in the normal flow of a system or program occurring in such a way that the flow can be resumed from that point at a later time. Interrupts are initiated by signals of two types: (1) signals originating within the computer system with the outside world (e.g., an operator or a physical process) or (2) signals originating exterior to the computer systems to synchronize the operation of the computer system with the outside world (e.g., an operator or a physical process).

Inverse kinematics Finding the required amount of motion at each joint for a given position of the end of the robot manipulator.

Jacobian A matrix that relates the joint velocities to the Cartesian velocities of the robot manipulator tip.

Joint A rotational or translational degree of freedom in a manipulator system. It connects two links and permits relative motion.

Joint interpolated motion A method of coordinating the movement of the joints, such that all joints arrive at the desired location simultaneously. This method of servocontrol produces a predictable path regardless of speed and results in the fastest cycle time for a particular move.

Joint space The space defined by a vector whose components are the angular or translational displacement of each joint of a multi-degree-of-freedom linkage relative to a reference displacement for each such joint.

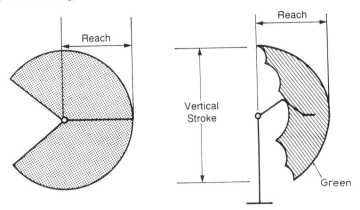

Jointed-arm robot work envelope.

Jointed-arm robot   A robot whose arm consists of two links connected by "elbow" and "shoulder" joints to provide three rotational motions. This robot most closely resembles the movement of the human arm.

Kinematic error   Kinematic errors of coordination between the various moving bodies that make up a machine, that is, deviations from ideal.

Kinematic mount   A mount that mechanically constrains an object by the minimum number of constraints necessary to prevent undesired motion.

Kinematics   Position, velocity, and acceleration relationships among the links of the robot manipulator.

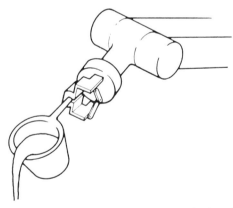

Robot ladle gripper mechanism. (From *Robotics in Practice* by Joseph F. Engelberger.)

Ladle gripper   Ladling hot materials such as molten metal is a hot and hazardous job for which industrial robots are well-suited. In piston casting, permanent mold die casting, and related applications, the robot can be programmed to scoop up and transfer the molten metal from the pot to the mold, and then do the pouring. In cases where dross will form, dipping techniques will often keep it out of the mold.

LaGrangian formulation   An approach toward deriving the dynamic equations of motion for manipulators using LaGrangian equations.

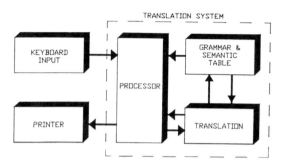

Block diagram of language translation.

Language translator A general term for any assembler, compiler, or other routine that accepts statements in one language and produces equivalent machine language instructions.

Leadthrough A means of teaching a robot by leading it through the operating sequence with a control console or a hand-held control box.

Light interferometer Robot sensors used when a greater accuracy is required. They generally use a short-wavelength light source and, like acoustic proximity systems, sense interfering patterns that occur as exact harmonics of the transmitted light.

Limit-detecting hardware A device for stopping robot motion independently from control logic.

Limit switch An electrical switch that is actuated when the limit of a certain motion is reached and the actuator causing the motion is deactivated.

Limited-degree-of-freedom robot A robot able to position and orient its end-effector in fewer than six degrees of freedom.

Limited sequence robot A simple or nonservo type of robot. Movement is controlled by a series of limit or stop switches. Also called bang-bang robot.

Limiting device To qualify as a means for restricting the work envelope, these devices must stop all motion of the robot independent of control logic.

Line synchronization The ability to synchronize the operation of an industrial robot with a moving production line so that the robot automatically compensates for variations in line speed.

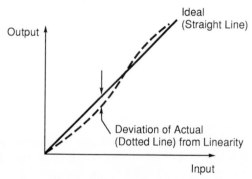

Graph of ideal versus actual linearity. (From NIST, *A Glossary of Terms for Robotics.*)

Linearity   The degree to which an input/output is a directly proportional relationship.

Link   Rigid bodies of a robot arm that form chains or linkages.

Load   The power delivered to a machine or apparatus. The weight (force) applied to the end of the robot arm. A device intentionally placed in a circuit or connected to a machine or apparatus to absorb power and convert it into the desired useful form. To insert data into memory storage. In computer operations, the amount of scheduled work, usually expressed in terms of hours of work. In programming, to feed data or programs into the computer.

Load capacity   The maximum total weight that can be applied to the end of the robot arm without sacrifice of any of the applicable published specifications of the robot.

Load deflection   The difference in position of some point in a body between a nonloaded and an externally loaded condition. The difference in position of a manipulator hand or tool, usually with the arm extended, between a nonloaded condition and an externally loaded condition. Either or both static and dynamic loads may be considered.

Load-handling capacity   Considerations must be given to the weight of the work item being manipulated. The tool, the paint gun, the welder, or the items to be moved are at the end of the robot arm, and their weights and movements will impact the work volume.

Locating surface   Machined surfaces on a part that are used as reference surfaces for precise locating and clamping of the part in a fixture.

Long-term repeatability   Closeness of agreement of repeated position repeatability movements, under the same conditions, to the same location. The degree to which an industrial robot or other programmable mechanism can repeatedly locate either of the end points, the program path, or a cycle over a long period of time, under the same conditions.

Magnetic detector   Robot sensor that can sense the presence of ferromagnetic material. Solid-state detectors with appropriate amplification and processing can locate a metal object to a high degree of precision.

Major motion axes   May be described as the number of independent directions the robot arm can move the attached wrist and end-effector relative to a point of origin of the manipulator, such as the base. The number of robot arm axes required to reach world coordinate points is dependent on the design of the robot arm configuration.

Manipulation   The process of controlling and monitoring data table bits or words by means of the user's program in order to vary application functions. Grasping, releasing, moving, transporting, or otherwise handling an object.

Manipulator   A mechanism usually consisting of a series of segments, jointed or sliding relative to one another, for the purpose of grasping and moving objects usually in several degrees of freedom.

Manipulator-oriented language   Programming language for describing exactly where a robot's arm and gripper should go and when. To be contrasted with task-oriented languages for describing what the effect of robot action should be.

Manual control   A device containing controls that manipulate the robot arm and allow for the recording of locations and program motion instructions.

Master control relay   A mandatory hardwired relay that can be de-energized by any hardwired series-connected emergency stop switch. Whenever the master control relay is de-energized, its contacts must open to de-energize all applications I/O devices and power source.

Material-handling robot   A robot designed to grasp, move, transport, or otherwise handle parts of materials in a manufacturing operation.

Volvo material-handling system.

Material-handling system   System or systems used to move and store parts, as well as materials used in processing the parts (e.g., tools, coolant, wastes).

Material-processing robot   A robot designed and programmed so that it can machine, cut, form, or in some way change the shape, function, or properties of the materials it handles between the time the materials are first grasped and the time they are released in a manufacturing process.

Mechatronics   A term coined by the Japanese to describe the integration of mechanical and electronic engineering. The concept specifically refers to a multidisciplined, integrated approach to product and manufacturing system design and encompasses the next generation of machines, robots, and smart mechanisms for advanced manufacturing technology. The environments for mechatronics are primarily factory automation, office automation, and home automation.

Memory capacity   The number of actions that a robot can perform in a program.

Metal-arc welding   Arc welding with metal electrodes. Commonly refers to shielded metal-arc welding using covered electrodes.

Metal inert-gas welding   A method of joining two ferrous metal parts by passing a heavy electrical current from a metal rod to the grounded parts. The resulting electric discharge melts the metal rod and the part joints together to form a weld. This process normally is conducted with a shielding gas that prevents oxidation of the molten joint and thus increases weld integrity.

Microprocessor   A compact element of a computer central processing unit constructed as a single integrated unit, and increasingly used as a control unit for robots.

Minor axes   The robot axes may be described as the number of independent attitudes that the wrist can orient the attached end-effector. Relative to the mounting point of the wrist assembly on the arm. In machine vision, the axis of minimum elongation of a blob in a plane. Derived from second moment calculations.

Mobile robot   A robot mounted on a movable platform. The motions of the robot about the workplace are controlled by the robot's control system.

Motion axis   The line defining the axis of motion, either linear or rotary, of a machine element.

Motor controller   A device or group of devices that serves to govern, in a predetermined manner, the electrical power delivered to a motor.

Net load capacity   The additional weight or mass of a material that can be handled by a machine or process without failure over and above that required for a container, pallet, or other device that necessarily accompanies the material.

Network security   The measures taken to protect a network from an unauthorized access, accidental or willful interference with normal operations, or destruction, including protection of physical facilities, software, and personnel security.

Newton–Euler formulation   An approach toward deriving the dynamic equations of motion for manipulators using Newton–Euler equations.

Noise immunity   The ability of the computer or robot controller to reject unwanted noise signals.

Object-oriented language   In robotics, a synonym for task-oriented language. In general use, a programming language in which procedures for doing things are accessed through descriptions of the things to be worked on.

Object-oriented programming   A programming approach focused on objects that communicate by message passing. An object is considered to be a package of information and descriptions of procedures that can manipulate that information.

Off-line programming   Defining the sequences and conditions of actions on a computer system that is independent of the robot's "on-board" control. The prepackaged program is loaded into the robot's controller for subsequent automatic action of the manipulator.

On-line programming   A means of programming a robot on a computer that directly controls the robot. The programming is performed in real time.

Open-loop control   A system of robot control that does not rely on a feedback loop for measuring performance. In open-loop control, communication is in one direction only.

Operating range The reach capability of a robot. Also called work envelope.

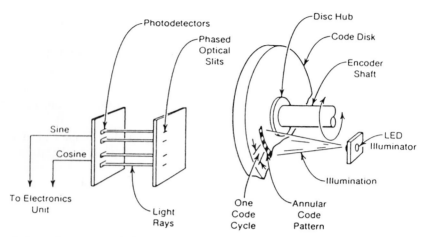

An optical encoder measures shaft rotation by detecting the light that passes through a rotating code disk. (From *Robotics and Automated Manufacturing* by Richard C. Dorf.)

Optical encoder A device that measures linear or rotary motion by detecting the movement of markings past a fixed beam of light.

Optical proximity sensor Robot sensor that measures visible or invisible light reflected from an object to determine distance. Light sources can be from incandescent lights, light-emitting diodes (LED), or, for greater precision, from laser sources.

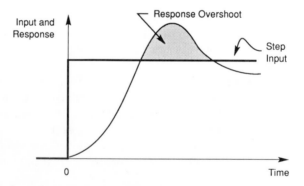

Illustration of overshoot response curve. (Source: NIST, *A Glossary of Terms for Robotics.*)

Overshoot The degree to which a system response to a step change in reference input goes beyond the desired value. The amount of overtravel beyond the command position. The amount of overshoot is related to factors such as system gain, servoresponse, mechanical clearances, and inertia factors relating to mass, feedrate, and strain.

Payback period A measure of the economic benefit of a capital expenditure. It is the year when the cash flow of the investment equals the cash flow of the expense; when cumulative revenue equals cumulative expenditure.

Payload   The mass that can be moved by the robot, given its specified performance in terms of accuracy, speed, repeatability, and the like. Larger payloads may sometimes be accommodated at reduced performance by the robot (e.g., slower speed). Maximum weight carried at normal speed—also called workload.

Pendant   Any portable control device, including teach pendants, that permits an operator to control the robot from within the work envelope of the robot.

Pendant control   A control panel mounted on a pendant cable that enables the human operator to stand in the most favorable position to observe, control, and record the desired movements in the robot's memory.

Perception   A robot's ability to sense its environment by sight, touch, or some other means, and to understand it in terms of a task, for example, the ability to recognize an obstruction or find a designated object in an arbitrary location. An active process in which hypotheses are formed about the nature of the environment or sensory information is sought to confirm or refute hypotheses.

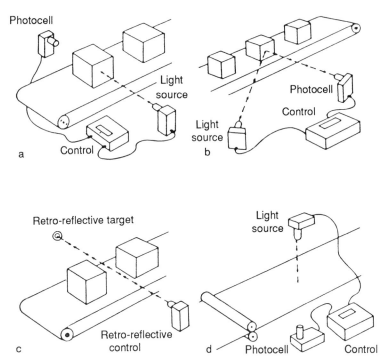

Examples of photoelectric proximity sensor controls. (a) Interrupted light system using dark-operated counter or control, (b) reflected light system using light-operated counter or control, (c) typical arrangement of a retroreflective system used for jam control or empty-line control, (d) interrupted light system using light-operated control to detect break in material. (Courtesy of Scanning Devices Company.)

Photoelectric proximity sensor   A version of the photoelectric tube and light source. These sensors are well-adapted for controlling the motion of a robot manipulator. They consist of a solid-state light-emitting diode (LED) that acts as a transmitter of infrared light and a solid-state photodiode that acts as a receiver. Both are mounted in a small package.

Pick-and-place robot　A simple robot often with only two or three degrees of freedom. A pick-and-place robot transfers items from place to place by means of point-to-point moves. Little or no trajectory control is available. Often referred to as a bang-bang robot.

Pitch　Rotation of the end-effector in a vertical plane around the end of the manipulator arm.

Playback accuracy　Difference between a position command recorded in an automatic control system and that actually produced at a later time, when the recorded position is used to execute control. Difference between actual position response of an automatic control system during a programming or teaching run and that corresponding response in a subsequent run.

Playback robot　A manipulator that can produce, from memory, operations originally executed under human control. A human operator initially operates the robot to input instructions. All the information relevant to the operations (sequence, conditions, and positions) is put in memory. When needed, this information is recalled (or played back, hence its name) and the operations are repetitively executed automatically from memory.

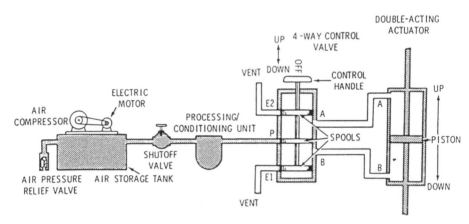

Simple pneumatically driven robot system.

Pneumatically driven robot　Robots in which compressed air drives the robot mechanical arm and often used for small, limited-sequence activities, for example, pick and place, where speed or precision is not critical. They tend to be lightweight, fast, and comparatively inexpensive—partly because of their limited capabilities—and their relative simplicity keeps the reliability high and the corresponding maintenance cost down. Such robots are employed in places where there is already a source of compressed air available that is being used for other purposes.

Point-to-point motion　A type of robot motion in which a limited number of points along a path of motion is specified by the controller, and the robot moves from point to point rather than in a continuous smooth path.

Polar coordinate system　A coordinate system, two of whose dimensions are angles and the third being a linear distance from the point of origin. These three coordinates specify a point on a sphere.

Position error　In a servomechanism that operates a manipulator joint, the difference between the actual position of that joint and the commanded position.

Positioning accuracy and repeatability A term often used to denote the difference between the true displacement of a machine and that recorded by the machine measurement system (scale). The term is ambiguous in that the line of measurement must be specified because of Abbe offsets on any real machine. Accuracy is a measure of the robot's ability to move to a programmed position. Repeatability is its ability to do this time after time. With the pick-and-place robot, accuracy and repeatability are interchangeable. With a programmable robot, repeatability can be improved by fine-tuning the controls.

Presence-sensing safeguarding device A device designed, constructed, and installed to create a sensing field or area to detect an intrusion into such a field or area by personnel, robots, or other objects.

Prismatic joint A joint that allows only translational relative motion between links.

Prismatic part A rectangular or box-shaped part, usually processed on a machining center.

Process control Pertaining to systems whose purpose is to provide automation of continuous operations, and characterized by in-line adjustments to regulate an operation. This is contrasted with numerical control, which provides automation of discrete operations.

Process simulation A program utilizing a mathematical model created on the system to try out numerous process design iterations with real-time visual and numerical feedback. Designers can see on the CRT what is taking place at every stage in the manufacturing process. They can therefore optimize a process and correct problems that could affect the actual manufacturing process downstream.

Product definition Data required to describe and communicate the characteristics of physical objects as manufactured products.

Programmable Capable of being instructed to operate in a specified manner of accepting set points or other commands from a remote source. A feature of a robot that allows it to be instructed to perform a sequence of steps, and then to perform this sequence in a repetitive manner. It can then be reprogrammed to perform a different sequence of steps if desired.

Programmable controller A solid-state control system that has a user-controller programmable memory for storage of instructions to implement specific functions such as I/O control logic, timing, counting, arithmetic, and data manipulation. A personal computer consists of a central processor, input/output interface, memory, and programming device that typically uses relay-equivalent symbols. The personal computer is purposely designed as an industrial control system that can perform functions equivalent to a relay panel or a wired solid-state logic control system.

Programmable logic controller A stored program device intended to replace relay logic used in sequencing, timing, and counting of discrete events. Instead of physical wiring relay, push buttons, limit switches, and so on, a programmable logic controller is programmed to test the state of input lines, to set output lines in accordance with input state, or to branch to another set of tests. The instruction sets of these machines generally exclude all arithmetic and Boolean operators but do include vital decision instructions such as skip, transfer unconditional, transfer conditions, and even transfer and link.

Programmable manipulator A device that is capable of manipulating objects by executing a stored program resident in its memory.

Programming   The creation of a series of movements and/or work actions for the robot system, including step sequencing, time delays, speed conditions, direction, distance, tool actuation, and other conditional instructions.

Proximal   Close to the base, away from the robot end-effector of the arm.

Proximity sensor   A device that senses that an object is only a short distance (e.g., a few inches or feet) away and/or measures how far away it is. Proximity sensors work on the principles of triangulation of reflected light, elapsed time for reflected sound, intensity-induced eddy currents, magnetic fields, back pressure from air jets, and others. A noncontact sensor that determines when one object is close to another. Devices that sense and indicate the presence or absence of an object without requiring physical contact. Five of six major types of proximity sensors available commercially are radio frequency, magnetic bridge, ultrasonic, permanent-magnet hybrid, and photoelectric. Noncontact sensors have widespread use, such as for high-speed counting, indication of motion, sensing presence of ferrous materials, level control, reading of coding marks, and noncontact limit switches.

Query   A request for data entered while the computer system is processing. In data communication, the process by which a master station asks a slave station to identify itself and to give its status.

Queue   Waiting lines resulting from temporary delays in providing service. A series of elements, one waiting behind the other; a waiting line.

Range sensor   Range sensors are designed to measure the distance from the sensor to the object. If the sensor is located on the end of the robot arm, then the precise location of the arm has been specified. For industrial applications, the device should be able to measure distances from 1 to 10 feet with accuracies no less than one part in 300, and preferably one part in 1000. The device could then be useful to locate not only the manipulator, but other objects in the work area as well.

Raster   Parallel horizontal lines drawn by an electron gun on the face of a video monitor to display a video image. There are approximately 240 noninterlaced raster lines or 420 interlaced raster lines visible on a CRT.

Rated load capacity   A specified weight or mass of a material that can be handled by a machine or process that allows for some margin of safety relative to the point of expected failure.

Reach   Reach defines the robot's arm movement or work envelope. The work envelope usually has one of three shapes—cylindrical, spherical, or spheroidal—depending on the basic configuration of the arm and on the major axes of motion. For practical purposes, the description of the work envelope can be simplified by citing only its three major parameters: (1) degrees of rotation about the center axis (horizontal arm sweep); (2) vertical motion at both minimum and maximum arm extension; and (3) radial arm extension, measured from the center axis.

Record-playback robot   A manipulator for which the critical points along desired trajectories are stored in sequence by recording the actual values of the joint position encoders of the robot as it is moved under operator control. To perform the task, these points are played back to the robot servosystem.

Rectangular coordinate robot   A robot whose manipulator arm moves in linear motions along a set of Cartesian or rectangular axes. The work envelope forms the outline of a three-dimensional rectangular figure.

Rectilinear-Cartesian robot   A continuous path extended-reach robot that offers the versatility of multiple robots through the use of a bridge and trolley construction that enables it to have a large rectangular work envelope. Being ceiling mounted, such devices can service many stations with many functions, leaving the floor clear. x and y motions are performed by bridge and trolley, the vertical motions are performed by telescoping tubes, and additional axes can be used.

Relative coordinate system   A coordinate system whose origin moves relative to world or fixed coordinates.

Remote center compliance   A compliant device used to interface a robot or other mechanical workhead to its tool or working medium. The remote center compliance allows a gripped part to rotate about its tip or to translate without rotating when pushed laterally at its tip. The remote center compliance thus provides general lateral and rotational "float" and greatly eases robot or other mechanical assembly in the presence of errors in parts, jigs, pallets, and robots. It is especially useful in performing very close clearance or interference insertions.

Resistance welding   Welding with resistance heating and pressure, the work being part of the electrical circuit. Examples are resistance spot welding, resistance seam welding, projection welding, and flash butt welding.

Resolved motion rate control   A control scheme whereby the velocity vector of the end point of a manipulator arm is commanded and the computer determines the joint angular velocities to achieve the desired result.

Resolver   A transducer that converts rotary or linear mechanical position into an analog electrical signal by means of the interaction of electromagnetic fields between the movable and the stationary parts of the transducer.

Restricted work envelope   That portion of the work envelope to which a robot is restricted by limiting devices that establish limits that will not be exceeded in the event of any reasonably foreseeable failure of the robot or its controls. The maximum distance that the robot can travel after the limiting device is actuated shall be considered the basis for defining the restricted work envelope of the robot.

Revolute joint   A joint that allows only one rotational relative motion between links.

Right-handed Cartesian coordinate system   A coordinate system in which the axes are mutually perpendicular and are positioned in such a way that, when viewed along the positive z axis toward the origin, the positive x axis can be made to coincide with the positive y axis by rotating the x axis 90 degrees in the counterclockwise direction.

Robot   A reprogrammable multifunctional manipulator designed to move material, parts, tools, or specialized devices through variable programmed motions for the performance of a variety of tasks.

Robot motions   Types of work motions include: (1) anthropometric motion—motions of a robot as in a shoulder, an elbow and a wrist, developing a modified spherical work envelope; (2) cylindrical motion—motion of a robot's arm when mounted on a cylindrical axis; (3) polar motion—motions of a robot by two axes or rotation that create a modified spherical work envelope; (4) rectilinear motion—motions of a robot in three dimensions along straight lines (slides or channels).

Robot programming language A computer language especially designed for writing programs for controlling robots.

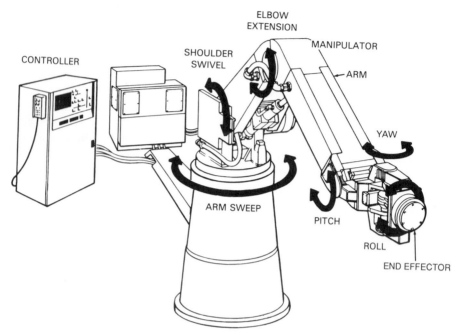

ELBOW
EXTENSION

MANIPULATOR

SHOULDER
SWIVEL

CONTROLLER

ARM

YAW

ARM SWEEP

PITCH

ROLL

END EFFECTOR

The controller, manipulator, and end-effector are the basic elements of a robot system. (Courtesy of Cincinnati Milacron.)

Robot system A robot system includes the robot hardware and software, consisting of the manipulator, power supply, and controller; the end-effector(s); any equipment, devices, and sensors the robot is directly interfacing with; any equipment, devices, and sensors required for the robot to perform its task; and any communications interface that is operating and monitoring the robot, equipment, and sensors.

Robot vision The use of a vision system to provide visual feedback to an industrial robot. Based on the vision system's interpretation of a scene, the robot may be commanded to move in a certain way.

Robotics The study of robots or the practice of using robots. The science of designing, building, and applying robots.

Roll Rotation of the end-effector in a plane perpendicular to the end of the manipulator arm.

Rotational motion A degree of freedom that defines motion of rotation about an axis.

SCARA robot (selective compliance assembly robot arm) A low-cost, high-speed assembly robot moving almost entirely on a horizontal plane. The mechanism originated with the Japanese.

Search function The search function in a robot system can adjust the position of data points within an existing cycle, based on changes in external equipment and workpieces. One use of the search function is in stacking operations, especially when the stacked items are fragile or have irregular thicknesses. The time delay inherent in deceleration from the input signal activation will permit some movement beyond the robot's receipt of the signal; so if the signal originates through a limit switch that is closed upon contact with the stack, some compliance must be built into the robot gripper. A fragile workpiece would also require a slow velocity during the search segment.

Semi-kinematic A robot mount that approximates a kinematic mount.

Sensor A sensor converts a pressure, temperature, or other physical parameter into an electrical signal, often for use in a control system. A transducer whose input is a physical phenomenon and whose output is a quantitative measure of that physical phenomenon. A "transducer" that takes in information about the physical state of things and converts it to an electrical signal that can be processed by a control system. Sensors can be simple, such as a temperature monitor on a machine tool, or highly complex, such as a machine vision system. Other sensors monitor things like torque on a robot wrist, the pressure exerted by robot grippers, or the vibrations in a workpiece being machined.

Sensory control Control of robot based on sensor readings. Several types can be employed: (1) sensors used in threshold tests to terminate robot activity or to branch to another activity, (2) sensors used in a continuous way to guide or direct changes in robot motions (see also active accommodation), (3) sensors used to monitor robot progress and to check for task completion or unsafe conditions, and (4) sensors used to retrospectively update robot motion plans prior to the next cycle.

Sensory-controlled robot A robot whose program sequence can be modified as a function of information sensed from its environment. Robot can be servoed or non-servoed.

Sequence robot A robot whose physical motion and trajectory follows a preprogrammed sequence.

Sequencer A controller that operates an application through a fixed sequence of events.

Characteristics	Nonservo	Servo Controlled	
		Point-to-Point	Continuous Path
Payload (lb)	2–1000	2–1250	10–100
Programming	Manual	Leadthrough	Walkthrough
Accuracy (in)	±0.0005–0.025	+0.0006–0.125	±0.030–0.200
Repeatability (in)	±0.0004–0.015	±0.0001–0.200	±0.002–0.160
Power rating (kVA)	Up to 4	Up to 32	Up to 10
Price range	$10,000–$30,000	$25,000–$75,000	$50,000–$200,000
Typical applications	Materials handling, assembly, inspection, machine loading	Materials handling, assembly, inspection, machine loading, spot welding, arc welding, machining	Arc welding, spraying, flame cutting, machining

Comparison of performance between nonservo to servo controlled robot.

Servo controlled robot The control of a robot through the use of a robot closed-loop servosystem, in which the position of a robot axis is measured by feedback devices and compared with a predetermined point stored in the controller's memory.

Servo mechanism   A mechanical or electromechanical device whose driving signal is determined by the difference between the commanded position and the actual position at any point in time. An automatic feedback control system for mechanical motion. A control system for the robot in which the computer issues commands, the air motor drives the arm, and a sensor measures the motion and signals the amount of the motion back to the computer. This process is continued until the arm is repositioned to the point requested. A powerful amplifying device that takes an input signal from some low-energy source and directs an output requiring large quantities of energy. A type of closed-loop control system in which mechanical position is the controlled variable.

Shaft encoder   A rotary encoder used to encode or determine the position of the rotary shaft.

Shoulder   The manipulator arm link joint that is attached to the robot base.

Smart robot   A robot that can make sophisticated decisions and behavioral choices through its sensing and recognizing capabilities.

Smart sensor   A sensing device whose output signal is contingent on mathematical or logical operations that are based on internal data or additional sensing devices.

Solenoid   An electromagnet with a movable core or plunger that, when it is energized, can move a small mechanical part a short distance.

Spatial resolution   Spatial resolution, a significant parameter in robot design, refers to the minimum or smallest dimension to which the system can define the work space. This resolution determines the smallest error that can be sensed by the robot, as limited by the minimum resolution of the controller or the minimum resolving increment of the servosystem, whichever is less.

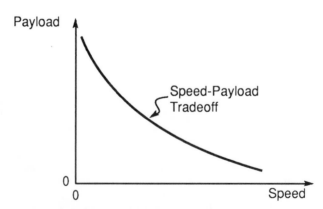

Speed–payload trade-off curve. (Source: NIST, *A Glossary of Terms for Robotics.*)

Speed–payload trade-off   The relationship between corresponding values of maximum speed and payloads with which an operation can be accomplished to some criterion of satisfaction, with all other factors remaining the same.

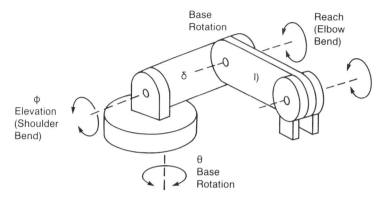

Spherical coordinate robot work envelope.

Spherical coordinate robot   A robot whose construction consists of a horizontally rotating base, a vertically rotating shoulder, and a linear transversing arm connected in such a way that the envelope traced by the end of the robot arm at full extension defines a sphere in space.

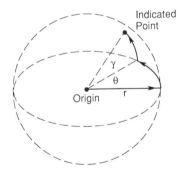

Illustration of origin, r, θ, and γ to indicated point. (Source: NIST, *A Glossary of Terms for Robotics.*)

Spherical coordinate system   A coordinate system, two of whose dimensions are angles and the third being a linear distance from the point of origin. These three coordinates specify a point on a sphere.

Spot welding   A method of fastening sheet metal parts together in which a heavy electric current is passed through the plates at a spot. This current rapidly heats and melts the two sheet metal plates together, forming a small round spot weld. Welding of lapped parts in which fusion is confined to a relatively small circular area. It is generally resistance welding but may also be gas-shielded tungsten-arc, gas-shielded metal-arc, or submerged-arc welding.

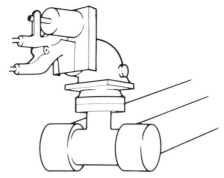

Example of a spot welding gun. (From *Robotics in Practice* by Joseph F. Engelberger.)

Spot welding gun   A general-purpose industrial robot can maneuver and operate a spot welding gun to place a series of spot welds on flat, simple-curved, or compound-curved surfaces.

Standard branching   Term for the way truly general-purpose industrial robot systems select or alter the programmed path and function, based on changes in the environment around them. The name given to such a facility may vary, but the purpose is the same. The robot reaches some point and interrogates an input signal to determine whether it is electrically active, or the robot is interrupted by activation of another input signal. In either case, the robot path "branches" to a section of the path/function program; if no signal is present at this decision point, or no interrupt occurs, the robot continues in a normal path sequence.

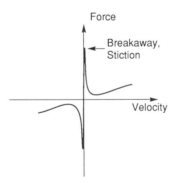

Illustration of static friction force elements. (Source: NIST, *A Glossary of Terms for Robotics.*)

Static friction   The force required to initiate sliding or rolling motion between two contacting bodies; also called stiction.

Statics   The relationship between the force and torque that the manipulator is exerting on the environment and the forces and torques at the robot links.

Supervisory-controlled robot   A robot incorporating a hierarchical control scheme whereby a device having sensors, actuators, and a computer and capable of autonomous decision making and control over short periods and restricted conditions is remotely monitored and intermittently operated directly or reprogrammed by a person.

Switch sequencing   A method of establishing logic sequences by setting a limit switch sequencing device and physical hardstops to control the axes' travel. A robot is considered reprogrammable if its switch sequencing and stop settings can be adapted to effect new motions without modifying the basic design.

Tactile   Perceived by the touch or having the sense of touch.

Tactile sensor   Sensors that respond to contact forces that arise between themselves and solid objects; the object must actually be touched, unlike proximity sensors. Tactile sensors can be classified into two groups: touch sensors and stress sensors. Touch sensors indicate contact; stress sensors indicate the magnitude of the contact forces. The most common touch sensor is the microswitch, while the most common stress sensor is the strain gage. A device, normally associated with the hand or gripper part of an industrial robot, which senses physical contact with an object, thus giving an industrial robot an artificial sense of touch. A transducer that is sensitive to touch.

Teach   To program a manipulator arm by guiding it through a series of points or in a motion pattern that is recorded for subsequent automatic action by the manipulator. To move a robot to or through a series of points to be stored for the robot to perform its intended task.

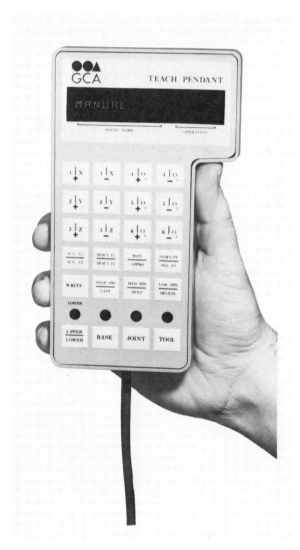

Typical teach pendant.

Teach pendant   The control box that an operator uses to guide a robot through the motions of its tasks. The motions are recorded by the control memory for future playback.

Teach restrict   A facility whereby the speed of movement of a robot during teaching, which during normal operation would be considered dangerous, is restricted to a safe speed.

Teleoperator   A master–slave device that produces movements identical to or in direct proportion to actions or motions of a remotely located human operator. The device communicates certain feedback information such as position, forces, and the like to the human operator. A device having sensors and actuators for mobility and/or manipulation that is remotely controlled by a human operator. A teleoperator can extend the human's sensory-motor function to remote or hazardous environments

Touch sensor   A sensor that detects the presence of an object by coming into contact with it.

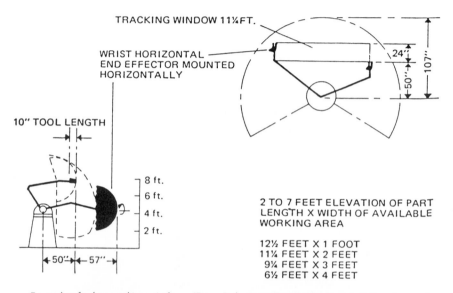

Example of robot tracking windows. (From *Robotics in Practice* by Joseph F. Engelberger.)

Tracking window   There are many parameters that influence the length of working range of the robot in the direction parallel to the moving line. This working range of the robot parallel to the line is termed the "tracking window." The height of the part on the conveyor, the distance of the robot from the conveyor, and the length and configuration of the end-effector all play a part in determining the tracking window. Therefore, every tracking application must be considered separately so that the robot is positioned correctly, relative to the conveyor, to ensure the optimum tracking window.

Trajectory   The motions of a robot. Trajectory consists of a time sequence of positions, velocities, and accelerations of some point such as the end-effector or manipulator tip.

Trajectory planning   The process of computing a sequence of positions, velocities, and accelerations for a given task. The resulting position, velocities, and accelerations are usually those in joint space.

Translational motion   Movement of a robot arm along one of three axes without rotation.

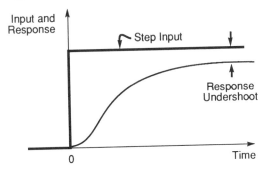

Illustration of undershoot response curve. (Source: NIST, *A Glossary of Terms for Robotics.*)

Undershoot   The degree to which a system response to step changes in reference input falls short of the desired value.

Upper arm   That portion of a jointed-arm robot that is connected to the shoulder.

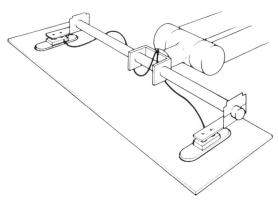

Illustration of a vacuum cup hand mechanism. (From *Robotics in Practice* by Joseph F. Engelberger.)

Vacuum cup hand   The vacuum pickup has the virtues of the magnetic pickup and is much less susceptible to workpiece sideslip. For light- to moderate-weight glass, plastic, ferrous, and nonferrous parts, the vacuum pickup is often an excellent choice.

Vision sensor   A sensor that identifies the shape, location, orientation, or dimensions of an object through visual feedback, such as a television camera.

Volatile memory   A memory system in a computer or control system that requires a continual source of electric current to maintain the data it is storing intact. Removal of power from a volatile memory system results in the loss of the data being stored.

Walkthrough programming   A method of programming a robot by physically moving the manipulator arm through a complete operating cycle. This is typically used for continuous path robots.

Work coordinates   The coordinate system referenced to the workpiece, jig, or fixture.

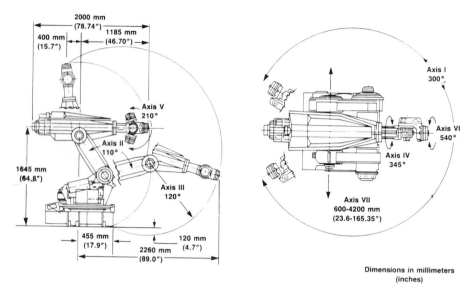

Work envelope for an industrial robot.

Work envelope   The set of points representing the maximum extent or reach of the robot hand or working tool in all directions. The work envelope can be reduced or restricted by limiting devices that establish limits that will not be exceeded in the event of any foreseeable failure of the robot or its controls. The maximum distance that the robot can travel after the limit device is actuated will be considered the basis for defining the restricted (or reduced) work envelope.

Working space or volume   The physical space bounded by the robot's working envelope in physical space. See Fig. 2-18.

Workpiece   Any part in any stage of manufacture prior to its becoming a finished part. The piece of metal that is being worked.

World coordinate   A device-independent Cartesian coordinate system used by the application program to organize two-dimensional or three-dimensional modeled objects for display. The effect of applying the composite modeling transformation to modeling coordinates is to produce world coordinates.

Wrist   A set of rotary joints between the arm and robot end-effector that allows the end-effector to be oriented to the workpiece.

Wrist force sensor   A sensor that consists of a structure with some compliant sections and transducers that measure the compliant sections along three orthogonal axes, as a result of the applied force and torque. There are different types of force transducers, such as strain gage, piezoelectric, magnetostrictive, magnetic, and others. A robot wrist force sensor measures the three components of force and three components of torque between the hand and the terminal link of the manipulator.

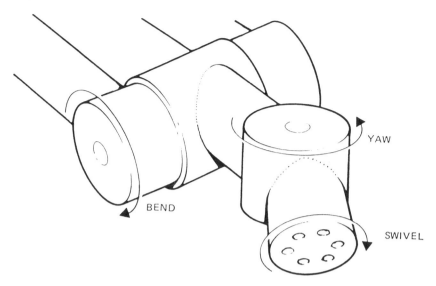

Typical wrist articulations. (From *Robotics in Practice* by Joseph F. Engelberger.)

Wrist movement   A robot ability that can make a minor contribution to the shape and size of the work envelope. However, the main significance of wrist movement is the ability to orient the gripper or any other end-of-arm tooling. Pitch refers to wrist movement in the vertical plane; yaw represents movement in the horizontal plane (swing); and the ability to rotate is denoted by roll.

Yaw   Rotation of the end-effector in a horizontal plane around the end of the manipulator arm. The angular displacement of a moving body about an axis that is perpendicular to the line of motion and to the top side of the body. Side-to-side motion at an axis.

Z Axis   The vertical direction in three-dimensional space.

APPENDIX B: POINTS
OF CONTACT

Robot Associations

National Service Robot Association
900 Victors Way
P.O. Box 3724
Ann Arbor, Michigan 48106
(313) 994-6088

Robotic Industries Association
900 Victors Way
P.O. Box 3724
Ann Arbor, Michigan 48106
(313) 994-6088

Robotics International of SME
One SME Drive
P.O. Box 930
Dearborn, Michigan 48121

Michael Kassler & Associates Party,
    Ltd. (Australia)
2 W. Crescent St., Suite 2
McMahnons Point
New South Wales 2060 Australia
Contact: Dr. M. Kassler

Flemish Organisation for Robotics
    and Automation
(FLORA) (Belgium)
Brouwersvliet 15, bus

B-2000 Antwerp, Belgium
Contact: Mr. A. Van den Bossche
        Managing Director
        (03) 231 16 60

Belgisch Institut voor Regel-techniek
    en Automatizering
(BIRA) (Belgium)
Jan Van Rijswijcklaan 58
B-2018 Antwerp, Belgium
Contact: Mr. F. Denis
        President
        32321609 96

Association de Robotique
    Industriella Athena, a.s.b.l.
Centre de Services de Lauzelle
avenue de Lauzelle, 61
1348 Ottingnies
Louvain-la-Neuve, Belgium
Contact: Mr. P. Van der Wielen
        General Secretary
        010/41 29 79

Ontario Robotics Center
743 Monaghan Road
Peterborough, Ontario
Canada
Contact: Mr. I.A. Barrie
        (705) 876-1611

Technical University of Kosice
  (Czechoslovakia)
Svermova 9
04001 Kosice, Czechoslovakia
Contact: Professor Jan Buda
         30016

Danish Industrial Robot Association
  (DIRA)
Secretariat
Teknologiparken
8000 Aarhus C, Denmark
Contact: Mr. H. Knudsen
         President
         06-14 2400 or 02-99 6611

Robotics Society of Finland
P.O. Box 55
0331 Helsinki 33, Finland
Contact: Mr. Vuorilehto
         President
         358 9 56271

Association Francaise de Robotique
  Industrielle (AFRI)
61 avenue de President Wilson
94230 Cashan, France
Contact: Dr. M. Parent
         President
         33 1 547 69 33

Societe Italian Robotique Industrielle
  (SIRI)
Etas Kompas Periodici Tecnici
via Mantegna 6
1-20154 Milano, Italy
Contact: Prof. D. Fabrizi
         President
         347 051/312 041

Japan Industrial Robot Association
  (JIRA)
c/o Kikaishinko Building
3-5-8 Shibakoen
Tokyo, Japan
Contact: Mr. K. Yonemoto
         Executive Director
         03434 2910

Dutch Robotic Association (CIR--
  Contactgroep Industriele Robots)

c/o Hoogovens Ijmuiden BV
Research Lab. (3J22)
1970 CA Ijmuiden, The Netherlands
Contact: Ir. J.C. Groothuizen
         Secretary
         02510-94143

Technical University of Warsaw
A1 Niepodleglosci
  222r 206
00-663 Warsaw, Poland
Contact: Professor A. Morecki
         210070

Singapore Robot Association
Maxwell Road
P.O. Box 392
Singapore 9007
Contact: Mr. S. Choo
         2657740

Association Esponala de Robotics
  (AER)
Rambla de Cataluna 70 30 2a
08007 Barcelona, Spain
Contact: Mr. J.M. Muxi
         (93) 215 57 60

Swedish Industriale Robot
  Association (SWIRA)
Sveriges Makanforbund
Box 5506
S-11485 Stockholm, Sweden
Contact: Mr. Bo Halbert
         468-63 50 20

Institute de Microtechnique Ecole
  Polytechnique Federale
Ecublens
CH-1015 Lausanne, Switzerland
Contact: Prof. C.W. Burchardt
         021 47 38 25

British Robot Association
28-30 High St.
Kempston
Bedford MK427AJ United Kingdom
Contact: Mr. Thomas E. Brock
         Executive Secretary
         0234 854477

IPA Stuttgart
Nobelstrasse 12
7000 Stuttgart 80, West Germany
Contact: Dr. R.D. Schraft
        Deputy Director
        0711 781602

Robot Manufacturers

Adept Technology Inc.
150 Rose Orchard Way
San Jose, California 95134
(408) 432-0888

AKR Robotics Inc.
35367 Schoolcraft Road
Livonia, Michigan 48154
(313) 261-8700

Allen-Bradley Co.,
   Industrial Computer Group
747 Alpha Drive
Highland Heights, Ohio 44143
(216) 449-6700

American-Monarch Machine Co.,
   Inc.
503 N. Niles
Metamora, Illinois 61548
(309) 367-2325

Anorad Corporation
110 Oser Avenue
Hauppauge, New York 11788
(516) 231-1995

ASEA Brown Boveri (ABB)
   Robotics Inc.
16250 W. Glendale Drive
New Berlin, Wisconsin 53151-2840
(414) 785-3400

Automatix Incorporated
755 Middlesex Turnpike
Billerica, Massachusetts 01821
(508) 667-7900

Binks Manufacturing Company
9201 W. Belmont Avenue
Franklin Park, Illinois 60131
(312) 671-3000

CIMCORP Inc.
615 N. Enterprise Street
P.O. Box 2032
Aurora, Illinois 60507-2032
(312) 851-2220

Cimflex Teknowledge Corp.
160 Industry Drive
Pittsburgh, Pennsylvania 15275
(412) 787-3000

Cincinnati Milacron
Industrial Robot Division
795 West Alexander Ave.
Greenwood, South Carolina 29648
(803) 227-6000

The DeVilbiss Company
300 Phillips Avenue
P.O. Box 913
Toledo, Ohio 43692
(419) 470-2169
1-800-DEV-4448

Elicon
940 S. Leslie Street
La Habra, California 90631
(714) 870-6647

GMF Robotics Corp.
2000 South Adams Road
Auburn Hills, Michigan 48057
(313) 377-7000

General Numeric Corporation
390 Kent Avenue
Elk Grove Village, Illinois 60007
(312) 640-1595

Graco Robotics Inc.
12898 Westmore Avenue
Livonia, Michigan 48150
(313) 523-6300

Hitachi America Ltd.
6 Pearl Court
Allendale, New Jersey 07401
(201) 825-8000

Hobart Brothers Company
600 W. Main Street

Troy, Ohio 45373
(513) 332-5611

IBM
1000 N.W. 51st Street
Boca Raton, Florida 33432
(407) 443-2000

Intelledex
4575 S.W. Research Way
Corvallis, Oregon 97333
(503) 758-4700

International Robomation/
    Intelligence
2281 Las Palmas Drive
Carlsbad, California 92009
(619) 438-4424

I.S.I. Manufacturing, Inc.
31915 Groesbeck Highway
Fraser, Michigan 48026
(313) 294-9500

Lamson Corporation
P.O. Box 4857
Syracuse, New York 13221
(315) 432-5500

Lincoln Electric Co., The
22801 St. Clair Avenue
Cleveland, Ohio 44117-1199
(216) 481-8100

Mack Corporation
P.O. Box 1756
Flagstaff, Arizona 86002
(602) 526-1120

Mazak Corp.
8025 Production Drive
Florence, Kentucky 41042
(606) 727-5700

Medar, Inc.
38700 Grand River Avenue
Farmington Hills, Michigan 48018
(313) 478-9330

Mitsubishi Elec. America
800 Biermann Court
Mount Prospect, Illinois 60056
(312) 298-9223

Panasonic Industrial Co.
One Panasonic Way
Secaucus, New Jersey 07094
(201) 348-7000

Pentel of America, Ltd.
2715 Columbia Street
Torrance, California 90503
(213) 320-3831

Pickomatic Systems
37900 Mound
Sterling Heights, Michigan 48310
(313) 939-9320

Positech Corporation
Rush Lake Road
Laurens, Iowa 50554
(712) 845-4548

Prab Robots, Inc.
6007 Sprinkle Road
P.O. Box 2121
Kalamazoo, Michigan 49003
(616) 329-0835

Reis Machines
1320 Holmes Road
Elgin, Illinois 60123
(312) 741-9500

Rhino Robots
308 S. State Street
Champaign, Illinois 61820
(217) 352-8485

Schrader Bellows/Scovill Inc.
200 W. Exchange Street
Akron, Ohio 44309
(216) 375-5202

Sigma
3401 E. LaPalma Avenue
Anaheim, California 92806
(714) 632-0474

Sormel/Black and Webster
219 Bear Hill Road
Waltham, Massachusetts 02254
(617) 890-9100

Sterling Detroit Company
261 E. Goldengate Avenue
Detroit, Michigan 48203
(313) 366-3500

Swanson-Erie Corp.
814 E. 8th Street
P.O. Box 1217
Erie, Pennsylvania 16512
(814) 453-5841

TecQuipment Inc.
P.O. Box 1074
Acton, Massachusetts 01720
(508) 263-1767

Thermwood Corp.
Old Buffaloville Road
Dale, Indiana 47523
(812) 937-4476

Westinghouse
200 Beta Drive
Pittsburgh, Pennsylvania 15238
(412) 963-4000

Robot Manufacturers (Europe)

Akronics Robot Systems AB
Box 11073
250 11 Heisingborg, Sweden
042/183110

Amysa-Yverdon SA
Route de Lausanne 10
CH-1400 Yverdon, Switzerland
(024) 215121

A.O.I.P. Kremlin Robotique
6 rue Maryse Bastie
9100 Evry
France

AST GmbH
Postfach 100125
D-3500 Kassel, West Germany
(561) 83016

ATM Automation, Ltd.
Earls Way
Church Hill
Thurmaston, Leicester, England
  LE4 8DH
533-693396-7

BCIRA
Alvechurch
Birmingham, England B48 7QB

Bilsing Robot Systeme
Am Zollstock 6
5952 Attendorn, West Germany
02722-3051 and 3052

Blohm + Voss AG
Hermann-Blohm-Str. 3
D-2000 Hamburg 11, West Germany
(040) 3119-2750

British Federal Ltd.,
  Castle Mill Works
Birmingham New Road
Dudley, West Midlands DY1 4DA
  England
0384 54701-7

British Federal Welder and Machine
  Co., Ltd.
Castle Mill Works
Dudley
West Midlands, DY1 4DA
United Kingdom

Camel Robot SRL
Palozzolo Milanese
Italy

Climax Automation
Avenue De Chateauoun BP 1039
41007 Blois CEDEX, France
(33) 54745505

Concentric Production Research Ltd.
Upper Holland Road, Sutton
  Coldfield
W. Midlands B72 1RD England
021-355-1266

Dainichi Sykes Robotics, Ltd.
Walton Summit Centre
Bamber Bridge, Preston, Lancs,
    England
0772 322444

Digital Electronics Automation SpA
Co Torino 70
Moncalieri, Piemonte 10024
Italy

Electrolux AB
Industrial Systems
S-105 45 Stockholm
Sweden

Elettronica San Giorgio—Elsag SpA
Via G. Puccini 2
16154 Genova, Italy
39-10-60011

Fiat Auto SpA
CSO Agnelli 200
Torino, Piemonte
Italy

Gaiotto Impianti SpA
26010 Vaiano Cremasco
Cremona, Italy
0373/791254

GEC Robot Systems
Boughton Road
Rugby, Warwickshire, England
    CV21 1BU
Rugby (44) 0788 2144

Geveke Intern Transport B.V.
Maltaweg 12
1044 AJ Amsterdam, Netherlands
020-5867177

Hahn and Kolb Engineering
KLonig Str. 14
7000 Stuttgart, West Germany
0049 711 224974

Hall Automation Limited
Colonia Way
Watford
Herts, WD2 4FG
United Kingdom

Jungheinrich
Unternelmensverwaltung
Friedrich-Ebert-Dabb 129
2000 Hamburg 70
West Germany
ASEA AB
S-72183 Vasteras
Sweden

KUKA
Schweissanlagen and Roboter GmbH
P.O. Box 431280
Zugspitzstr. 140
D-8900
Augsburg 43
West Germany

lemme Italia SpA
Via Erba 106
20037 Paderno Dugnano, Milano,
    Italy
(02) 9103842

Mecman Engineering AB
Box 1008
611 29 Nykoping, Sweden
0155/97000

MEPAL
G Avenue du bois de l'Epine
91000 Evry, France
(33) 160771112

Microbo S.A.
Rue de la Gare 8, CH-2024
St. Aubin, Switzerland
(038) 55 32 62

Mouldmation Limited
2 Darwin Close
Burntwood, Walsall
Staffs WS7 9HP
United Kingdom

Nimak
Werkstrabe
Postfach 86
5248 Wissen/Sieg
West Germany

Nokia AB
Box 42037
126 12 Stockholm, Sweden
08/7447500

Olivetti SpA
Controllo Numerico
Fr S Bernardo
V Torino 603
Ivrea, Piemonte
Italy

Pendar
Bridgwater
Somerset
United Kingdom

Prima Industrie S.p.A.
via Antonelli 32
10097 Regina Margherita Di Collegno
  (TO) Italy
011-411-13-22

Rafra Industriale
Via Villa Eleonora
7-27100 Pavia, Italy
0382-460839

Regie Nationale des
Usines renault SA
66Av Edouard Vaillaut
Boulogne-Billancourt
France

Renault-Automation, Etablissement
  Sirtes
204 roud-point du Pont de Sevies
92516 Boulogne, France
46 08 9112

R. Kaufeldt AB
P.O. Box 42139
S-126 Stockholm
Sweden

Sormel
rue Becquerel
25009 Besanicon Cedex
France

Spine Robotics AB
Flojelbergsgatan 14, 431 37 Molndal,
  Sweden
(+46) 31-87 0710

Syke Instrumentation, Ltd.
117 Station Road
Liss, Hants GU33 7AJ England
0730 893821

Taylor Hitec
77 Lyons Lane
Chorley Lancs, England
(02572) 65825

Tecno systems
Via G. Di Vittorio 13
15033 Casale Monferrato, AL, Italy
0192 75851

Tecnogamma S.N.C.
V. Arno, 1/3
Castiglione Olona, Varese, Italy
0331/850606

Tecnologie E Prodotti Per
  L'Automazione-T.P.A. SpA
Via Vincenzo Monti
8 Milano, Italy
(02) 878580

Thorn EMI Robotics, Ltd.
855 Ringwood Road
Bournemouth, England BH11 8NE
0202 570811

Trallfa
Paint-Welding Robot Systems
P.O. Box 113
4341 Bryne
Norway

Unimation, Inc.
Units A3/A4
Stafford Park 4
Telford, Salop
United Kingdom

Voest-Alpine AG
P.O. Box 2
A-4010 Linz, Austria
0732-585-8079

Volkswagenwerk AG
Abt. Industrieverkauf
3180 Wolfsburg
West Germany

Volvo Automated Systems of North
America,
Div. of Volvo of North America
Corp.
7000 Nineteen Mile Road
Sterling Heights, MI 48078

VSI Automation Co. Ltd.
7 Factory Road
Upton Industrial Estate
Poole, Dorset, England

Robot Manufacturers (Japan)

Daihen Corp.
5-1, Minamisenrioka, Settsu
Osaka 566, Japan
06-383-1662

Dainichi Kiko Co., Ltd.
Kosai-cho
Nakakomagun Yeamanshi Pref.
400-04
Japan

Fanuc, Ltd.
3-5-1
Asahigoaka, Hino City
Tokyo
Japan

Hitachi, Ltd.
Shin-Maru Bldg.
1-5-1
Marunouchi, Chiyoda-ku
Tokyo
Japan

Kamiuchi Electric Works, Ltd.
5-31, 2-Chome, Tagawa
Yodogawa-Ku, Osaka, Japan 532
06-308-3861

Kawasaki Heavy Industries Ltd.
World Trade Center Bldg.

2-4-1 Hamamatsucho, Minato-ku
Tokyo 105
Japan

Matsushita Industrial Equipment Co.
Ltd.
3-1-1 Inazumachi
Toyonaka City Osaka Pref.
Japan

Mitsubishi Heavy Industries Ltd.
2-5-1
Marunouchi, Chiyoda-ku
Tokyo
Japan

Okura Yusoki Co., Ltd.
900 Furuouchi, Noguchi-Chu
Hyogo, Japan
0794-26-181

Osaka Denki co., Ltd.
3-31, Nishimikuni 4-Chome
Yodogawa-Ku, Osaka, Japan
06-394-1191

Sanko Senzai Kogyo Co., Ltd.
14, Nishiura-Cho
Umezu, Ukyo-Ku, Kyoto,
Japan
075-8818121

Sankyo Seiki Mfg. Co., Ltd.
1-17-2
Shunbashi, Minati-ku
Tokyo 105
Japan

Skinko Electric Co., Ltd.
3-Chome
12-2 Nihonbashi Chuo-Ku
Tokyo, Japan
03-274-1121

Tokico Ltd.
1-6-3
Funta, Kawasaki-ku
Kawasaki City
Kanagaw Pref.
Japan

Yaskawa Electric Mfg. Co. Ltd.
Ohtemachi Bldg.
1-6-1
Ohtemachi, Chiyoda-ku
Tokyo
Japan

YUASA International,
Div. of YUASA Battery (America),
    Inc.
620 Washington Avenue
Carlstadt, New Jersey 07072
(201) 935-9000

Robot Rental/Lease Firms

Hi-Tech Assembly
8130 N. Knox
Skokie, Illinois 60076
(312) 676-0080

Thermwood Machinery
    Manufacturing Co. Inc.
P.O. Box 436
Dale, Indiana 4752
(812) 937-4476

Rob-Con Ltd.
12001 Globe Road
Livonia, Michigan 48150
(313) 591-0300

Robot Consulting/ Applications Firms

Automation Systems/American
    Technologies
1900 Pollitt Drive
Fair Lawn, New Jersey 07410
(201) 797-8200

Blanarovich Engineering
Box 292
Don Mills, Ontario M3C 2S2
Canada
(416) 438-6313

Franklin Institute Research
    Laboratory, Inc.
The Benjamin Franklin Parkway

Philadelphia, Pennsylvania 19103
(215) 448-1000

Productivity Systems Inc.
21999 Farmington Road
Farmington Hills, Michigan 48024
(313) 474-5454

RMT Engineering Ltd.
P.O. Box 2333, Station B
St. Catherines, Ontario L2M 7M7
Canada
(416) 937-1550

Robot Systems, Inc.
50 Technology Parkway
Norcross, Georgia 30092
(404) 448-4133

Technology Research Corporation
8328-A Traford Lane
Springfield, Virginia 22152
(703) 451-8830

U.S. Robotics Research Organizations

Arizona State University
Center for Automated Engineering
    and Robotics Research
Engineering Research Center 552
Tempe, Arizona 85287
(602) 965-3709

Carnegie-Mellon University
The Robotics Institute
Schenley Park
Pittsburgh, Pennsylvania 15213
(412) 578-2597

Charles Stark Draper Laboratory,
    Inc.
Robotics Assembly System Division
555 Technology Square
Cambridge, Massachusetts 02139
(617) 258-2901

Environmental Research Institute of
   Michigan
Robotics Program
P.O. Box 8618
Ann Arbor, Michigan 48107
(313) 994-1200

George Washington University
725 23rd Street NW
Washington, DC 20052
(202) 676-6083

Georgia Institute of Technology
Material Handling Research Center
765 Ferst Drive, N.W.
Atlanta, Georgia 30332-0205
(404) 894-2362

Hughes Research Laboratories
3011 Malibu Canyon Road
Malibu, California 90265

Industrial Technology Institute
P.O. Box 1485
Ann Arbor, Michigan 48106
(313) 769-4000

IIT Research Institute
Manufacturing Productivity Center
10 West 35th Street
Chicago, Illinois 60616

Jet Propulsion Labs
Robotics Group
4800 Oak Grove Drive
Pasadena, California 91103
(213) 354-6101

Lehigh University
Institute for Robotics
Harold S. Mohler Building No. 200
Bethlehem, Pennsylvania 18015
(215) 758-4826

MIT
Artificial Intelligence Lab
545 Technology Square
Cambridge, Massachusetts 02139
(617) 253-6218

National Institute of Standards and
   Technology
Bldg. 220, Room A123
Washington, DC 20234
(30l) 921-2381

Naval Research Laboratory
Code 7505
Washington, DC 20375
(202) 545-6700

North Carolina State University
Raleigh, North Carolina 27650
(919) 737-2336

Purdue University
School of Electrical Engineering
West Lafayette, Indiana 47906
(317) 749-2607

Rensselaer Polytechnic Institute
Center for Manufacturing
   Productivity
JEC 5001
Troy, New York 12180-3590
(518) 266-6021

Stanford University
Artificial Intelligence Lab
Stanford, California 94305
(415) 497-2797
Dr. John McCarthy, Director

SRI International
Artificial Intelligence Center
Menlo Park, California 94025
(415) 859-2311

Texas A&M University
Dept. of Industrial Engineering
College Station, Texas 77840
(713) 845-5531

United States Air Force
AFWAL/MLTC (USAF ICAM)
Wright Patterson AFB
Ohio 45433
(513) 255-2232

University of Central Florida
College of Engineering
P.O. Box 25000

Orlando, Florida 32816
(305) 275-2236

University of Cincinnati
Institute of Applied Interdisciplinary
   Research
Loc #72
Cincinnati, Ohio 45221

University of Florida
Institute for Intelligent Machines and
   Robotics
Room 300, Mechanical Engr.
Gainesville, Florida 32601
(904) 392-0814

University of Michigan
Robotics Program
ECE Department
Ann Arbor, Michigan 48109
(313) 764-7139

University of Rhode Island
Robotics Research Center
Kirk Building, Upper College Road
Kingston, Rhode Island 02881
(401) 792-2514

University of Utah
Center for Engineering Design
3168 Merrill Engineering Building
Salt Lake City, Utah 84112
(801) 581-6499

University of WI
1513 University Avenue
Madison, Wisconsin 53706
(608) 262-3543

Worchester Polytechnic Institute
MEAC Department
Worchester, Massachusetts 01609
(617) 793-5335

BIBLIOGRAPHY

Books

Aleksander, Igor, *Artificial Vision for Robots*. New York: Chapman & Hall, 1983.

Aleksander, Igor, *Computing Techniques for Robots*. New York: Chapman & Hall, 1985.

Aleksander, Igor, *The World Yearbook of Robotics Research and Development*. Kogan Page, London, 1985.

Asfahl, C.R., *Robotics and Manufacturing Automation*. New York: Wiley, 1985.

Asimov, Isaac, and Karen A. Frenkel, *Robots—Machines in Man's Image*. New York: Harmony Books, 1985.

Ballard, D.H., and C.M. Brown, *Computer Vision*. Englewood Cliffs, New Jersey: Prentice–Hall, 1982.

Baranson, T.P., *Robots in Manufacturing—Key to International Competitiveness*. Lomond, 1983.

Brady, J.M., *Computer Vision*. Amsterdam: North-Holland, 1981.

Brady, J.M., *et al.*, *Robot Motion: Planning and Control*. Cambridge, Massachusetts: MIT Press, 1982.

Brady, J.M., *et al.*, *Robotics and Artificial Intelligence*. New York/Berlin: Springer-Verlag, 1984.

Brownell, James R., *et al.*, *Robotics Research and Research Needs: An Exploratory Study*. New York: Kappa Systems, Inc., February 1982.

Coiffet, Philippe, *Robot Technology: Volume I—Modelling and Control*. Englewood Cliffs, New Jersey: Prentice–Hall, 1983.

Coiffet, Philippe, *Robot Technology: Volume II—Interaction with the Environment*. Englewood Cliffs, New Jersey: Prentice–Hall, 1983.

Coiffet, Philippe, and Michel Chirouze, *An Introduction to Robot Technology*. New York: McGraw–Hill, 1983.

Considine, Douglas M., *Standard Handbook of Industrial Automation*. New York: Chapman & Hall, 1986.

Craig, J.J., *Introduction to Robotics: Mechanics and Control*. Reading, Massachusetts: Addison–Wesley, 1986.

Critchlow, Arthur, *Introduction to Robotics*. New York: Macmillan Co., 1985.

Dodd, G.G., and L. Rossol, *Computer Vision and Sensor-Based Robots*. New York: Plenum, 1979.

Dorf, Richard C., *Robotics and Automated Manufacturing*. Reston, Virginia: Reston Publishing, 1983.

Dorf, Richard C., *International Encyclopedia of Robotics,* Vols. 1–3. New York: Wiley–Interscience, 1988.

Duffy, J., *Analysis of Mechanisms and Robot Manipulators.* New York: Wiley, 1980.

Dun and Bradstreet, Inc., *An Analysis of the Robotics Industry.* New York: Dun and Bradstreet, 1983.

Engelberger, J.F., *Robotics in Practice.* New York: Amacom Division of American Management Associations, 1980.

Faugeras, O., *Fundamentals in Computer Vision.* New York/London: Cambridge Univ. Press, 1983.

Fisk, J.D., *Industrial Robots in the United States: Issues and Perspectives,* Congressional Research Service, The Library of Congress, Report No. 81–78 E, March 30, 1981.

Goldberg, Joel, *Electronic Servicing of Robotic Equipment.* Englewood Cliffs, New Jersey: Prentice–Hall, 1985.

Hanafusa, H., and H. Inoue, *Robotics Research: The Second International Symposium.* Cambridge, Massachusetts MIT Press, 1985.

Hartley, John, *Robots at Work—A Practical Guide for Engineers and Managers.* London: Kogan Page, 1983.

Heath, Larry, *Fundamentals of Robotics: Theory and Applications.* Reston, Virginia: Reston Publishing, 1985.

Holland, John, *Basic Robotic Concepts.* Indianapolis, Indiana: Howard Sams, 1983.

Horn, Berthold Klaus Paul, *Robot Vision.* Cambridge, Massachusetts: MIT Press, 1986.

Hunt, V. Daniel, *Industrial Robotics Handbook.* New York: Industrial Press, 1983.

Hunt, V. Daniel, *Smart Robots.* New York: Chapman & Hall, 1985.

Hunt, V. Daniel, *Artificial Intelligence and Expert Systems Sourcebook.* New York: Chapman & Hall, 1986.

Hunt, V. Daniel, *Dictionary of Advanced Manufacturing Technology.* Amsterdam: Elsevier, 1987.

Hunt, V. Daniel, *Mechatronics—Japan's Newest Threat.* New York: Chapman & Hall, 1988.

Hunt, V. Daniel, *Robotics Sourcebook.* Amsterdam: Elsevier, 1988.

Hunt, V. Daniel, *Computer-Integrated Manufacturing Handbook.* New York: Chapman & Hall, 1989.

Kafrissen, E., and M. Stephans, *Industrial Robots and Robotics.* Reston, Virginia: Reston Publishing, 1984.

Koren, Yoram, *Robotics for Engineers.* New York: McGraw–Hill, 1985.

L'Hote, Francois, *et al., Robot Technology:* *Volume IV—Robot Components and Systems.* Englewood Cliffs, New Jersey: Prentice–Hall, 1983.

Martin, Lee, and Danial Kuban, *Teleoperated Robotics in Hostile Environments.* Dearborn, MI: Society of Manufacturing Engineers, 1985.

Mason, Matthew, and Kenneth Salisbury, *Robot Hands and the Mechanics of Manipulators.* Cambridge, Massachusetts: MIT Press, 1985.

Masterson, J.W., E.C. Poe, and S.W. Fardo, *Robotics.* Reston, Virginia: Reston Publishing, 1985.

McCormick, Peter, *Developing and Applying End of Arm Tooling.* Dearborn, Michigan: Society of Manufacturing Engineers, 1986.

Minsky, Marvin, *Robotics.* New York: Anchor Press/Doubleday, 1985.

Morecki, A., *et al., Theory and Practice of Robots and Manipulators.* Cambridge, Massachusetts: MIT Press, 1985.

Morgan, Chris, *Robots: Planning and Implementation.* New York/Berlin: Springer-Verlag, 1984.

Nof, S.Y., *Handbook of Industrial Robotics.* New York: Wiley, 1985.

Owens, Tony, *Assembly with Robots.* Englewood Cliffs, New Jersey: Prentice–Hall, 1985.

Paul, R. *Robot Manipulators: Mathematics, Programming, and Control.* Cambridge, Massachusetts: MIT Press, 1981.

Pugh, A., *Robot Vision.* New York/Berlin: Springer-Verlag, 1983.

Ranky, P.G., and L.Y. Ho, *Robot Modelling: Control and Applications with Software.* New York/Berlin: Springer-Verlag, 1985.

Rathmill, Keith, *Robotic Assembly.* New York/Berlin: Springer-Verlag, 1985.

Rathmill, Keith, *et al., Robot Technology and Applications.* New York/Berlin: Springer-Verlag, 1985.

Rehg, James, *Introduction to Robotics—A Systems Approach.* Englewood Cliffs, New Jersey: Prentice– Hall, 1985.

Rifkin, Susan B., *Industrial Robots: A Survey of Foreign and Domestic U.S. Patents,* U.S. Department of Commerce, National Technical Information Service, August 1982.

Robillard, Mark, *Advanced Robot Systems.* Indianapolis, Indiana: Howard Sams, 1984.

Robillard, Mark, *Microprocessor Based Robotics.* Indianapolis, Indiana: Howard Sams, 1984.

Robot Institute of America, *Robot Institute of America Worldwide Robotics Survey and Directory.* Dearborn, Michigan: RIA, 1982.

Smith, Donald N., and Peter Heytler, Jr., *Industrial Robots—Forecasts and Trends,* Delphi

Study, 2nd ed. Dearborn, Michigan: Society of Manufacturing Engineers/The University of Michigan, 1985.

Snyder, Wesley, *Industrial Robots: Computer Interfacing and Control*. Englewood Cliffs, New Jersey: Prentice–Hall, 1985.

Strubhar, Peter, *Working Safely with Industrial Robots*. Dearborn, Michigan: Society of Manufacturing Engineers, 1986.

Susnjara, Ken, *A Manager's Guide to Industrial Robots*. Shaker Heights, Ohio: Corinthian Press, 1982.

Todd, D.J., *Walking Machines—An Introduction to Legged Robots*. New York: Chapman & Hall, 1985.

Toepperwein, L., Blacknow, M.T., *et al.*, ICAM Robotics Application Guide, Report AFWAL-TR-80-4042, Vol. II. Air Force Wright Aeronautical Laboratories, Materials Laboratory, Wright-Patterson Air Force Base, Ohio, 1980.

Toepperwin, L., *Machine Vision*. Dearborn, Michigan: Society of Manufacturing Engineers, 1984.

Special Reports

Department of Commerce, International Trade Administration, *A Competitive Assessment of the U.S. Flexible Manufacturing Systems Industry*, July 1985.

Department of Commerce, Office of Industry Assessment, Industry Analysis Division, *A Competitive Assessment of the U.S. Manufacturing Automation Equipment Industries*, U.S. Department of Commerce technical publication, June 1984.

Office of Technology Assessment, U.S. Congress, *Computerized Manufacturing Automation: Employment, Education, and the Workplace*, U.S. Government Printing Office, OTA-CIT-235, April 1984.

Conference Proceedings

Brady, M., and R. Paul, *Robotics Research: The First International Symposium*. Cambridge, Massachusetts: MIT Press, 1984.

Robots Conference Proceedings, Robotics International of SME, One SME Drive, P.O. Box 930, Dearborn, Michigan 48128

Directories

Industrial Robots
Society of Manufacturing Engineers
Marketing Services Division

One SME Drive
P.O. Box 930
Dearborn, Michigan 48128

Robotics Product Database
TECSPEC
P.O. Box 617024
Orlando, Florida 32861-7024

Robotics World Directory
Communications Channels, Inc.
6255 Barfield Road
Atlanta, Georgia 30328
(404) 256-9800

Related Periodicals

Assembly Engineering
Hitchcock Publishing Company
New York, New York

High Technology Magazine
High Technology Publishing Corporation
Boston, Massachusetts

Image and Vision Computing
Butterworth Scientific Ltd.
P.O. Box 63
Westbury House, Bury St.
Guildford, Surrey GU1 5BH
United Kingdom

Industrial Robots International
158 Linwood Plaza
P.O. Box 13304
Fort Lee, NJ 07024

Journal of Robotic Systems
John Wiley & Sons, Inc.
605 Third Avenue
New York, New York 10158

le nouvel Automatisme
41, rue de las Grange-aux Belles
75483 Paris Cedex 10
France

Managing Automation
Thomas Publishing Company
New York, New York

Material Handling Engineering
Penton/IPC
Cleveland, Ohio

Manufacturing Engineering
Society of Manufacturing Engineers
Dearborn, Michigan

Manufacturing Technology Horizons
P.O. Box 206
Lake Geneva, Wisconsin 53147

Production Engineering
Penton/IPC
Cleveland, Ohio

Robomatics Reporter
EIC/Intelligence
38 W. 38th Street
New York, New York 10018

Robotech Japan
Topika Inc.
Nagatani Bldg.
7-17-4, Ginza
Chuko-ku, Tokyo 104
Japan

Robotica
Cambridge University Press
32 E. 57th Street
New York, New York 10022

Robotics Engineering
174 Concord Street
Peterborough, New Hampshire 03458

Robotics Technology Abstracts
Cranfield Press
Management Library
Cranfield Institute of Technology
Cranfield Bedford MK43 OAL
United Kingdom

Robotics Today
Society of Manufacturing Engineers
One SME Drive
P.O. Box 930
Dearborn, Michigan 48128

Robotics World
Communications Channels, Inc.
6255 Barfield Road
Atlanta, Georgia 30328

Robot Insider
Fairchild Publications
7 E. 12th Street
New York, New York 10003

Robot News International
IFS (Publications) Ltd.
35-39 High Street
Kempston, Bedford
MK42 7BT England

Sensors
North American Technology, Inc.
174 Concord Street
Peterborough, New Hampshire 03458

The Industrial Robot
IFS (Publications) Ltd.
35-39 High Street
Kempston, Bedford
MK42 7BT England

The International Journal of Robotics Research
The MIT Press
28 Carleton Street
Cambridge, Massachusetts 02142

INDEX